# AIRCRAFT INSTRUMENTS AND AVIONICS

# FOR A&P TECHNICIANS

**JEPPESEN**

## by MAX F. HENDERSON

Jeppesen Sanderson, Inc.

Published in the United States of America
Jeppesen Sanderson, Inc.
55 Inverness Drive East, Englewood, CO 80112-5498
www.jeppesen.com

ISBN-13: 978-0-89100-422-6
ISBN-10: 0-89100-422-X

Jeppesen Sanderson, Inc.
55 Inverness Dr. East
Englewood, CO 80112-5498
Web Site: www.jeppesen.com
Email: Captain@jeppesen.com
© 1993 Max F. Henderson
All Rights Reserved. Published 1993
Printed in the United States of America

JS312666-001

# Table of Contents

# About This Book

This textbook is intended to be used in the instruction of students in an aviation maintenance technician training program. The descriptions, drawings and graphics in this book are for instructional purposes only and should not be used as a technical reference source for specific maintenance tasks on aircraft or aircraft systems or for other operational purposes. Excerpts from Federal Aviation Regulations and other sources have been paraphrased and simplified in order to save space and time.

The author wishes to express his appreciation for permission to use material from the technical publications of the following aviation companies.

Beechcraft Aircraft Corp. (Wichita, Kansas)
Canadair Group, Bombardier Inc. (Montreal, Quebec, Canada)
Cessna Aircraft Co. (Wichita, Kansas)
Comant Industries Inc. (Sante Fe Springs, California)
Dayton-Granger Inc. (Fort Lauderdale, Florida)
Dorne and Margolin Inc. (Bohemia, New York)
Flight Dynamics Inc. (Portland, Oregon)
Piper Aircraft Corp. (Vero Beach, Florida)
Sensor Systems (Chatsworth, California)
Terra Avionics (Albuquerque, New Mexico)
United Technologies — Pratt & Whitney Canada Inc. (Longueuil, Quebec, Canada)

The Canadair drawings which appear throughout this book are the proprietary property of Bombardier Inc, Canadair Group. As such, it is forbidden to copy these drawings without the express written permission of Bombardier Inc., Canadair Group. Readers are cautioned that the drawings are training material only and as such are not subject to revision. They are not to be used in lieu of approved technical manual illustrations for the purposes of carrying out any maintenance procedure or any other activity on any Canadair aircraft or any other aircraft.

# About The Author

Max F. Henderson has been teaching Aviation Maintenance Technology subjects at Embry-Riddle Aeronautical University since 1982. Previous experience includes working as an Electronics Technician in the U.S. Air Force, as a Commercial pilot and A&P mechanic and as a Control Tower Operator. Mr. Henderson holds four FAA certificates:

1. Commercial Pilot Certificate — Ratings for single and multi-engine land, instruments, single-engine seaplanes and gliders.
2. Mechanic Certificate — Airframe and Powerplant ratings
3. Ground Instructor Certificate — Advanced rating
4. Control Tower Operator Certificate

During his years at Embry-Riddle Aeronautical University, Mr. Henderson has earned the following degrees: A.S. Degree in Aircraft Maintenance, B.S. Degree in Professional Aeronautics and a Master's Degree in Aeronautical Science. Mr. Henderson acquired his interest in aviation from his father Floyd B. Henderson whose flying and maintenance experience on aircraft began in 1932. Mr. Henderson's interest in aviation history is evidenced by a collection of books and photographs of early aviation dating back to the World War I era.

# CHAPTER I

# Basic Instruments

Chapter one begins with a study of the general requirements for aircraft instruments and their installation. The categories and types of instruments are covered before beginning a study of specific instruments.

The instruments examined in chapter one include pitot-static system instruments, gyro instruments, compass systems and electronic instruments. Reference will be made to Federal Aviation Regulations which apply to these areas, particularly FAR Part 1 Definitions and Abbreviations, FAR Part 23, FAR Part 43 and FAR Part 91.

## A. Why Study Instruments?

It is important for aircraft technicians to study aircraft instruments so that they will be able to inspect, install and troubleshoot them properly. There are also occasions when the technician will be running the aircraft's engines or other systems and will have to use the instruments himself. Many instruments are a part of a larger system and it is necessary to understand the interrelationships between the various parts of the system.

All certificated aircraft have instruments, although in the case of hot air balloons and gliders,

only a few basic instruments may be required. The number and variety of instruments has increased over the years so that a small single engine airplane of today has more instruments and more sophisticated instruments than airliners had in the 1940s or earlier. Figure 1-1 shows the instrument panel of a Piper Cub from the early 1940s with its six basic instruments. This airplane was a small two place airplane which did not have an electrical system, so all the instruments used mechanical means of operation. The instrument panel shown in figure 1-2 is that of a modern single engine airplane equipped for "blind flying" or IFR flight operations. This airplane has many more instruments and systems that increase the safety of flight and make it a more efficient means of transportation. The most important instruments are placed directly in front of the pilot and the radios are grouped together in the middle for easy access to the controls.

The most common and important types of aircraft instruments and avionics systems will be described in this book along with some FAA requirements for testing and installation. The categories for aircraft instruments and the basic FAA requirements will be covered first.

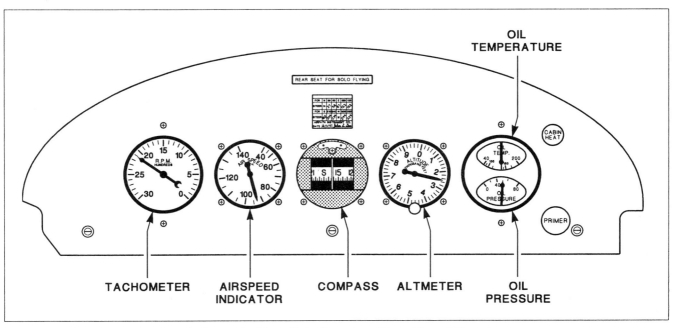

Figure 1-1. *The instrument panel of a 1940s Piper Cub. (Courtesy Piper Aircraft Corp.)*

## B. Aircraft Instrument Requirements

### 1. Instrument Categories

The instruments found on different types of aircraft have considerable variety, but they can be categorized according to either how they work or what kinds of information they present to the flight crew.

#### a. Categories According to Application

1. Powerplant Instruments — These give information related to the aircraft's powerplant or powerplants.
2. Flight and Navigation Instruments — These give information such as altitude, speed etc. or information required for navigating the aircraft.
3. Systems Instruments — These concern aircraft systems such as electrical, hydraulic, pressurization, bleed air systems etc.

#### b. Categories According to Means of Operation

1. Pressure Instruments — These measure the pressure of air, fuel, oil, etc.
2. Mechanical Instruments — These use a mechanical system to obtain and/or transmit information.
3. Gyro Instruments — These use the principles of a gyroscope and are primarily used for IFR flight.

4. Electrical and Electronic Instruments — This group has seen the most change in recent years due to advances in digital technology and other related fields.

### 2. Instrument Placement and Installation

While there is not a standard placement for all the instruments that might be found on either a small or large aircraft, some of the most important instruments will have a standard layout directly in front of the pilot. This makes it easier for the pilot to scan the important instruments and it makes it easier to transition to a different type of airplane.

Aircraft instruments are manufactured in a number of standard sizes. This mainly applies to the round instruments since some other types come in a wide variety of sizes. The standard sizes for round instruments are:

1. 1″ — Often a vacuum gauge on single-engine airplanes
2. 2″ Flangeless — Many turbine engine powerplant instruments are this type.
3. 2-1/4″ — A common size for many different instruments
4. 3-1/8″ — Considered to be a standard full-size instrument

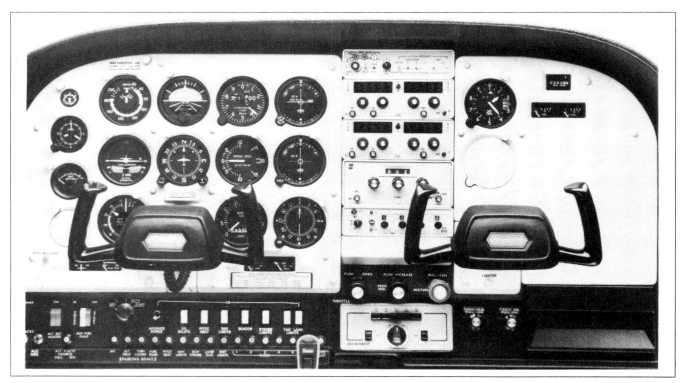

*Figure 1-2. Typical arrangement of instruments and radios in a single engine airplane.*

5. 4″ — The older style gyro instruments were often this size, but it is seldom used on a modern aircraft.

Examples of the 1″, 2-¼″ and 3-⅛″ sizes can be seen on the instrument panel in figure 1-2.

There are a number of methods used to install instruments into the aircraft instrument panel. The three most common methods are:

1. Screws — Non-magnetic fine thread machine screws are used, brass screws with a black oxide finish are very common.

2. Circumferential Clamps — These clamps are fastened to the back of the instrument panel and operate somewhat like a hose clamp (figure 1-3).

3. Brackets — small "L" or "U" shaped brackets are installed on studs to hold the instrument in place (figure 1-3).

Installing aircraft instruments is often made difficult by the fact that there isn't much room behind the instrument panel and access is limited. Some aircraft use sliding or hinged panels to improve access to this area.

### 3. Instrument Markings

Aircraft instruments often utilize colored markings so that safe operating values can be indicated to the pilot. For example, red usually means a maximum or minimum operating limitation for the airplane or engine. These markings are normally on the face of the instrument, inside the cover glass. It is permissible to apply colored markings with paint to the cover glass, but if this is done the marks must not interfere with reading the instrument and a white line must be applied to the cover glass and case to act as a slippage mark.

When applying or inspecting the markings on instruments, a suitable reference source must be used, the acceptable sources are:

1. Approved Aircraft Flight Manual or Pilot's Operating Handbook — This is an FAA-approved document which is a part of the required aircraft equipment.

2. Maintenance Manual or Service Manual.

3. Type Certificate Data Sheet or Specifications.

4. STC, Manufacturers Service Bulletins, and AD Notes — These would indicate a change from the original aircraft requirements.

There are standard meanings for the different colors and markings applied to instruments like powerplant and system instruments, they are:

1. Red Radial Line — This indicates a maximum or minimum operating limitation. Example: on an oil pressure gauge.

2. Red Arc — This indicates a prohibited range of operation. A common example is the red arc on a tachometer because of vibration problems at certain RPMS.

3. Yellow Arc — This indicates a caution range.

4. Green Arc — The normal operating range.

5. Blue Arc or Line — This has a meaning specified by the manufacturer. An example is a blue arc on a manifold pressure gauge for engine operation with a lean mixture.

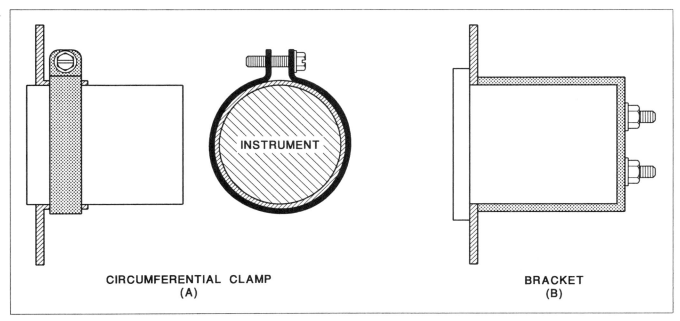

CIRCUMFERENTIAL CLAMP
(A)

BRACKET
(B)

*Figure 1-3. Two of the common methods used to install instruments in an aircraft instrument panel.*

The colored markings on an airspeed indicator have different and very specific meanings, this will be covered later. The colored markings found on an airspeed indicator are shown in figure 1-4, notice that both arcs and radial lines are used.

## 4. General Precautions for Installing Instruments

A number of things must be kept in mind when installing instruments, radios and related systems. Instruments are very delicate and must be handled with care. If an instrument must be sent to a repair station or other place for repair, it should be packed in an approved container with any ports or openings plugged and with a desiccant pack to prevent moisture damage if it is sensitive to moisture. When shock mounts are required for a particular installation, you should ensure that the shock mounts are in good condition and that the weight of the equipment does not exceed the weight carrying capability of the shock mounts. Figure 1-5 shows a shock mount unit for aircraft equipment with a bonding jumper installed. Figure 1-6 illustrates the use of a shock mounted sub-panel for the flight instruments on a small airplane.

Many types of instruments can be damaged by static electricity and magnetic fields. Bonding jumpers, shielded wires and static wicks must be properly installed and maintained to prevent these kinds of problems.

Bonding jumpers have a number of functions when installed on an aircraft. Four of these functions are:

1. A ground return path for aircraft circuits that use single wire type systems.
2. Reducing radio frequency interference in sensitive aircraft systems.
3. Decreasing the possibility of damage due to lightning strikes on control surfaces and other areas.
4. Allowing static charges to move around easily and equalize. This prevents arcing which could create a fire hazard.

A bonding jumper is a small metal braid or metal strap which electrically connects together two parts on the airframe. Some of the recommendations for installing and maintaining bonding jumpers are:

1. Keep them as short as possible but allow for any movement that is necessary as on control surfaces.
2. Clean the contact areas to minimize resistance. This includes removing coatings such as anodizing.
3. Do not solder bonding jumpers. It makes them brittle.
4. Do not paint bonding jumpers. It makes them brittle.
5. Use multiple jumpers on shock mounted electrical equipment. One might break.
6. Ensure that the jumper is compatible with the structural material and hardware to prevent corrosion. Aluminum jumpers are recommended for aluminum aircraft parts and copper jumpers are recommended for stainless steel, cadmium plated steel, brass and bronze.

Some instrument and equipment installations require the use of shielded wire. Don't assume that both ends of the wire shield should be connected to ground. It is sometimes specified that only one end of the wire shielding be attached to ground.

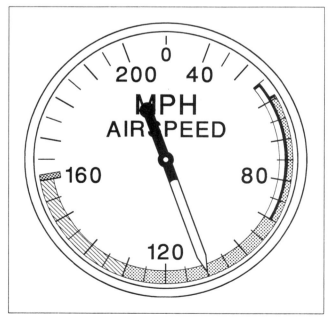

Figure 1-4. Operating limitations markings on an airspeed indicator.

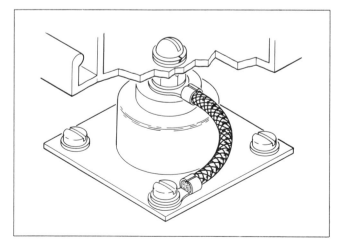

Figure 1-5. Bonding jumpers are installed on shock mounts to ensure proper grounding.

When installing an instrument that requires lighting, use care to ensure that the light is installed correctly and that it will not short out or cause a problem with another instrument. There are often many small wires behind the instrument panel for the light fixtures and they must be routed and tied carefully. There are four common types of instrument lighting systems found on aircraft:

1. Eyebrow Lights — These are small semi-circular fixtures that fit over the top of a round instrument and look like eyebrows.

2. Post Lights — These are small round lights that install into holes in the instrument panel (figure 1-7).

3. Internal Lights — These are inside the instrument case.

4. Flood Lights — These lights can be aimed at the instrument panel and are shielded so that they don't shine in the pilot's eyes. They are often fitted in addition to one of the other types as a back-up lighting system.

Figure 1-8 shows the fluorescent flood lighting system for a corporate jet airplane.

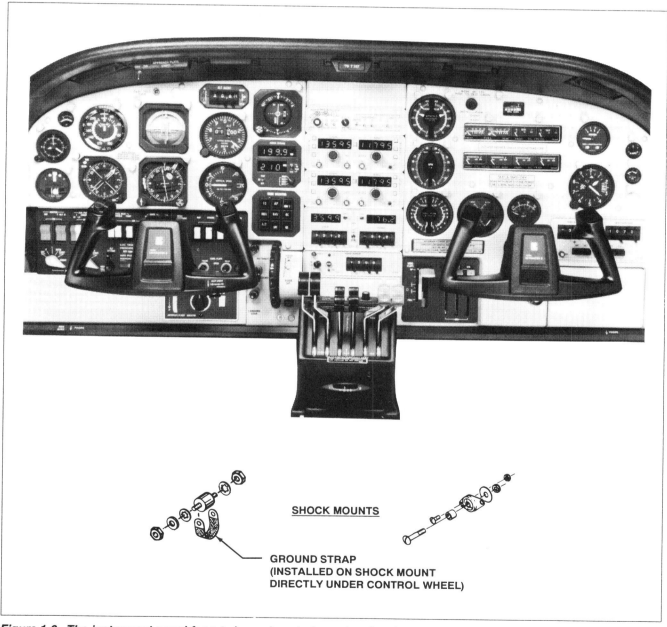

SHOCK MOUNTS

GROUND STRAP
(INSTALLED ON SHOCK MOUNT
DIRECTLY UNDER CONTROL WHEEL)

Figure 1-6. The instrument panel for a twin engine airplane showing the shock mounted sub--panel and two kinds of shock mounts. (Courtesy Cessna Aircraft Co.)

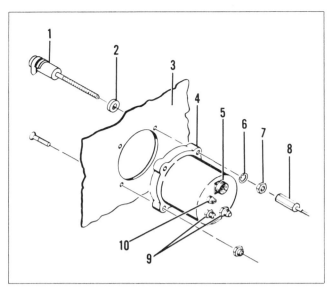

Figure 1-7. A post light type of lighting fixture (item 1) for aircraft instruments. (Courtesy Cessna Aircraft Co.)

Precipitation static, also known as P-static, is a build up of static electricity on the aircraft in flight. It can have an adverse effect on the operation of many instruments and radios. P-static is caused by friction between the aircraft structure and particles in the air such as rain, snow, ice and dust particles. It can also be caused by the hot exhaust of a turbine engine as it exits the large metal tailpipe or exhaust pipe. It cannot be prevented but the problems can be reduced by installing good static dischargers on the aircraft. These are normally installed on the trailing edges of main control surfaces and also occasionally on the tips of the wing and horizontal stabilizer.

## 5. FAA Regulations for Instruments

The FAA has many regulations that concern the installation of instruments in certificated aircraft. The examples that will be given apply to FAR Part 23 airplanes although the requirements for other categories of aircraft are often very similar. The requirements of FAR Part 91 would apply to any aircraft being operated under that section of the FARs. The FARs will not be quoted exactly, but

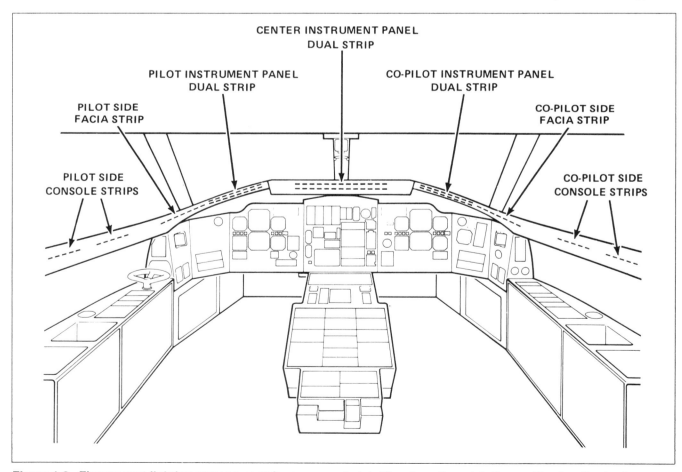

Figure 1-8. Fluorescent lighting arrangement for a corporate jet. (Courtesy Canadair Group, Bombardier Inc.)

**Figure 1-9. An un-supercharged reciprocating aircraft engine.**

will be paraphrased in order to simplify the wording and save space.

Since some of the FAR rules for instruments depend on what type of engine the aircraft uses, it is necessary to discuss the different types of powerplants found on certificated aircraft. A reciprocating engine is a piston engine which can either be supercharged or non-supercharged. The most common type of reciprocating engine on modern aircraft is the horizontally opposed type although many radial piston engines are still in service. Figure 1-9 shows an unsupercharged

horizontally opposed reciprocating engine. Figure 1-10 shows a radial engine with an internal supercharger. A turbine engine could be one of four types. The turbojet and turbofan engines are similar in that they are both rated in pounds of thrust. The difference is that with the turbofan engine some airflow bypasses the core of the engine and is acted upon only by the fan section as seen in figure 1-11. The turbojet engine illustrated in figure 1-12 does not use the bypass principle since all of the intake air passes through the length of the engine. In the FARs, the use of the term turbojet includes turbofan engines. The other two types of turbine engines are the turbo-propeller and turboshaft engines. These are both usually rated in horsepower because they deliver power to an output shaft (unlike turbojet and turbofan engines). The difference between the two is that the turboprop engine turns a propeller while the turboshaft engine powers the rotor drive gearbox of a helicopter. The reduction gearbox and output shaft of a turboprop engine can be seen on the left in figure 1-13.

---

**FAR Part 23**

This FAR covers the Airworthiness Standards for Normal, Utility, Acrobatic and Commuter category airplanes. Certain instrument requirements are a part of these Airworthiness Standards.

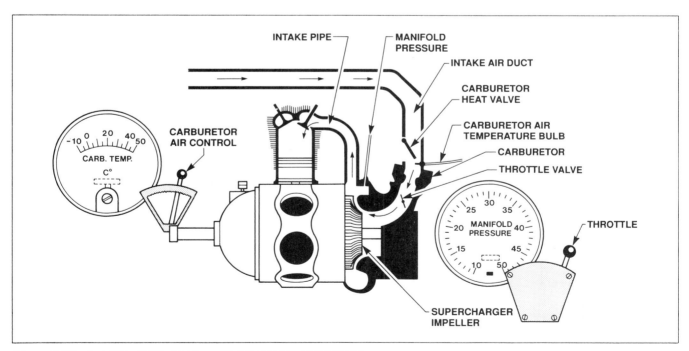

**Figure 1-10. A radial piston engine with internal supercharger.**

## FAR 23.841

The additional instruments required for pressurized airplanes are specified in this section. Figure 1-14 illustrates these instruments. Pressurized airplanes are required to have instruments to indicate:

1. Cabin differential pressure
2. Cabin altitude
3. Rate of change of cabin altitude (cabin rate of climb)

## FAR 23.1301

This FAR states that equipment must be labeled as to its identification, function and operating limitations. The colored markings on an airspeed indicator are examples of these required operating limitations.

## FAR 23.1303
### Required Flight and Navigation Instruments

1. Airspeed indicator
2. Altimeter
3. Magnetic direction indicator (compass)
4. Free air temperature for airplanes with turbine engines
5. Speed warning for turbine engine aircraft or others when Vmo/Mmo is greater than .8 Vd.

Notice that only the first three would be required for all FAR Part 23 airplanes.

## FAR 23.1305
### Required Powerplant Instruments

1. Fuel quantity for each tank.

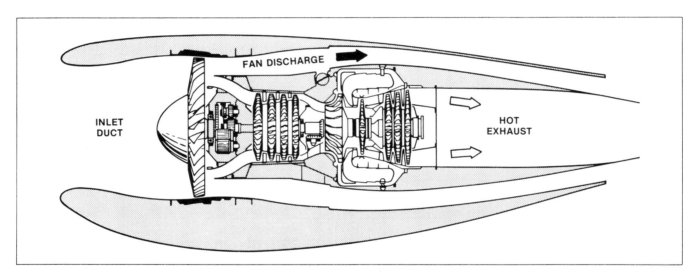

Figure 1-11. *A turbofan engine showing the bypass airflow which bypasses the core of the engine.*

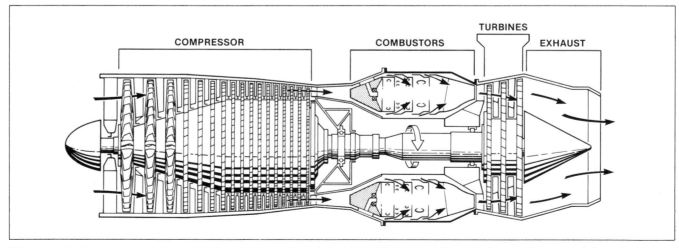

Figure 1-12. *A turbojet engine with the major sections identified. This type of engine has no bypass airflow.*

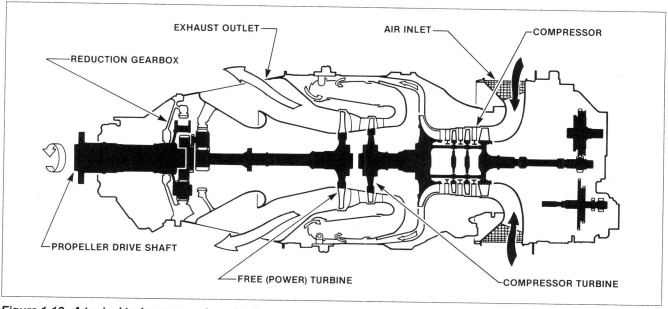

**Figure 1-13. A typical turboprop engine with the output shaft on the left. The engine could become a turboshaft engine if it was modified to drive the rotors of a helicopter.**

2. Oil pressure for each engine.

3. Oil pressure for each turbosupercharger (only with separate oil system).

4. Oil temperature for each engine.

5. Oil temperature for each turbosupercharger (only with separate oil system).

6. Tachometer for each engine.

7. Cylinder head temperature for:

   a. Air-cooled engines with cowl flaps.

   b. Reciprocating engine commuter category airplanes.

8. Fuel pressure if the engine is pump fed.

9. Manifold pressure for:

   a. Altitude engines.

   b. Reciprocating engine commuter category airplanes.

10. Oil quantity for each oil tank (if separate from engine).

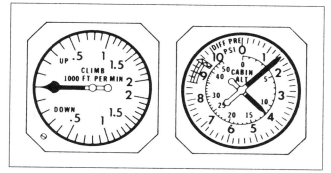

**Figure 1-14. The three instruments required for a pressurized aircraft.**

11. Gas temperature for turbine engines.

12. Fuel flowmeter for turbine engines.

13. Torquemeter for turbo-propeller engines.

14. EGT and carburetor inlet temperature for turbosupercharger installations if operating limitations can be exceeded.

Figure 1-15 shows a typical tachometer and manifold pressure gauge installation for a twin engine airplane with two pointers in each gauge for the left and right engines.

---

## FAR 23.1321
### Instrument Installation

1. Instruments must be plainly visible with minimum deviation of the pilot's position.

2. For multi-engine airplanes, identical instruments must be arranged to prevent confusion.

3. Instrument panel vibration must not damage the instruments.

4. For airplanes more than 6,000 lbs. maximum weight, the following instruments must be installed so that they are centered about the vertical plane of the pilot's vision in this order:

   a. Primary attitude instrument in the center.

   b. Airspeed indicator adjacent and to the left of the attitude instrument.

   c. Altitude instrument adjacent and to the right of the attitude instrument.

   d. Direction of flight instrument adjacent and below the attitude instrument.

The instrument referred to as the primary attitude instrument above would be an artificial horizon on smaller aircraft or an ADI on aircraft with more modern types of instruments. The direction of flight instrument in item 4 is not a magnetic compass. It would be a directional gyro on simple airplanes or an HSI on more sophisticated aircraft. In addition to the four standard instruments mentioned above as part of this "T" configuration, two other instruments are commonly installed in standard positions to make up an arrangement of six instruments. This is illustrated in figure 1-16. The actual appearance of the instruments in the standard configuration is shown in figure 1-17. The gyro instruments in figure 1-17 are the older style instruments.

## FAR 23.1322
### Warning, Caution and Advisory Lights

There are standard colors specified for certain indicator lights used in airplanes. A fire warning light for example would be red. The colors specified in this FAR are as follows:

RED — Warning — This is used when immediate attention is required.

AMBER — Caution — This is not as serious as a warning.

GREEN — Safe operation — normal operating range.

Any other color of indicator light can be used including white if it differs sufficiently from other colors and its meaning is specified by the manufacturer.

## FAR 23.1381
### Instrument Lights

Any instrument lights that are installed must make the instruments and controls easily readable and must be shielded so that they don't shine in the pilot's eyes. A cabin dome light is not acceptable as an instrument light.

## FAR 23.1541
### Markings and Placards

The airplane must have all placards required by the FARs and any additional placards that are required for safe operation if unusual design, handling or operational characteristics are present. In addition, each marking and placard:

1. Must be displayed in a conspicuous place.

2. Must not be easily erased, disfigured or obscured.

## FAR 23.1543
### Instrument Markings, General Requirements

1. When markings are on the cover glass, there must be a means to maintain the alignment of the glass with the dial (a slippage mark).

2. Each arc and line must be wide enough and located to be clearly visible to the pilot.

## FAR 23.1545
### Airspeed Indicator

The required markings are:

1. For the never exceed speed Vne, a red radial line.

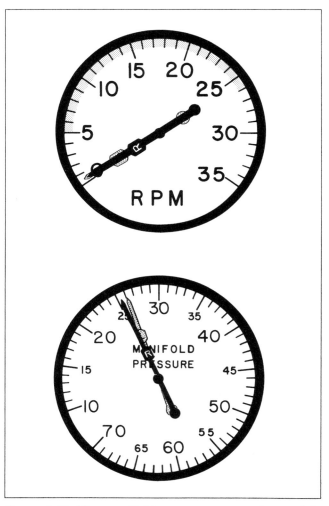

*Figure 1-15. The manifold pressure gauge is used in conjunction with a tachometer to set power on a supercharged engine.*

10

2. For the caution range, a yellow arc extending from the red radial line in item 1 to the upper limit of the green arc in item 3.

3. For the normal operating range, a green arc with the lower limit at Vs1 (maximum weight, landing gear and flaps retracted) and the upper

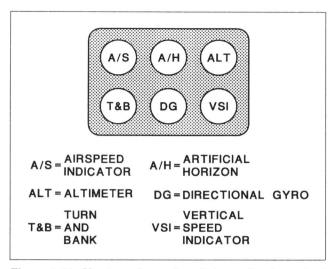

A/S = AIRSPEED INDICATOR      A/H = ARTIFICIAL HORIZON

ALT = ALTIMETER      DG = DIRECTIONAL GYRO

T&B = TURN AND BANK      VSI = VERTICAL SPEED INDICATOR

Figure 1-16. *Most modern aircraft have the important flight instruments installed in a standard configuration directly in front of the pilot.*

limit at Vno, maximum structural cruising speed.

4. For the flap operating range, a white arc with the lower limit at Vso and the upper limit at Vfe.

5. For the one-engine-inoperative best rate of climb speed, Vy, a blue sector extending from the Vy speed at sea level to the Vy speed at 5,000 ft. (or higher altitude as appropriate).

6. For the minimum control speed (one-engine-inoperative) Vmc, a red radial line.

Note: Items 1 through 3 do not apply to an aircraft for which a maximum operating speed, Vmo/Mmo has been established. These aircraft would need a maximum allowable airspeed indicator.

---

### FAR 23.1547
### Magnetic Direction Indicator

1. A placard must be installed on or near the magnetic direction indicator to show deviation error corrections.

2. The placard must show the calibration in level flight with the engines running.

Figure 1-17. *The types of instruments that might be found in the standard "T" configuration in a small airplane.*

3. The placard must state if calibration was made with radios on or off.
4. The placard must list the corrections for magnetic headings in increments of no more than 30°.
5. If the operation of electrical equipment can cause a deviation of more than 10°, the placard must identify that equipment.

## FAR 23.1549
### Powerplant Instruments

The required markings are:
1. Each maximum and minimum safe operating limit must be marked with a red radial line.
2. Each normal operating range must be marked with a green arc.
3. Each takeoff and precautionary range must be marked with a yellow arc.
4. Each engine or propeller range that is restricted because of vibration stresses must be marked with red arcs or red lines.

## FAR 23.1551
### Oil Quantity Indicator

It must be marked with sufficient increments to readily and accurately indicate the quantity of oil.

## FAR 23.1553
### Fuel Quantity Indicator

If the unusable fuel supply for any tank exceeds one gallon or 5% of tank capacity, whichever is greater, a red arc must be marked to extend from calibrated zero to the lowest reading obtainable in level flight.

## FAR 23.1563
### Airspeed Placards

There must be an airspeed placard in clear view of the pilot and as close as practical to the airspeed indicator. This placard must list:
1. The design maneuvering speed Va.
2. The maximum landing gear operating speed Vlo.

## FAR 43 Appendix A
### Appliance Major Repairs
1. Calibration and repair of instruments
2. Calibration of radio equipment

## FAR 43 Appendix D
### Scope and Detail of Items to Inspect For 100-Hour and Annual Inspections

(4) Instruments — inspect for poor condition, mounting, marking and where practical for improper operation.

## FAR 65.81
### General Privileges and Limitations

(a) A certificated mechanic may perform or supervise the maintenance, preventive maintenance or alteration of an aircraft or appliance or a part thereof, for which he is rated but excluding major repairs to and major alterations of propellers and any repair to or alteration of instruments.

## FAR 91.9
### Powered Civil Aircraft with Standard Category U.S. Airworthiness Certificates; Instrument and Equipment Requirements

Visual Flight Rules Day — For VFR, the following are required:
1. Airspeed indicator
2. Altimeter
3. Magnetic direction indicator
4. Tachometer for each engine
5. Oil pressure gauge for each engine
6. Temperature gauge for each liquid-cooled engine
7. Oil temperature gauge for each air-cooled engine
8. Manifold pressure gauge for each altitude engine
9. Fuel quantity gauge for each tank
10. Landing gear position indicator if landing gear is retractable

Visual Flight Rules Night — For night VFR in addition to the requirements for VFR day, the following are required:
1. Position lights
2. Anti-collision lights (red or white)
3. Adequate source of electrical energy for all electrical equipment
4. If operating for hire, one electric landing light
5. Spare fuses

Instrument Flight Rules — For IFR, the following are required
1. The equipment for VFR day and night as appropriate; PLUS
2. Two-way radio communications equipment
3. Radio navigation equipment

4. Gyroscopic rate-of-turn indicator (except aircraft with three attitude instruments)

5. Slip-skid indicator

6. Sensitive altimeter

7. Clock which displays hours, minutes and seconds

8. Generator or alternator

9. Gyroscopic bank and pitch indicator (artificial horizon)

10. Gyroscopic direction indicator (DG or equivalent)

11. For flight at and above 24,000 ft. MSL, a DME system

12. For Category II operations, additional equipment is required as listed in Appendix A.

A modern digital aircraft clock is shown in figure 1-18. The clock required for IFR does not have to be a digital clock, but it must display hours, minutes and seconds. The older type of aircraft clock was a conventional kind of round clock with three hands.

## C. Pitot-Static System Instruments

### 1. Methods of Pressure Measurement

Pressure instruments are those which obtain readings by measuring the pressure at one or more places in terms of a liquid or gas pressure.

Figure 1-18. A digital aircraft clock able to display hours, minutes and seconds. (Courtesy Canadair Group, Bombardier Inc.

### a. Pressure Measuring Sensors

There are three common types of sensors that can be used to mechanically measure a fluid pressure.

#### 1) Bourdon Tube

A bourdon tube is a curved, hollow tube made of a springy metal (often a specially treated brass material) (figure 1-19).

One end of the tube is anchored and the other is free to move and fastened through linkages to the indicator pointer or similar device. As pressure is applied to the inside of the bourdon tube, it will try to straighten out as a result of the imbalance of forces on the walls of the curved tube. This motion is transmitted to the indicator needle or pointer through gears and linkages. The bourdon tube is used to measure relatively high pressure, typically 20 PSI or more.

#### 2) Diaphragm

A diaphragm is a thin, lens shaped hollow metal container. It is used to measure relatively low pressures, as in an altimeter or airspeed indicator. Typically, it is made of a very thin, springy metal (beryllium copper is often used). One side is anchored and the other side is connected through gears and linkages to the pointer. See figure 1-20.

#### 3) Bellows

A bellows is somewhat similar to a diaphragm, but it is longer and has accordion folds to typically allow a greater range of motion. It measures relatively

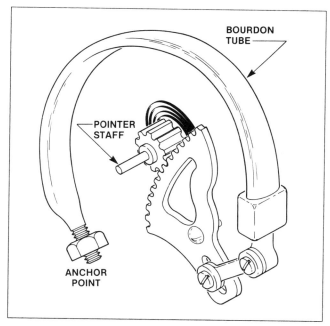

Figure 1-19. The bourdon tube pressure measuring device for instruments.

low pressures and a common use is to measure differential pressure. It that case the bellows would be divided into two separate chambers with a different pressure source connected to each one as seen in figure 1-21.

### b. Units of Measure for Pressure

Many different units of measure are used for pressure. In aviation, a number of units are in common use. Some examples are listed below.

1. Pounds per Square Inch — PSI
2. Inches of Mercury — in. Hg
3. Millibars — Mbar
4. Kilopascals — kPa

### c. Types of Pressure Measurement

Pressure is measured compared to some reference value. Standard abbreviations are used to designate what this reference level is for a particular pressure measurement. The three common designations are:

1. Absolute Pressure — This is a pressure compared to a perfect vacuum. No pressure can be below a vacuum, so there is never a negative absolute pressure. Examples of this designation are PSIA and in. Hg absolute.
2. Gauge Pressure — This is a pressure compared to ambient pressure, usually outside atmospheric pressure, as in PSIG, etc.
3. Differential Pressure — This is used to designate two different pressures in the aircraft that are compared to each other, as in PSID.

Examples of these using aircraft instruments are the manifold pressure gauge which measures absolute pressure, the oil pressure gauge measures gauge pressure and the cabin differential pressure gauge is calibrated in PSID.

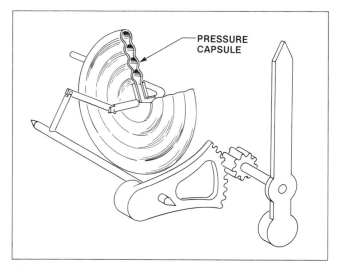

Figure 1-20. The diaphragm or aneroid pressure measuring device.

We will now examine the basic aircraft flight instruments that operate as pressure instruments. These are often referred to as the pitot-static instruments because they utilize pitot pressure and static pressure.

## 2. Standard Atmosphere Table

Altimeters and other instruments obtain readings by measurements of the pressure at various altitudes. The average or standard pressures and temperatures at different altitudes are contained in a table of the Standard Atmosphere. The values given in this table are accepted by virtually all countries of the world for scientific and aviation purposes (figure 1-22).

## 3. Altimeters

The altimeter is a basic required instrument for all certificated aircraft. It measures the atmospheric pressure and displays it as altitude in feet. This altitude is called mean sea level (MSL) since it is referenced to the average level of the major oceans. The measurement of altitude is based on the standard atmosphere table and the changes in pressure with altitude changes that it gives.

### a. Non-Sensitive and Sensitive Altimeters

### 1) Non-Sensitive Altimeter

A non-sensitive altimeter has only one pointer and it makes one complete revolution for each 10,000 ft. in altitude. If the pointer was on the number 8,

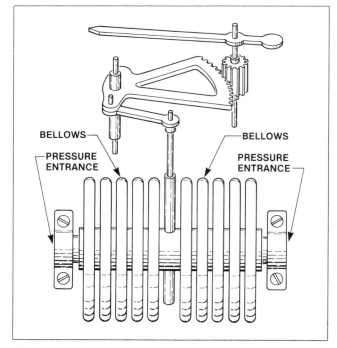

Figure 1-21. An example of a bellows being used to measure a differential pressure.

that would represent 8,000 ft.; but it could also indicate 18,000 ft. For this reason, this type of altimeter is only used for small, simple aircraft that don't operate at high altitudes. A non-sensitive altimeter is illustrated in figure 1-23.

### 2) Sensitive Altimeter

A sensitive altimeter is more sensitive and easier to read than the non-sensitive type. A sensitive altimeter may have three separate pointers or a single pointer and a drum readout.

On an altimeter with three pointers, the longest pointer makes one revolution for each 1,000 ft., the second pointer makes one revolution for each 10,000 ft., and the shortest pointer makes one revolution for each 100,000 ft. The three pointer

sensitive altimeter is shown in figure 1-24. A major problem with this type of altimeter is that the smallest pointer can be covered up by one of the other two pointers which makes it easy to misread the altimeter. The newer kind of three pointer altimeter

*Figure 1-23. A simple non-sensitive aircraft altimeter. (Courtesy Piper Aircraft Corp.)*

| ALTITUDE FT. | DENSITY RATIO $\sigma$ | PRESSURE RATIO $\delta$ | TEMPER-ATURE °F | SPEED OF SOUND $\alpha$ KNOTS |
|---|---|---|---|---|
| 0 | 1.0000 | 1.0000 | 59.00 | 661.7 |
| 1000 | 0.9711 | 0.9644 | 55.43 | 659.5 |
| 2000 | 0.9428 | 0.9298 | 51.87 | 657.2 |
| 3000 | 0.9151 | .08962 | 48.30 | 654.9 |
| 4000 | 0.8881 | 0.8637 | 44.74 | 652.6 |
| 5000 | 0.8617 | 0.8320 | 41.17 | 650.3 |
| 6000 | 0.8359 | 0.8014 | 37.60 | 647.9 |
| 7000 | 0.8106 | 0.7716 | 34.04 | 645.6 |
| 8000 | .07860 | 0.7428 | 30.47 | 643.3 |
| 9000 | 0.7620 | 0.7148 | 26.90 | 640.9 |
| 10000 | 0.7385 | 0.6877 | 23.34 | 638.6 |
| 15000 | 0.6292 | 0.5643 | 5.51 | 626.7 |
| 20000 | 0.5328 | 0.4595 | −12.32 | 614.6 |
| 25000 | 0.4481 | 0.3711 | −30.15 | 602.2 |
| 30000 | 0.3741 | 0.2970 | −47.98 | 589.5 |
| 35000 | 0.3099 | 0.2353 | −65.82 | 576.6 |
| *36089 | 0.2971 | 0.2234 | −69.70 | 573.8 |
| 40000 | 0.2462 | 0.1851 | −69.70 | 573.8 |
| 45000 | 0.1936 | 0.1455 | −69.70 | 573.8 |
| 50000 | 0.1522 | 0.1145 | −69.70 | 573.8 |
| 55000 | 0.1197 | 0.0900 | −69.70 | 573.8 |
| 60000 | 0.0941 | 0.0708 | −69.70 | 573.8 |
| 65000 | 0.0740 | 0.0557 | −69.70 | 573.8 |
| 70000 | 0.0582 | 0.0438 | −69.70 | 573.8 |
| 75000 | 0.0458 | 0.0344 | −69.70 | 573.8 |
| 80000 | 0.0360 | 0.0271 | −69.70 | 573.8 |
| 85000 | 0.0280 | 0.0213 | −64.80 | 577.4 |
| 90000 | 0.0217 | 0.0168 | −56.57 | 583.4 |
| 95000 | 0.0169 | 0.0134 | −48.34 | 589.3 |
| 100000 | 0.0132 | 0.0107 | −40.11 | 595.2 |

**\* GEOPOTENTIAL OF THE TROPOPAUSE**

*Figure 1-22. A reference table of the Standard Atmosphere.*

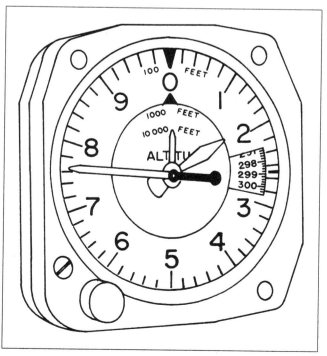

*Figure 1-24. The older style three-pointer sensitive altimeter.*

seen in figure 1-25 has been modified to make it easier to read. The pointer that makes one revolution in 100,000 ft. has been extended to the outside of the face with a small triangle on the end so it cannot be covered up. In addition, a small window shows a striped pattern below about 15,000 ft. (at higher altitudes the striped symbol disappears). The sensitive altimeter with one pointer as seen in figure 1-26 uses the drum readout and a single pointer which makes one revolution for each 1,000 ft. The drum readout may have three or five digits displayed, but in any case the combination of the two permits accurate reading of the altimeter.

### b. Altimeter Mechanism

The internal mechanism of the altimeter consists of three diaphragms in series. This creates an altimeter which is sensitive to very small changes in pressure and which has a large enough range of measurement to read altitudes of 35,000 to 50,000 ft. or more.

Inside the case of the altimeter is a bimetallic device which gives automatic compensation for temperature changes to ensure accurate readings. There is a knob on the front of the altimeter which operates a mechanism that compensates for non-standard atmospheric pressure. The standard atmosphere table gives the standard pressure at sea level as 29.92 in. Hg, but the actual atmosphere pressure in any given location seldom matches the

*Figure 1-25. The newer style three-pointer sensitive altimeter uses a different pointer and a striped symbol that is visible below about 15,000 ft. as aids to make reading the altimeter easier.*

values in the table. Weather systems with higher or lower pressure are constantly moving across the surface of the earth.

It is due to these variations in pressure that the knob on the front of the altimeter must be adjusted to the current barometric pressure setting for the area in which it is operating. There is a small window on the altimeter which displays the current barometric pressure setting. It is commonly called the Kollsman window. If for example a pilot received an altimeter setting of 30.01 from an air traffic controller, that number would be set into the Kollsman window of the altimeter. When the pilot sets the altimeter to the correct setting before takeoff, the indication on the altimeter will show the height of that airport above sea level. Outside the United Sates, a different unit of measurement is often used for barometric pressure settings. This unit of measurement is millibars (MB) and the altimeters found in many modern aircraft have two Kollsman windows: one for inches of mercury and one for millibars. Figure 1-26 shows the two windows and the barometric pressure setting knob.

### c. Altimeter Operation

The diaphragms of an altimeter are sealed at the factory. The case of the altimeter is connected to the static ports on the airplane. The static pressure outside the airplane is conducted to the instrument case by tubing and hose. If the airplane climbs, the reduced pressure in the case causes the diaphragms to expand and move the pointers to indicate a higher altitude.

The altimeter uses three diaphragms in series to increase the range of measurement. The mechanism uses very delicate gearing which is designed in such a way that a very small movement of the diaphragm causes a large motion of the pointer or pointers. Under certain circumstances it has a tendency to stick and some aircraft have a vibrator on the instrument panel or in the altimeter to prevent this sticking.

### d. Encoding Altimeter

An altimeter related device which is found on many aircraft is the encoding altimeter system. The purpose of this system is to send information concerning the aircraft's altitude to a radar system on the ground so that it can be displayed on a radar scope. The data is transmitted to the ground using a special aircraft radio called a transponder. An encoding altimeter system (also known as Mode C), supplies the electrical signal to the transponder that contains this altitude data. An aircraft encoding altimeter and transponder are required for three different conditions:

1. Flight operations within a TCA (terminal control area) or Class B airspace.
2. Flight operations within an ARSA (airport radar service area) or Class C airspace.
3. Flight operations above 10,000 ft. MSL and over 2500 ft. AGL.

The connections for the encoding feature of an altimeter and an altimeter vibrator can be seen in figure 1-27.

## 4. Airspeed Indicators

Airspeed indicators are required on all certificated aircraft except free balloons. This instrument gives the pilot an indication of his speed through the air, it does not measure groundspeed. The airspeed indicator is a pitot-static system instrument that is connected to both the pitot pressure source and the static pressure source. It measures the difference between these two pressures as indicated airspeed.

On aircraft operated in the United States, the unit of measurement for airspeed indicators is nautical miles per hour (knots), statute miles per hour (MPH) or both on the same instrument.

### a. Types of Airspeed

There are three types of airspeed associated with the airspeed indicator. This is because it is subject to a number of errors or inaccuracies. The three types of airspeed are:

1. Indicated Airspeed — This is the reading on the instrument
2. Calibrated Airspeed — This is indicated airspeed which has been corrected for position and instrument error. The pitot tube is mounted at a fixed angle to the longitudinal axis of the aircraft and at slow speeds and high angles of attack there will be an error. The pilot determines the correction for calibrated airspeed by consulting a table in the Pilot's Operating Handbook, an example of which is shown in figure 1-28.
3. True Airspeed — This is calibrated airspeed which has been corrected for altitude and temperature effects. At high altitudes the indicated airspeed will be much less than the actual speed through the air which is true airspeed. For example, at 41,000 ft. the indicated airspeed is only about half the true airspeed. At sea level on a standard day with the aircraft in level cruise flight, indicated and true airspeed are usually the same.

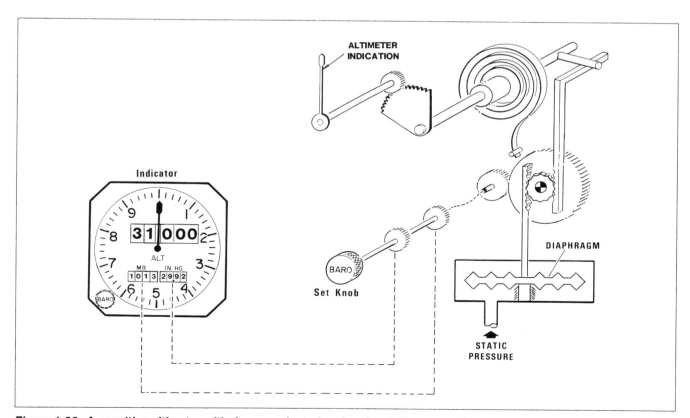

Figure 1-26. *A sensitive altimeter with drum readout showing the static connection to the outside of the diaphragm.*

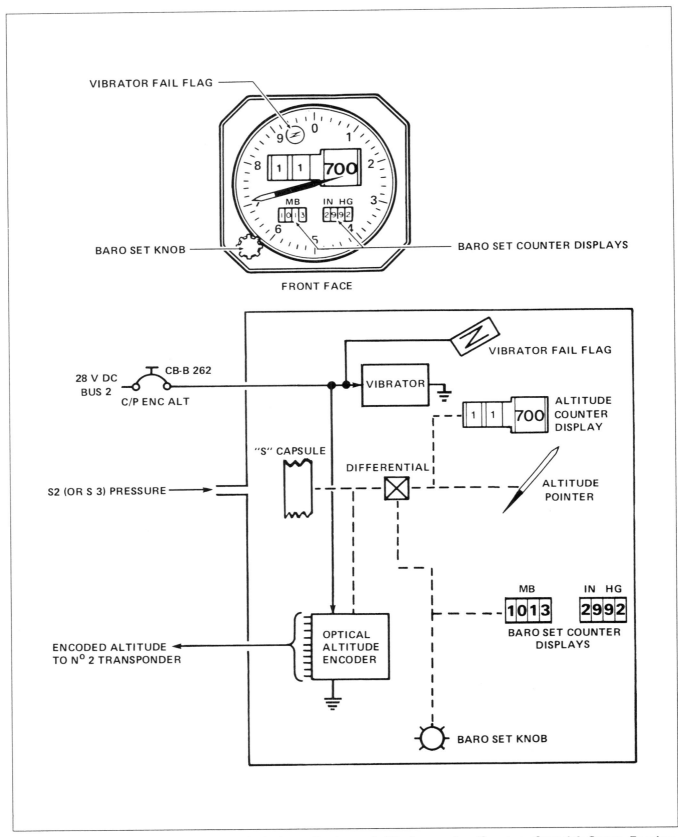

**Figure 1-27.** *An altimeter installation that includes a vibrator and altitude encoder. (Courtesy Canadair Group, Bombardier Inc.)*

18

## b. Airspeed Indicator Operation

The airspeed indicator uses a diaphragm that measures the differential pressure between pitot pressure and static pressure. Pitot pressure is connected to the inside of the diaphragm and static pressure to the outside as shown in figure 1-29. A pitot tube has an opening facing forward into the relative wind so that it measures ram pressure effects. The static ports simply measure outside atmospheric pressure. The faster the airplane goes, the greater will be the difference in pressure.

## c. Airspeed Indicator Markings

The operating limitations airspeeds that would be found on a general aviation twin-engine airplane are listed below.

| FLAPS UP | | | | | | | | |
|---|---|---|---|---|---|---|---|---|
| KIAS | 80 | 100 | 120 | 140 | 160 | 180 | 200 | 210 |
| KCAS | 81 | 101 | 120 | 139 | 159 | 177 | 196 | 206 |
| FLAPS 10° | | | | | | | | |
| KIAS | 70 | 80 | 90 | 100 | 120 | 140 | 160 | 175 |
| KCAS | 72 | 81 | 91 | 100 | 119 | 138 | 157 | 171 |
| FLAPS 30° | | | | | | | | |
| KIAS | 60 | 70 | 80 | 90 | 100 | 110 | 125 | - - - |
| KCAS | 64 | 72 | 80 | 89 | 98 | 108 | 123 | - - - |
| Note: For illustration only; not to be used for flight planning | | | | | | | | |

*Figure 1-28. The table of calibrated airspeed corrections for a twin-engine airplane. (Courtesy Cessna Aircraft Co.)*

1. Vso — Stall speed with gear and flaps down. This is shown by the bottom of the white arc.
2. Vs1 — Stall speed with gear and flaps up. The bottom of the green arc.
3. Vmc — Minimum control speed with critical engine failed. A red radial line in the lower range of indicated airspeeds.
4. Vfe — Maximum speed with flaps down. Top of white arc.
5. Vno — Maximum structural cruise. Top of green arc or bottom of yellow arc.
6. Vne — Never exceed speed. a red radial line at the highest permitted airspeed, also the top of the yellow arc.
7. Vyse — Best rate of climb speed with one engine inoperative. A blue line or sector.

The aircraft should only be operated in the yellow arc range with caution and in smooth air. Figure 1-30 shows the colored markings for the airspeed indicator on a single-engine airplane. A twin-engine airplane would have the additional markings for Vmc and Vyse. The principle of critical engine and Vmc is illustrated in figure 1-31. The critical engine is the engine whose failure would produce the most adverse effect on the handling characteristics of the airplane. Since the flight controls become more effective at higher speeds, the concept of Vmc involves high engine power and slow speeds such as occurs during takeoff. During initial climb after takeoff, the thrust from the propellers is offset to the right side as shown in figure 1-31 if both

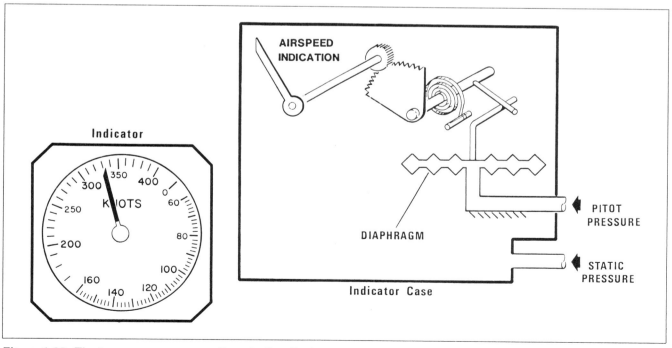

*Figure 1-29. The two pressure connections to the diaphragm in an airspeed indicator.*

propellers rotate clockwise. In this case, the critical engine is the left engine since the thrust line for the right engine is farther from the longitudinal axis of the airplane. Some twin engine airplanes are designed so that the propellers rotate in opposite directions. In that case, the two engines are equally critical. The Vmc speed would be the same no matter which engine failed. The reason that the Vmc marking is red is that maintaining a speed above Vmc can be very important to prevent loss of control. If an engine fails after takeoff and the airplane is below Vmc speed, the airplane will start to turn and roll and the motion cannot be stopped with full opposite control inputs. This has caused many accidents and many deaths. Vmc is a critical operating limitation that the pilot must keep in mind. The speed for Vyse is obviously higher than Vmc, it is the speed the pilot would use after an engine failure to get the best rate of climb possible.

A table of airspeed indicator operating limitations markings for a small twin engine airplane is shown in figure 1-32.

All of the important operating limitations airspeeds will not be shown on the airspeed indicator. Some of them will be displayed on a placard next to the airspeed indicator like that seen in figure 1-33 and others will only be found in the Pilot's Operating Handbook or Airplane Flight Manual.

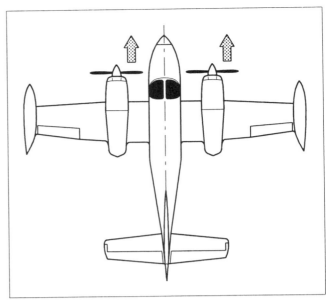

*Figure 1-31. An illustration of why the left engine is the critical engine when both propellers turn clockwise. At slow speeds, the thrust lines from the propellers are offset to the right which places the thrust line of the right engine farther from the center line of the aircraft. Vmc is the slowest speed at which control can be maintained when the critical engine fails.*

| MARKING | KIAS VALUE OR RANGE | SIGNIFICANCE |
|---|---|---|
| Red Radial | 65 | Minimum Control Speed |
| White Arc | 58-125 | Full Flap Operating Range. Lower limit is maximum weight $V_{S_O}$ in landing configuration. Upper limit is maximum speed permissible with flaps extended. |
| Green Arc | 66-175 | Normal Operating Range. Lower limit is maximum weight $V_S$ at most forward C.G. with flaps retracted. Upper limit is maximum structural cruising speed. |
| Blue Radial | 97 | Single Engine Best Rate-of-Climb Speed at Maximum Weight. |
| Yellow Arc | 175-210 | Operations must be conducted with caution and only in smooth air. |
| Red Radial | 210 | Maximum speed for all operations. |
| Note: For illustration purposes only; not to be used for flight planning. | | |

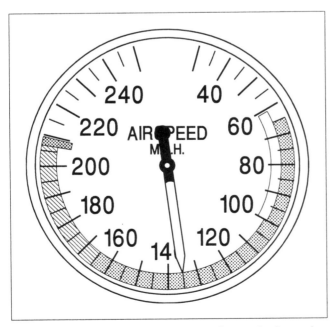

*Figure 1-30. The airspeed indicator for a single engine airplane showing the colored operating limitations markings.*

*Figure 1-32. A table of airspeed indicator markings for a twin engine airplane. This table is found in the Pilot's Operating Handbook or Approved Airplane Flight Manual. (Courtesy Cessna Aircraft Co.)*

### d. Maximum Allowable Airspeed Indicator

On high speed aircraft that operate at high altitudes, it is not practical to use the colored markings on the airspeed indicator because the values change significantly as the aircraft climbs to higher altitudes.

These aircraft would use a different type of airspeed indicator called the maximum allowable airspeed indicator. It is found on turboprop airplanes, bizjets and air carrier jets.

The maximum allowable airspeed indicator has two pointers; one gives the normal indicated airspeed and the second one, which has a striped or checked pattern, is connected to a separate diaphragm and it shows the Vmo speed at the existing altitude. The two pointers can be seen in figure 1-34. On a jet airplane, the maximum allowable airspeed indicator will also usually include a Mach number display as shown in figure 1-34.

### e. Machmeter

A machmeter is required for jet airplanes because they will have a maximum safe operating speed expressed in Mach numbers. This is in addition to the maximum safe indicated airspeed. This is necessary because if the safe Mach number is exceeded, the airplane can become difficult or impossible to

| MAX SPEED KIAS | |
|---|---|
| MANEUVERING | 148 |
| EXTEND GEAR | 175 |
| RETRACT GEAR | 150 |
| GEAR DOWN | 210 |

Note: For illustration purposes only; not to be used for flight planning.

*Figure 1-33. The airspeed limitations placard that would be installed near the airspeed indicator for a twin engine airplane. (Courtesy Cessna Aircraft Co.)*

control. Mach number indicates the ratio of the aircraft's true airspeed compared to the speed of sound. A speed of Mach 0.8 means the aircraft is traveling at 80% of the speed of sound. The speed of sound is about 760 MPH at sea level, but it is affected by temperature. As the temperature decreases, the speed of sound is also decreased. Since temperature decreases with an increase in altitude, the speed of sound is reduced at higher altitudes. At 35,000 ft. the speed of sound would be about 660 MPH. If an airplane climbed from sea level to 35,000 ft. at a constant true airspeed, the Mach number would steadily increase. Most civilian jet airplanes have an Mmo (maximum operating Mach number) of about 0.8 to 0.87. As an airplane approaches its critical Mach number, a shock wave begins to form on the upper surface of the wing as seen in figure 1-35. This will occur at flight speeds below Mach 1 because the air accelerates as it moves over the top of the wing. This shock wave disrupts airflow and causes the center of pressure to shift aft. As aircraft speed gets closer to Mmo, the shock wave gets stronger until a point is reached where control of the aircraft may be lost. A loss of control at high speed and high altitude can and has resulted in the loss of the aircraft—it is an important operating limitation for jet airplanes. The machmeter instrument has a diaphragm like a normal airspeed indicator that is connected to pitot and static pressure. It also has an additional diaphragm which modifies the movement of the pointer to compensate for the effects of altitude and temperature (figure 1-36).

## 5. Vertical Speed Indicator

The last of the three basic pitot-static system instruments is identified by several names: a vertical speed indicator (VSI), a rate of climb indicator (ROC)

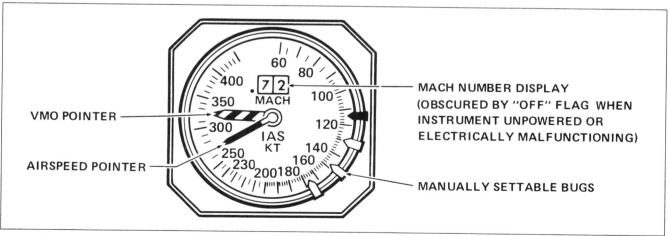

*Figure 1-34. The combined maximum allowable airspeed indicator and Machmeter for a corporate jet airplane. (Courtesy Canadair Group, Bombardier Inc.)*

and a vertical velocity indicator (VVI). This instrument measures the rate of change of static pressure. Since static pressure decreases with an increase in altitude, it can measure the rate of climb or descent of the aircraft. The unit of measurement is feet per minute (FPM) as seen on the instrument face in figure 1-37.

### a. Basic Operation of VSI

Static pressure is connected directly to the inside of the diaphragm, but it is connected to the case pressure (outside of the diaphragm) by a small orifice or restrictor opening as indicated in figure 1-38. If the airplane climbs, the pressure will decrease more rapidly inside the diaphragm than outside

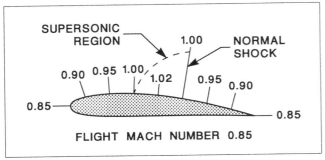

Figure 1-35. *A shock wave will form on the upper surface of the wing when the airplane is traveling at less than the speed of sound.*

of it. The diaphragm will be compressed and that will move the pointer to show the rate of change of altitude in feet per minute. The opposite occurs during descents. When the aircraft levels off, the pressures equalize and the pointer returns to zero. The instrument case usually includes an overpressure valve to prevent damage at rates of climb or descent in excess of the maximum reading for that instrument.

Because of the very small size of the restrictor opening, the pointer tends to react slowly to rapid changes in altitude. This problem is reduced in the instrument called an Instantaneous Vertical Speed Indicator (IVSI).

### b. Instantaneous Vertical Speed Indicator

The IVSI has two little cylinders with pistons and springs which can be seen in figure 1-39. They are called accelerometer operated dashpots. When the aircraft pitches up or down suddenly, the pistons will move and force air into or out of the diaphragm to get the pointer moving quickly. In a steady rate climb or descent, they will have no effect on the pointer.

### c. Variometer

The variometer is a very sensitive version of the VSI which is used by gliders. The mechanism uses a movable vane in a small air tight metal container.

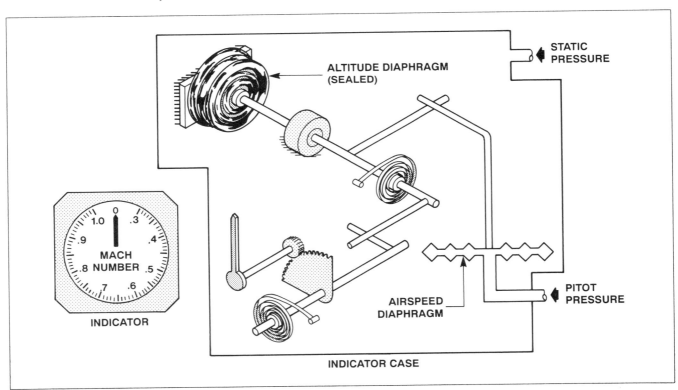

Figure 1-36. *The Machmeter has an extra diaphragm to compensate for altitude effects.*

The vane divides the container into two chambers. One chamber is connected to the static port and the other is connected to an air bottle. The air storage bottle is used because it will hold more air than a small instrument case and this improves sensitivity. With the variometer, even small changes in rate of climb or descent can be detected.

## 6. Accelerometer

The accelerometer is an instrument that measures the "G" forces or acceleration forces on an aircraft in flight. The common application is in an aerobatic airplane where the pilot needs to know how much "G" force the airplane is being subjected to in order to prevent overstress of the structure.

The mechanism of the accelerometer consists of a weight which is connected by a cord and pulleys to the shaft that operates the pointer. The internal arrangement of an accelerometer is shown in figure 1-40. The weight is supported by a guide shaft which only allows it to move up and down relative to the guide shaft. A positive G acceleration will cause the weight to move downward and rotate the pointer to show a higher positive G loading. There is a balance spring on the pointer shaft pulley to balance the forces. The instrument is installed in the airplane so that it measures acceleration along the vertical axis of the airplane. The normal at rest indication on the ground or in level flight is +1 Gs. The instrument face of an accelerometer is shown in figure 1-41. The instrument has three pointers connected to the operating mechanism. One pointer gives a readout of the current acceleration force along the vertical axis. The other two pointers have a ratchet device so that they will

remain at the highest reading recorded for positive and negative forces. A knob is included on the instrument to reset the two recording pointers.

## 7. Pitot-Static Systems

### a. Pitot and Static Ports

The system of ports and tubing on the aircraft which supplies pitot and static pressure for the instruments is called the pitot-static system. The pitot tube is an open tube which faces forward into the relative wind in flight. It measures the ram pressure of the airstream. On small airplanes, the pitot tube is usually installed below the wing. On other aircraft, it is installed on the nose section of the aircraft.

The static ports are openings at right angles to the relative wind so that they will measure static pressure and not be affected by the speed of the aircraft. The static ports are most often located in pairs along the sides of the fuselage. On some aircraft, the static ports are along the sides or top and bottom surfaces of the pitot tube so that both pressures are measured with the same probe. A pitot tube which includes static ports and electric heaters to prevent icing is shown in figure 1-42.

With the static ports in pairs on opposite sides of the fuselage, any errors caused by sideslip will be eliminated. Aircraft that must operate in adverse weather conditions will require an electrical heating system for the pitot tubes and static ports to prevent icing. Air carrier jets and similar types of aircraft usually employ multiple pitot tubes and static ports for safety. A typical arrangement of this kind with three pitot tubes and three sets of static ports is illustrated in figure 1-43. Notice that the instruments on the left and right sides of the cockpit

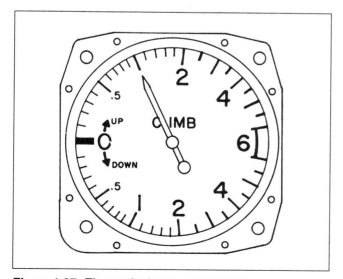

Figure 1-37. The vertical speed indicator has two scales: one for climbs and one for descents.

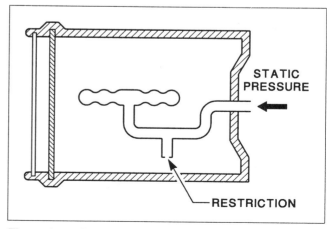

Figure 1-38. The VSI has a restrictor in the connection to the case which causes a difference between diaphragm and case pressure during climbs and descents.

are operated by totally separate pressure sources. By routinely cross checking the instrument indications from the left and right sides, a faulty indication can be identified.

### b. Blockage of Ports

When pitot-static lines or ports become blocked by ice or other factors, it can cause the instruments to give improper readings. If the static pressure is blocked, the altimeter will remain at the current indication and the VSI will continue to read zero even when the aircraft climbs or descends. This problem would usually be noticed by the pilot. The airspeed indicator uses both pitot and static pressure and a blockage in flight could be more difficult to detect.

Let's use the example of an airplane that is flying at 10,000 ft. when the static ports become blocked. The pressure in the static system will be sealed in and won't change when the aircraft climbs or descends. If the airplane climbs at a constant speed, the airspeed indicator will show a decreasing airspeed. If the airplane descends, the airspeed indicator will indicate a higher than actual airspeed. Just the opposite would happen if the pitot tube iced over or was blocked in some other way in flight. A climb would cause the airspeed indicator to read higher than it should and a descent would cause it to read lower than actual airspeed.

The lines and connections in a pitot-static system should be maintained in good condition. Even though they don't have to handle high pressures, the instruments are very sensitive to small changes in pressure so that even very small leaks can cause errors in the instruments.

The tubing and hoses that are used are not very strong and should be inspected carefully for damage. The fittings and connections should be installed with care and torqued to specified values.

### c. Altimeter System Tests and Inspections

There are some FAR requirements for testing of altimeter systems. These will be covered next along

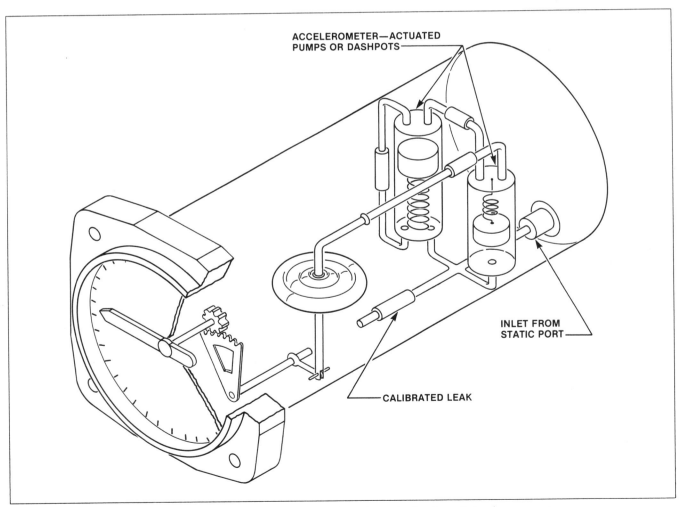

***Figure 1-39. The acceleration actuated dashpots in the IVSI reduce the lag in pointer movement.***

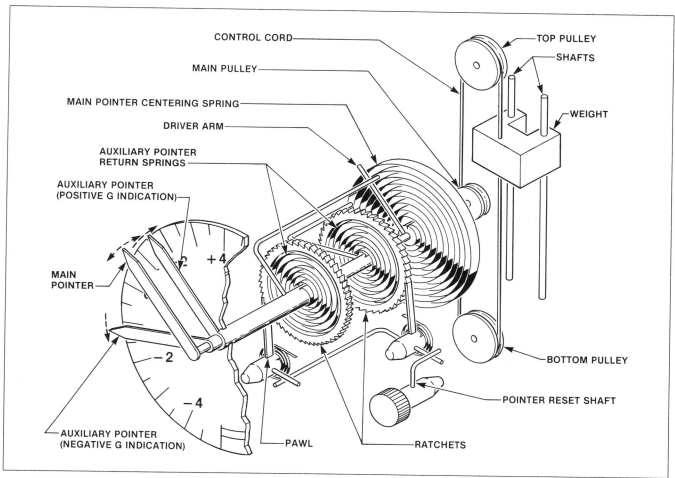

*Figure 1-40. The internal mechanism of a three-pointer accelerometer.*

*Figure 1-41. Accelerometer instrument face with three pointers.*

with the procedures for other tests which might not be required at specific intervals but would be conducted whenever a problem was suspected. A portable pitot-static system test set that could be used for these tests is seen in figure 1-44.

## FAR 91.411

### Altimeter System and Altitude Reporting Equipment Tests and Inspections

a. No person may operate an airplane, or helicopter, in controlled airspace under IFR unless:

1. Within the preceding 24 calendar months, each static pressure system, each altimeter instrument, and each automatic pressure altitude reporting system has been tested and inspected and found to comply with Appendix E of Part 43 of this chapter;

2. Except for the use of system drain and alternate static pressure valves, following any opening and closing of a static pressure system, that system has been tested and

inspected and found to comply with paragraph (a) Appendices E and F of Part 43 of this chapter; and

3. Following installation or maintenance on the automatic pressure altitude reporting system of the ATC transponder where any error could have been introduced, the entire system has been tested, inspected and found to comply with paragraph (c) Appendix E of part 43 of this chapter.

b. The tests required by paragraph (a.) of this section must be conducted by:

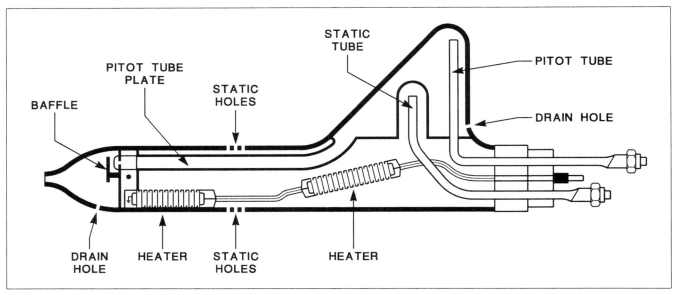

Figure 1-42. A pitot tube which also contains static ports and electric heating elements.

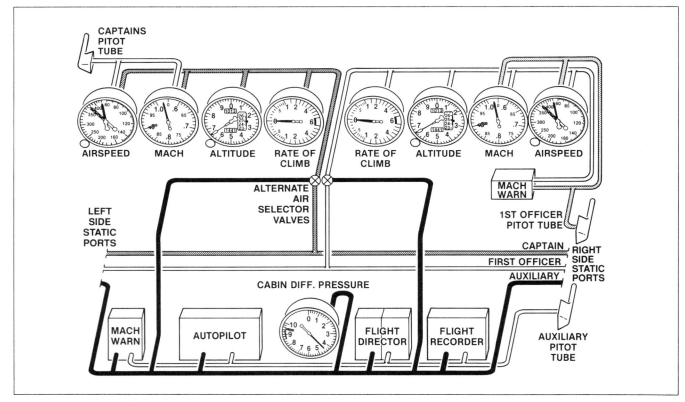

Figure 1-43. The pitot-static system for a large jet airplane showing the instruments and equipment operated by the three pitot tubes and three sets of static ports.

1. The manufacturer of the airplane or helicopter;
2. A certificated repair station with appropriate rating;
3. A certificated mechanic with an airframe rating (but only for the static pressure system tests and inspections).

## FAR 43 Appendix E
### Altimeter System Test and Inspection

Each person performing the altimeter system tests and inspections required by FAR 91.411 shall comply with the following:

a. Static pressure system;
   1. Ensure freedom from entrapped moisture and restrictions.
   2. Determine that leakage is within the tolerances established in FAR 23.1325 or 25.1325 whichever is applicable.
   3. Determine that the static port heater, if installed, is operative.
   4. Ensure that no alterations or deformation of the airframe surface have been made that would affect the relationship between air pressure in the static pressure system and true ambient static pressure for any flight condition.

b. Altimeter — omitted here

c. Automatic pressure altitude reporting system — omitted here

## FAR 23.1325
### Static Pressure System

b. If a static pressure system is necessary for the functioning of instruments, systems or devices, it must comply with the provisions of paragraphs (1) through (3) of this section.
   1. The design and installation of the static pressure system must be such that
      i. Positive drainage of moisture is provided
      ii. Chafing of tubing and excessive distortion or restriction in bends is avoided; and
      iii. The materials used are durable, suitable for the purpose and protected against corrosion.
   2. A proof test must be conducted to demonstrate the integrity of the static pressure system in the following manner
      i. Unpressurized Airplanes — Evacuate the static pressure system to a pressure differential of approximately 1 inch of mercury or to a reading of 1,000 ft. above the aircraft elevation at the time of the test. Without additional pumping for a period of one minute, the loss of indicated altitude must not exceed 100 ft. on the altimeter.
      ii. Pressurized Airplanes — Evacuate the static pressure system until a pressure differential equivalent to the maximum cabin pressure differential for which the airplane is type certificated is achieved. Without additional pumping for a period of 1 minute, the loss of indicated altitude must not exceed 2 percent of the equivalent altitude or 100 ft., whichever is greater.
   3. Each static pressure port must be designed and located so that errors will not result when the aircraft encounters icing conditions. An anti-icing means or alternate static ports may be used to show compliance.

### d. Pitot System Tests

There is no specific test for pitot systems as there is for static systems other than the normal inspections of the entire aircraft. If a problem is reported or suspected with a pitot system, there is a general leak test procedure in AC 43.13-1A, as well as some general guidelines for pitot-static system maintenance. The procedure for leak testing the pitot system is: Apply pressure to the pitot tube to cause the airspeed indicator to show 150 knots. Seal off for 1 minute and the maximum loss of indicated airspeed should not exceed 10 knots.

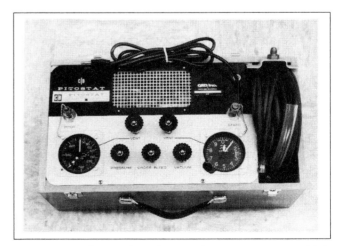

*Figure 1-44. A portable pitot-static system tester which can be used for leak tests and other maintenance functions.*

## Precautions in Testing Pitot-Static System

1. Perform all maintenance and inspections before leak testing.
2. Use a system diagram.
3. Check the test unit for leaks before beginning the test.
4. Run full range tests only if you are thoroughly familiar with both the aircraft and the test equipment.
5. Pressure in the pitot system must always be equal to or greater than the pressure in the static system.
6. The rate of change of pressure during testing should not exceed the limits for any installed instrument.
7. After testing make sure that the system is returned to flying condition, such as removing tape from ports and drain holes.

There is an FAR that concerns the altimeter setting which is set by the pilot in the Kollsman window.

## FAR 91.121
### Altimeter Settings

Each person operating an aircraft shall maintain the altitude of the aircraft by reference to an altimeter that is set:

1. Below 18,000 ft. MSL, to
   i. The current reported altimeter setting of a station along the route of flight and within 100 nautical miles of the aircraft
   ii. If there is no station within 100 nm, the nearest appropriate station altimeter setting
   iii. If the aircraft has no radio, the elevation of the departure airport or the setting available before takeoff shall be used.
2. At and above 18,000 ft. MSL, the altimeter shall be set to 29.92.

### e. Air Data Computer Systems

Aircraft that operate at high speeds and high altitudes can have significant errors in the pitot-static system instruments with the simple probes used on smaller aircraft. These aircraft will use an Air Data Computer (ADC) to operate the airspeed indicator, altimeter, VSI and any other systems that require this data. The air data computer is placed in the system between the sensor ports and the instruments to automatically apply corrections in order to increase accuracy.

The air data computer has three inputs; pitot pressure from the pitot tube, static pressure from the static ports and total air temperature (TAT) from a special TAT probe. The TAT measurement is needed to correct the instrument indications for friction heating of the air at high speeds. The TAT probe also permits the calculation of SAT (static air temperature) which is used to apply corrections for non-standard temperatures for any flight altitude. The outputs of the air data computer supply a number of cockpit instruments. The three basic pitot-static instruments are operated by the ADC and often several others are added. The common inputs and outputs associated with an air data computer are shown in figure 1-45.

High speed jet airplanes require a machmeter; this could be a separate instrument or included with the airspeed indicator.

Aircraft with an air data computer usually have a digital display on the instrument panel which gives a calculated true airspeed and total air temperature or static air temperature. TAT includes the heating effect of the friction at high speed whereas SAT is just ambient outside air temperature. The temperature indications are especially important for turbine engines which are affected by the temperature of the intake air.

The air data computer system automatically compensates for both temperature effects and the compressibility of the air at higher Mach numbers. This helps to ensure accurate instrument readings throughout a wide range of altitudes and airspeeds. Air data computers are typically found on turboprop airplanes and jet airplanes.

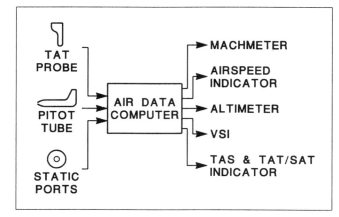

*Figure 1-45. An air data computer provides more accurate readings on the pitot-static instruments for high performance aircraft. Total air temperature is measured by a special probe and provided as an input to the ADC.*

## D. Gyro Instruments

The instruments know as gyro instruments are required for IFR flight and can also be an aid to accurate flying in VFR conditions. These instruments utilize the principles of a spinning gyroscope to give the pilot information about the aircraft's pitch and roll attitude, heading and rate of turn. A gyroscope is a device which consists of a weighted wheel or rotor which spins at high speed and is held in an arrangement of hinged mounting rings called gimbals (figure 1-46).

The gyro has three axes and one is always the spin axis. Depending on the type of gimbals used, it will be able to move relative to the mounting base around one or both of the remaining axes. If it has 1 degree of freedom, it can move around one axis and if it has two degrees of freedom it can move around both. A gyro with two degrees of freedom is also called a free gyro.

### 1. Principles of Gyroscopes

There are two main properties of a spinning gyro which are of importance to aircraft use, they are:

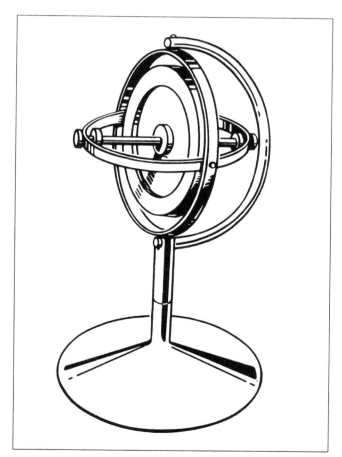

Figure 1-46. A simple gyroscope with both inner and outer gimbals.

1. Rigidity in Space — This means that the gyro rotor will try to maintain its position in space even when its mounting base is tilted and rotated. This is illustrated in figure 1-47.

2. Precession — This effect will cause a gyro, when it is acted upon by an outside force, to tilt or rotate as if the disturbing force was applied to it 90 degrees ahead in the direction of rotation of the rotor (figure 1-48).

Gyros are also subject to other effects such as oscillation. Oscillation is a problem caused by the mass of the gimbals. It can be reduced by making the gimbals lighter. A number of things can be done to make the gyro more stable and more efficient. One way is to concentrate the mass of the rotor on its rim and reduce the mass of the web and shaft which connects it to the bearings. Another way to make it more efficient is to increase the speed of rotation. There are two common methods used to spin the rotor of an aircraft gyro instrument. Pneumatics makes use of a stream of air directed at the rim of the rotor to make it spin at about 8,000 RPM. Electric motors can also be used to spin the rotor and will usually produce a speed of about 24,000 RPM. A gyro can become unstable which is called tumbling. Some aircraft gyro instruments have a caging knob or mechanism which is designed to return the gyro to a stable condition so that it will give correct instrument readings. A caging knob can be seen at the bottom left of figure 1-49. The latest types of gyro instruments are non-tumbling and as long as the instrument is in good condition it will not tumble, even in unusual attitudes. The three common types of aircraft gyro instruments are the directional gyro (DG), the artificial horizon and the turn and bank instrument.

### 2. Directional Gyro

The directional gyro is the primary heading reference for IFR flight. The magnetic compass is not a good

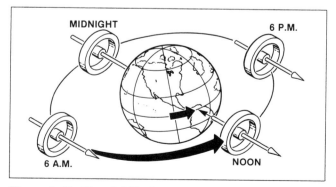

Figure 1-47. The rigidity in space characteristic causes the gyro rotor to try to maintain its orientation in space.

heading reference for IFR because it tends to oscillate and is not as stable as a DG. This instrument uses a free gyro with a horizontal spin axis. The DG will drift due to precession errors and must be reset every 15 to 20 minutes using the magnetic compass as a reference. Older style DGs had a rectangular window on the face through which the numbers representing the magnetic heading could be read. This older style DG presentation is shown in figure 1-50. Newer style DGs show a full compass card with the indicated magnetic heading under the index mark at the top of the instrument as seen in figure 1-51.

The newer style DG with a full compass card is often called a heading indicator. Another name for a DG type instrument is a gyro compass. The DG uses a free gyro because the spin axis must remain horizontal to give accurate readings. When the airplane banks, for example, the rotor will maintain its horizontal spin axis. On many modern aircraft a more sophisticated instrument replaces the DG, this instrument is the horizontal situation indicator or HSI.

The HSI shown in figure 1-52 is an example of a modern integrated instrument. It has a gyro stabilized compass card like a DG that indicates the aircraft's magnetic heading. Unlike the DG however, this compass card is slaved to a remote compass so it does not have to be reset every 15 to 20 minutes. The HSI is called an integrated instrument because it combines several different types of displays which would normally be found in separate

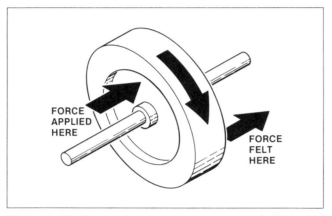

Figure 1-48. Precession causes a gyro rotor to tilt as if a disturbing force was applied 90° ahead in the direction of rotation from the actual point of application.

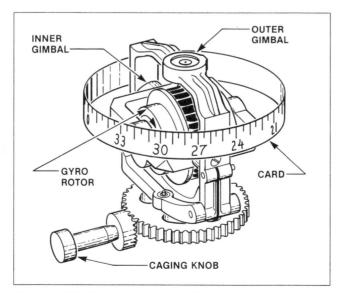

Figure 1-49. The rotor in a directional gyro has a horizontal spin axis and two degrees of freedom.

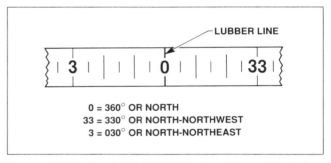

0 = 360° OR NORTH
33 = 330° OR NORTH-NORTHWEST
3 = 030° OR NORTH-NORTHEAST

Figure 1-50. The old style DG displayed a small window like a magnetic compass. This type of presentation can be difficult to read.

Figure 1-51. The modern DG or heading indicator has a display which shows a complete compass card. This type is easier to use.

instruments. The wide split bar in the middle is connected to navigational radios and tells the pilot whether to turn right or left to follow the radio navigational signals. The indicators on the right side and at the top are connected to other navigational radios to provide additional information to the pilot.

## 3. Artificial Horizon

The artificial horizon is the pilot's most important instrument for IFR flying. As the name implies, it replaces the natural earth horizon that a pilot uses in VFR flying to maintain the correct pitch and roll attitude of the aircraft. When an aircraft is flying in the clouds, the pilot must rely on the

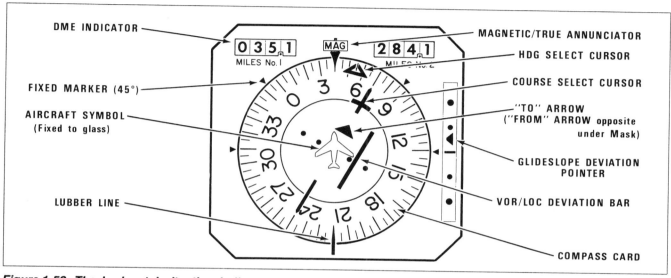

*Figure 1-52. The horizontal situation indicator is an integrated instrument that displays many additional kinds of information besides gyro stabilized heading data.*

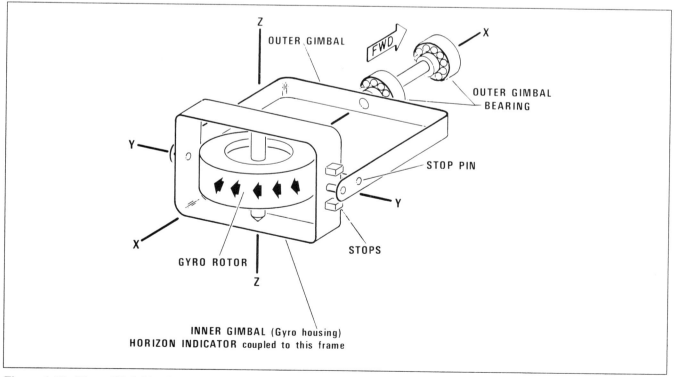

*Figure 1-53. The artificial horizon uses a gyro rotor with a vertical spin axis and two degrees of freedom.*

artificial horizon to determine the aircraft attitude and prevent a loss of control. The artificial horizon is also known as a gyro horizon, an attitude indicator, an attitude gyro and a bank and pitch instrument. The arrangement of the spin axis and gimbals for an artificial horizon is illustrated in figure 1-53. The artificial horizon is a free gyro with a vertical spin axis; this allows it to measure the angular displacement of the aircraft in both pitch and roll. The internal mechanism of the artificial horizon must have some means to maintain the spin axis in a vertical orientation. There are two common devices used to accomplish this function, the pendulous vane and ball erector systems.

The ball erector system uses a number of steel balls similar to ball bearings that are free to roll around on a plate mounted above or below the gyro rotor. One type of erector system that uses steel balls is shown in figure 1-54. When the gyro tilts away from the vertical, the balls roll to the low side and this produces a force which pushes the gyro back to the vertical position. This device will maintain the required vertical spin axis of the gyro rotor. The ball erector is usually found on electric motor driven artificial horizons. When an air-driven gyro is used, the pendulous vane erector mechanism is utilized.

The pendulous vanes in this type of erector mechanism are small gravity operated air valves. When the rotor tilts away from the vertical, the

vanes move to open the air valves in such a way that streams of air are directed to push the rotor back to the vertical position. The swing of the pendulous vanes to open and close the air valves can be seen in figure 1-55.

The artificial horizon has a presentation which shows an airplane symbol with the horizon behind it. It includes index marks to show the angle of bank. Some indications of an artificial horizon for different flight attitudes are illustrated in figure 1-56. The newer types of artificial horizon have a more user friendly presentation on the instrument face. Different colors are used above and below the horizon line to make it easier to read. Converging lines are placed below the horizon line to create perspective and additional markings for pitch attitude are included. These features can be seen on the newer type artificial horizon in figure 1-57.

The small knob on the front of the artificial horizon is used to move the airplane symbol up and down

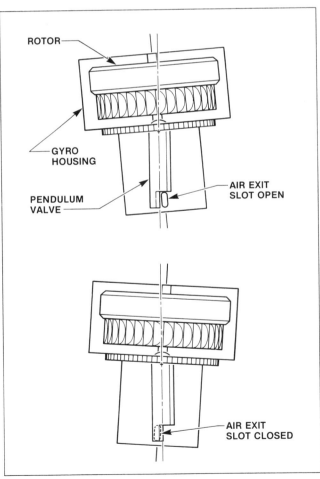

Figure 1-55. *The pendulous vanes used in the erector mechanism of an air-driven gyro horizon are opened and closed by gravity.*

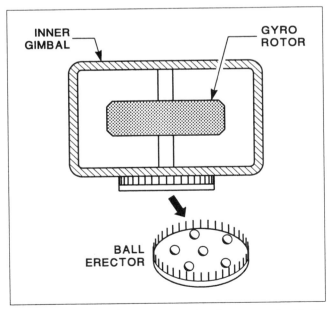

Figure 1-54. *The ball erector mechanism uses steel balls that move to the low side of the plate to supply a force that corrects the artificial horizon back to a vertical spin axis.*

to adjust for different aircraft flight attitudes and for tall and short pilots. There also may be a control for quick erect that can be used to stabilize the gyro if it tumbles. There is a newer type of integrated instrument which replaces the artificial horizon on many modern aircraft. This instrument is called the attitude director indicator (ADI). It includes command bars that are operated by a flight director. The flight director is a computer which receives signals from navigational radios and other sources and calculates the correct pitch and roll attitudes to keep the aircraft on course or return it to the desired flight path. The output signals from the flight director computer move the command bars on the ADI and the pilot follows these commands.

An example of the use of these command bars on an ADI is found in figure 1-58.

The latest kinds of ADIs use different shapes for the airplane symbol and the command bars as can be seen in figure 1-59. The airplane symbol is a triangle that resembles a delta wing airplane and the command bars are two converging triangular shapes above the airplane symbol. They often use different colors as well to make it easier to distinguish between the airplane symbol and command bar symbol. Some ADIs also include indicators for other aircraft systems in addition to the flight director indicator. The indicator pointer on the right side of the ADI is operated by the aircraft autothrottle system. The pointer on the left side is

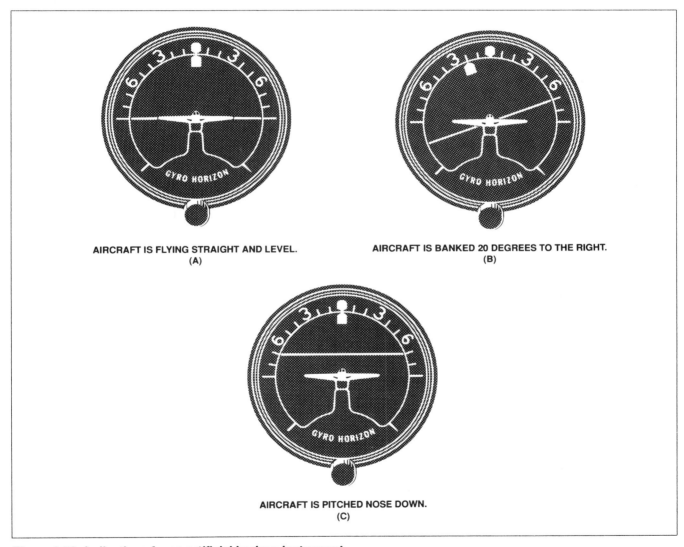

AIRCRAFT IS FLYING STRAIGHT AND LEVEL.
(A)

AIRCRAFT IS BANKED 20 DEGREES TO THE RIGHT.
(B)

AIRCRAFT IS PITCHED NOSE DOWN.
(C)

Figure 1-56. Indications for an artificial horizon instrument.
(A) The airplane is straight and level.
(B) The airplane is in a 20° bank to the right with the nose on the horizon.
(C) The wings are level, but the nose is below the horizon.

operated by a glideslope radio receiver and gives the pilot information needed for an instrument ILS approach. An ADI is an integrated instrument that gives pitch and roll attitude data like an artificial horizon and additional displays of information from radio navigation sources and other aircraft systems like the flight director. On sophisticated aircraft which have backup gyro instruments, a turn and bank is not installed, so the inclinometer is installed at the bottom of the ADI as can be seen in figure 1-59.

### 4. Turn and Bank

The last of the three basic gyro instruments is the oldest and simplest. It is called the turn and bank and it is really two instruments in one. The gyro part of the instrument measures the rate of turn for the aircraft. The inclinometer or slip-skid indicator is a simple mechanical instrument that consists of a ball in a liquid filled glass tube. This tube is curved and the ball reacts to gravity and centrifugal force. It is used by a pilot to coordinate the use of aileron and rudder control. If the pilot keeps the ball centered, the aircraft is being flown in a coordinated manner. This instrument is especially helpful when the aircraft is turning. When the ball is not centered, it means the aircraft is

flying a little sideways. The gyro rotor of the turn and bank is designed to measure the rate of turn of the aircraft. It is the only one of the three basic gyro instruments which is a rate gyro.

The other two basic gyro instruments measure angular displacement about the aircraft's axes. The turn and bank has a gyro with a horizontal spin

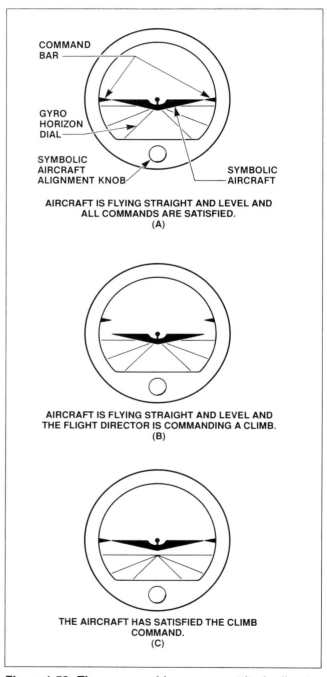

*Figure 1-58. The command bars on an attitude director indicator show the pilot the pitch and roll attitude that is needed to satisfy the commands of the flight director.*

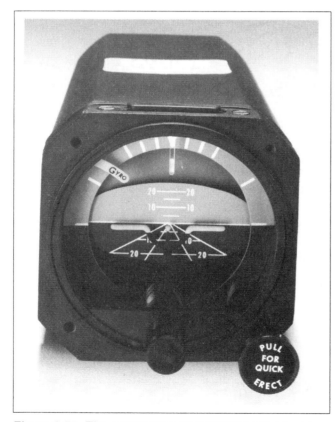

*Figure 1-57. The newer type of artificial horizon uses a presentation that is easier to interpret.*

axis and one degree of freedom. The feature that makes it a rate gyro are the springs that are connected to the gimbals. These springs oppose the precession force which is caused by the aircraft turning. These features of the turn and bank can be seen in figure 1-60.

When the aircraft turns, the gimbal holding the gyro rotor tilts over against the tension of the spring and moves the pointer to indicate the direction and rate of turn. The turn and bank gives readings based on the concept of a standard rate turn. A standard rate turn is a turning rate of 3° per second. This is also called a 2 minute turn because it would take 2 minutes to turn 360° at this rate. A standard rate turn is not suitable for a high speed aircraft because it would require a steep angle of bank.

These higher speed aircraft would use a ½ standard rate turn which is 1-½° per second or a 4 minute turn. Turn and banks are manufactured in both types; 2 minute turn and 4 minute turn, both of which are shown in figure 1-61. The turn and bank indicator is also called a turn and slip indicator and a needle and ball. The face of the instrument shows a needle to indicate turn direction and rate and a ball which is the slip-skid indicator or inclinometer.

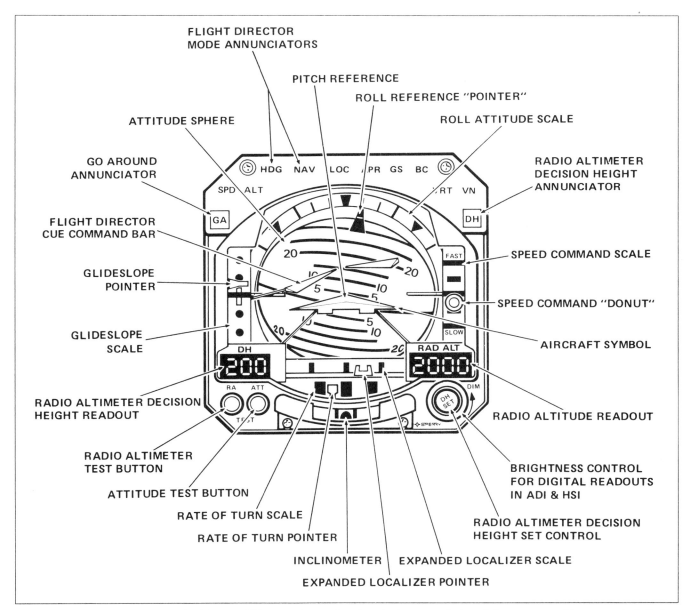

**Figure 1-59. The newer type of ADI uses different shapes for the airplane symbol and the command bars symbol. It also may include additional displays for other systems. (Courtesy of Canadair Group, Bombardier Inc.)**

The turn and bank is shown in figure 1-61. The pointer is the rate of turn indicator and the glass tube is the inclinometer.

The index marks on either side of the center position of the pointer on the lower instrument are called dog houses. When the pointer is lined up with a dog house, it indicates a 2-minute turn on the bottom instrument. A 2-minute turn on the upper instrument would be indicated by a one needle width deflection of the turn needle. The turn and bank is considered to be a backup instrumnet for the artificial horizon. If the artificial horizon fails, it is possible to fly the aircraft using the turn and bank in its place.

Another gyro instrument called the turn coordinator is a modified version of the turn and bank. The only significant difference in the internal mechanism is the fact that the tilt axis for the gimbal is changed to a 30° angle from the horizontal as shown in figure 1-62. This causes the gyro rotor

to react to rotation around the longitudinal axis as well as the vertical axis. The turn and bank only measures rotation rate about the vertical axis so that it cannot be used accurately to level the wings. The turn coordinator is a better back-up instrument for the artificial horizon for this reason. Since the turn coordinator is not the same as a turn and bank and doesn't give the same kind of information, it has a different appearance so that pilots won't confuse the two instruments.

The turn coordinator as illustrated in figure 1-63 uses a rear view of a small airplane as the indicator. When the wing tip of the airplane symbol is lined up with an index mark, it indicates a standard rate turn for the 2 minute type. The turn coordinator also includes an inclinometer, like the turn and bank.

## 5. Gyro Instrument Power Sources

Aircraft gyro instruments can be powered by electricity or air. The electric gyros can use 14 or

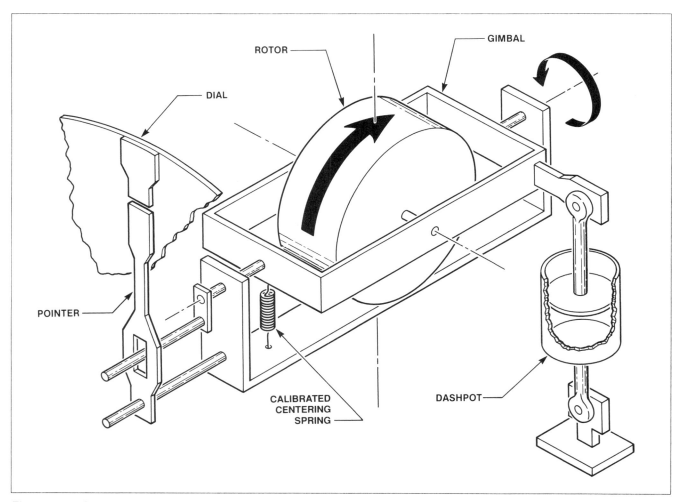

Figure 1-60. *The turn-and-bank instrument has a gyro rotor with a horizontal spin axis and one degree of freedom. It also has a centering spring on the gimbal.*

28 volts DC or several different values of AC. The gyros that are air driven can use either an air pump or bleed air from turbine engines. Air-driven gyros can either use suction pressure or positive pressure. Those that use suction pressure are usually called vacuum driven gyros. Some older aircraft used vacuum venturis to power the air-driven gyro instruments. The venturi for gyros is mounted on the fuselage of the aircraft and the airflow caused by the forward motion of the aircraft creates a low pressure or suction in the throat of the venturi. A major problem with using a venturi for IFR flight is that the venturi tends to become blocked with ice under some flight conditions. Another disadvantage of the venturi tube is that the aircraft must maintain a certain minimum airspeed to generate enough vacuum for the gyros. The gyros will not be spun-up and stable during takeoff for example. Examples of 2″ and 4″ venturis

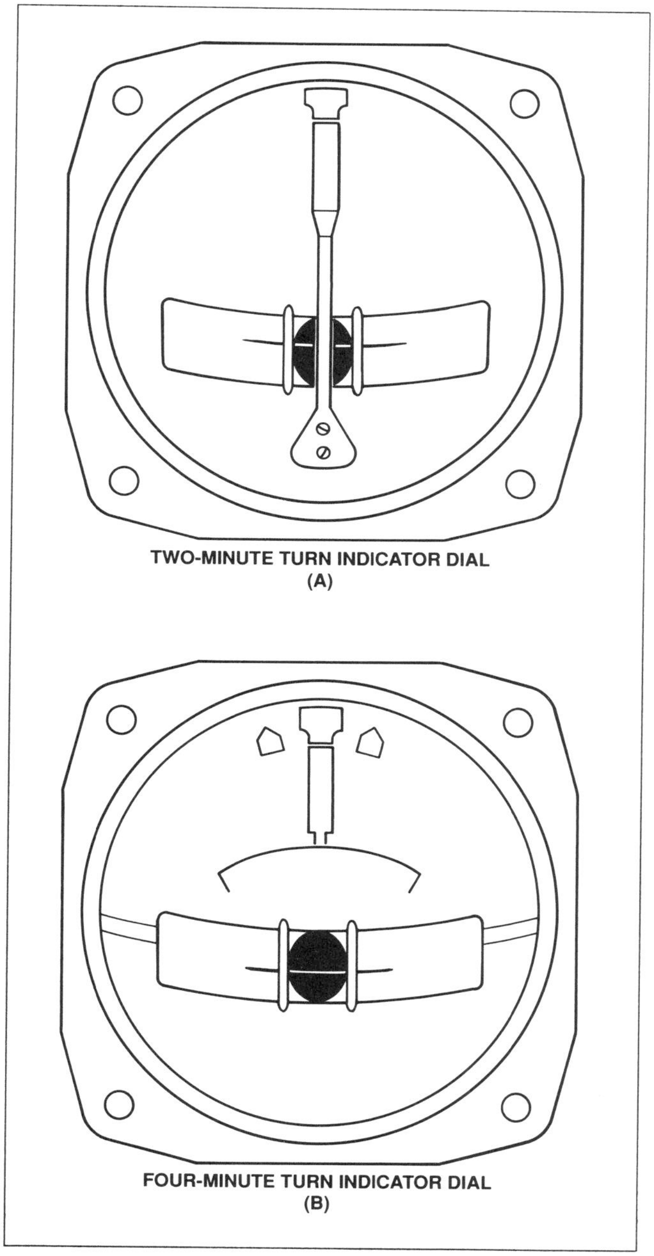

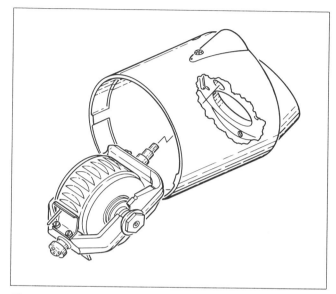

**Figure 1-62. By mounting the gimbal at an angle to the horizontal, the turn coordinator senses rotation about both the roll and yaw axes of the aircraft.**

**TWO-MINUTE TURN INDICATOR DIAL**
**(A)**

**FOUR-MINUTE TURN INDICATOR DIAL**
**(B)**

**Figure 1-61. Both 2-minute and 4-minute turn and bank instruments are available.**

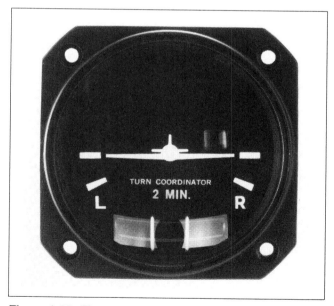

**Figure 1-63. The presentation on the face of the turn coordinator is different from that of a turn and bank so that the two instruments will not be confused with each other.**

are found in figure 1-64. The 2″ and 4″ are not physical dimensions. They refer to the amount of suction in inches of mercury that each is designed to provide.

The most common type of air pump used on modern airplanes for the gyro instruments is called a dry air pump. It does not use any oil for sealing or lubrication. It is a vane type pump and the vanes are made of a carbon based material which gradually wears away in service from rubbing against the cylinder walls. Figure 1-65 shows a dry air pump connected to operate as a vacuum pump. Notice that the gyro instruments and gauge are installed in parallel. Figure 1-66 shows the same kind of dry air pump that has been connected to operate as a positive pressure pump. In the vacuum pump

system the output of the pump is dumped overboard and the cockpit air is filtered before it flows into the instruments. A filter is required on the regulator of the vacuum system because air is drawn in at that point to regulate the vacuum pressure. An advantage of the positive pressure system is that it is better for aircraft that operate at higher altitudes of 15,000 to 18,000 ft. The positive pressure system requires a filter on the inlet side of the pump and a filter on the outlet side ahead of the instruments. A filter is not required on the regulator in the positive pressure system. There is also a wet pump for air driven gyros which uses engine oil for cooling and lubrication. It can only be used as a vacuum pump and requires an air/oil separator to return oil to the airplane's engine. Figure 1-67 shows the

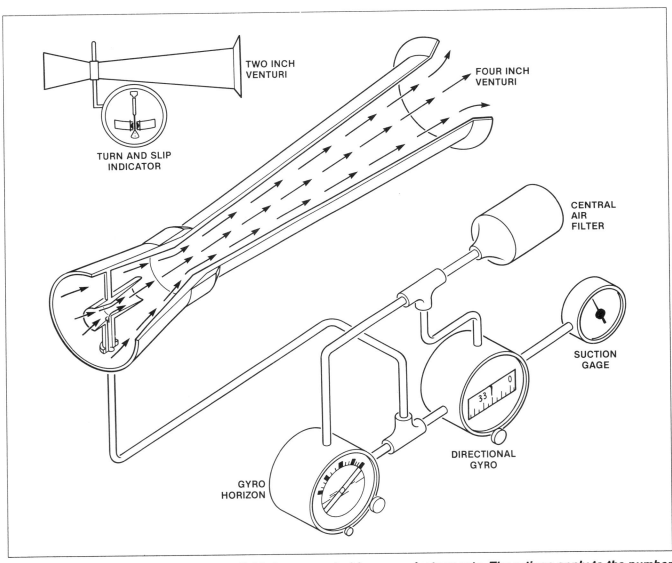

**Figure 1-64.** *A 2 ″ and 4 ″ venturi are available to power air-driven gyro instruments. The ratings apply to the number of inches of Mercury vacuum that are provided, not to physical size.*

air/oil separator in a wet pump system as well as a suction reducer that is used to drop the pressure for the turn and slip indicator. An air driven turn and bank or turn and slip requires about 2 inches of mercury while the other two basic types of gyros require 4-5 inches of mercury.

For any kind of air driven gyros, it is very important to change the filters regularly to ensure that only very clean air reaches the gyro instruments. The instruments are very delicate and can wear out rapidly if dust and dirt are allowed to enter with the air supply. A typical air filter for aircraft gyro instrument systems is shown in figure 1-68. The small filter installed on vacuum regulator valves can be seen in figure 1-69. The tubing and hose in an air driven gyro system must be checked to make certain that no restrictions are present which would create higher than normal resistance to the flow of air. The only lubricant approved for vacuum system fittings is usually a silicone spray. Thread lubricants and Teflon® tape should not be used as they might get drawn into the system and cause damage.

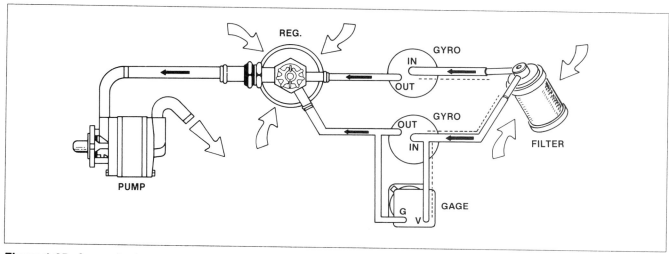

Figure 1-65. A gyro instrument vacuum system that uses a dry air pump.

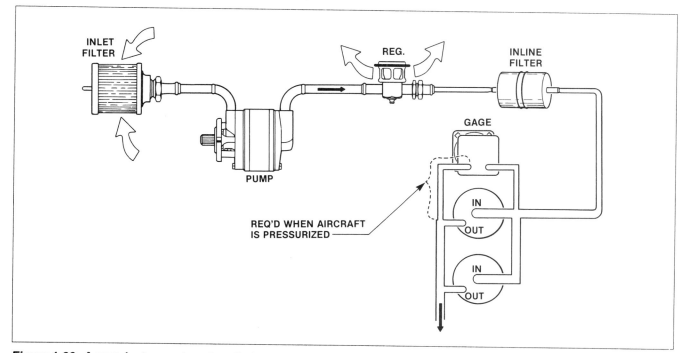

Figure 1-66. A gyro instrument system that uses a dry air pump to supply positive rather than negative pressure.

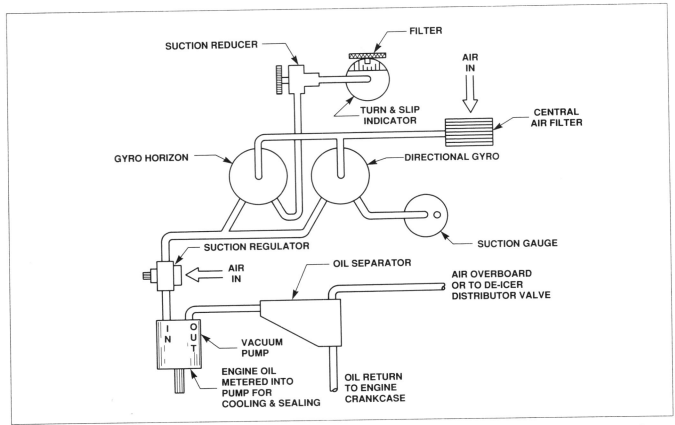

*Figure 1-67. A wet pump vacuum system to operate three gyro instruments. A suction reducer is needed in the line to the turn and slip since it requires less vacuum pressure.*

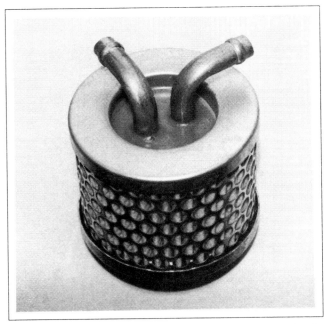

*Figure 1-68. A typical replaceable filter used with air-driven gyro instruments.*

## 6. Inspection and Maintenance of Gyro Systems

Some recommended practices for gyro system maintenance are:

1. Check the time it takes for the gyro instruments to come up to full speed and stabilize. This should normally be about 2–4 minutes.

2. Listen for unusual noise when the gyros are spinning. Noise is easier to detect after the engines are stopped.

3. When power to the gyros is removed, measure the run-down time. If there is a shortening of the normal run-down time, it indicates the bearings are getting worn or some other problem exists.

4. Check tubing and hose condition. They should not be worn or restricted. Check for kinks and dents.

5. Fittings should be in good condition and with wide radius bends. Do not over tighten.

6. Use only approved lubricants for fittings. Silicone spray is the most common recommendation.

7. Route tubing carefully to avoid rubbing and abrasion.

8. If it becomes necessary to blow the lines to remove dirt or moisture, ensure that instruments are completely disconnected. Apply air pressure to instrument end of the lines.

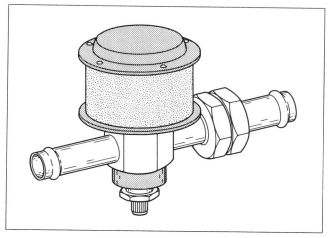

*Figure 1-69. A vacuum regulator for gyro instruments includes an air filter.*

9. Replace filters at recommended intervals—more often in dusty conditions or if smokers ride in the aircraft.

When installing additional air-driven gyro instruments or if a problem is suspected, the load on the pump should be evaluated. Each gyro instrument requires a certain volume of air which is stated in cubic feet per minute (CFM). Add up the requirement in CFM for all the instruments and ensure that it does not exceed the rated CFM for the pump. You must also evaluate the pressure drop requirements for the instruments and lines. Artificial horizons and directional gyros usually require 4.0–5.0 in. Hg. The turn and bank requires 2.0–2.5 in. Hg. The loss or pressure drop in all the lines and tubing should not exceed 2 in. Hg. If it does, you may have to use larger diameter tubing.

## E. Compass Systems

### 1. Magnetic Compass

The aircraft magnetic direction indicator or compass is a completely independent instrument. It does not require any electrical or tubing connections. It contains a compass card with magnets that line up with

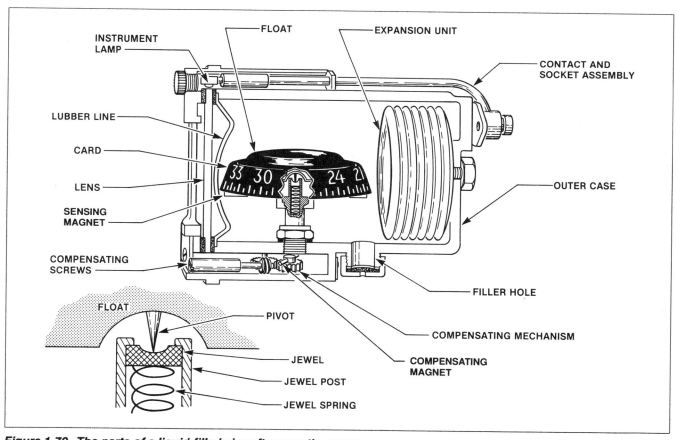

*Figure 1-70. The parts of a liquid-filled aircraft magnetic compass.*

the magnetic flux lines of the earth. Figure 1-70 shows the following basic parts of a magnetic compass.

1. A compass card or float which is mounted on jeweled bearings. It has numbers and direction markings so that the magnetic heading of the aircraft can be read from the instrument.

2. The case is filled with a light oil (usually refined kerosene) which dampens float motion and lubricates the bearings.

3. A diaphragm or bellows accommodates thermal expansion and contraction.

4. The compensator is two small moveable magnets used to adjust the compass for deviation error.

5. The lubber line is a marker against which readings are taken.

The face of a typical liquid filled magnetic compass is shown in figure 1-71. The indicated magnetic heading is 035°.

## 2. Compass Errors

The magnetic compass is subject to a number of errors which affect its operation. These include variation, deviation, acceleration error, northerly turning error and oscillation error. Variation error is simply the fact that a magnetic compass will give indications based on the magnetic north pole and not the north geographic pole. The normal grid lines on an aeronautical chart are in true directions based on the geographic poles and the equator. As can be seen in figure 1-72, the north magnetic pole is hundreds of miles from the north geographic

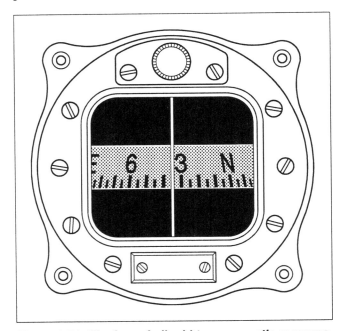

**Figure 1-71. The face of a liquid-type magnetic compass.**

pole. In most locations, there will be a difference between true and magnetic directions. This is variation. Figure 1-73 shows how the amount of variation is drawn on aeronautical charts for pilots to use. There are some locations where true and magnetic directions are the same. This would be along the line called the agonic line. Everywhere else the pilot would consult the variation markings on the map and add or subtract the appropriate number of degrees to convert from true to magnetic headings.

Acceleration error and north turning error are both a result of compass dip. The earth is round so that at high latitudes in the northern hemisphere, the compass card will tilt downward toward the north magnetic pole. This compass dip causes both of these errors. If an airplane is flying east and it accelerates, the compass will momentarily indicate a turn to the north. If it decelerates, it will indicate a turn to the south. North turning error occurs when the aircraft is flying north or south. If a turn is made from a north heading, the compass will indicate a turn in the opposite direction momentarily and then it will lag behind the actual heading during the turn. Turns from south will cause the compass to lead the actual heading or indicate a higher than actual turning rate. Oscillation error is caused by the very delicate bearings in the compass. In rough air, the compass will oscillate back and forth 40°, 50° or more. The compass may never settle down as long as the turbulence persists. This forces the pilot to have to estimate the actual compass reading.

Deviation error is the most important one for maintenance technicians because they usually perform the checks and adjustments for deviation error. This error is also called magnetic influence error since it is caused by magnetic influences within the aircraft. All aircraft have some steel parts that may have some permanent magnetism. Most aircraft also have electrical circuits that can produce electromagnetic fields. Both of these can affect the magnetic compass and cause errors. The compensator magnets in the compass are used to adjust this error to a minimum. This process is called swinging the compass. It should be performed whenever equipment is installed that could cause a change or when a problem with the compass accuracy is suspected.

Swinging the compass—the basic procedure is:

1. Locate a compass rose on a ramp area which is accurate and can be used as a reference. A compass rose is a circle with magnetic directions indicated as shown in figure 1-74.

2. Configure the aircraft for the checks by turning on electrical equipment and radios, running the engines and establishing a level attitude.

3. Set the compensators to zero (there are two little screws labeled N-S and E-W)

4. Point the aircraft north on the compass rose and adjust the N-S screw to zero error or as close to zero error as possible.

5. Point the aircraft east and adjust the E-W screw to zero error or as close to zero error as possible.

6. Point the aircraft south and remove half the error.

7. Point the aircraft west and remove half the error.

The process so far has averaged the error for all headings. Now you are ready to record the error.

8. Point the aircraft on all headings every 30°, and record the compass heading for each.

9. Prepare a placard which lists the deviation error at least each 30°. Place it on or near the compass and make a logbook entry.

The compass correction card is used to record the deviation error for the aircraft's compass. An example is shown in figure 1-75.

A newer type of compass is called the vertical card compass. It operates like the other types of

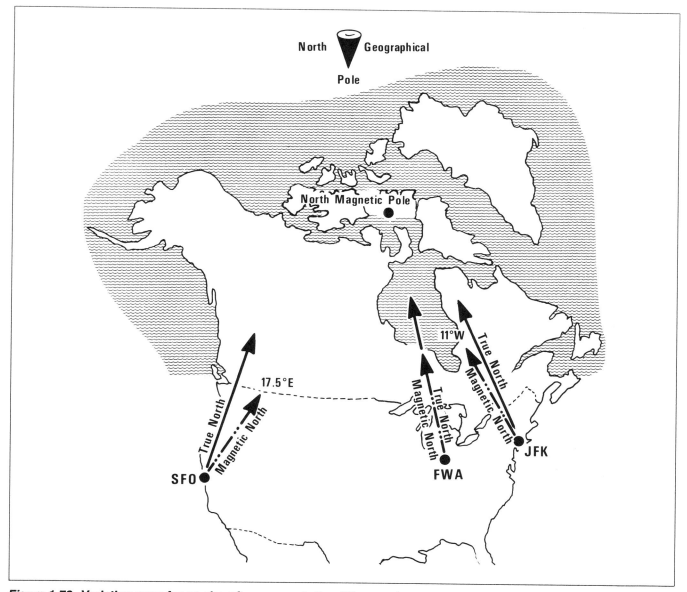

*Figure 1-72. Variation error for an aircraft compass is the difference between true headings and magnetic headings. It is caused by the fact that the north geographic pole and the north magnetic pole are not in the same location.*

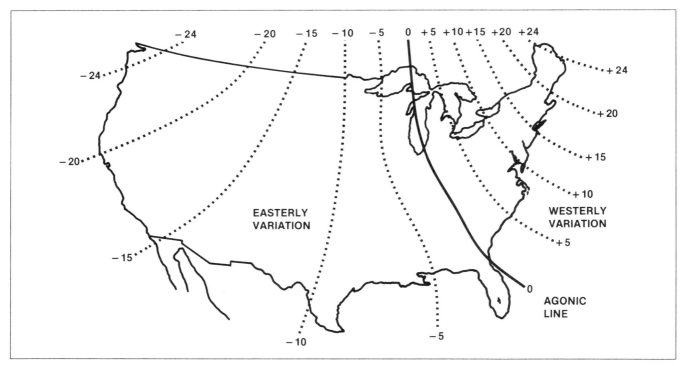

**Figure 1-73. Lines of variation are drawn on aeronautical charts so that pilots can apply the proper corrections during flight planning.**

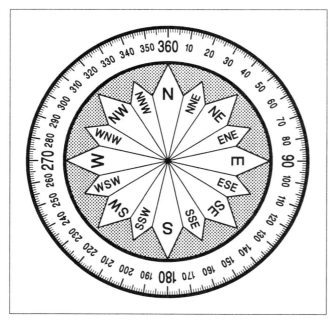

**Figure 1-74. A compass rose contains the markings and numbers needed for magnetic direction references.**

magnetic compass but the presentation on the face of the instrument is a full compass card which is easier to read. It sometimes eliminates the use of oil and employs eddy current damping. See figure

1-76 for an illustration of the appearance of a vertical card compass.

The full compass card presentation of the vertical card compass makes it easier to read. If the pilot wants to turn to a heading of 180°, the presentation makes it easier to determine if it is quicker to turn left or right to reach that heading. The compensator screws can be seen at the bottom of the vertical card compass.

### 3. Flux Gate Compass

The flux gate compass is a special type of remote mounted compass which is more stable than a standard magnetic compass and usually eliminates the problems of acceleration and north turning errors.

The sensor used with a flux gate compass system is called a flux valve or flux gate. It is a wheel shaped device made of a ferrous material with three spokes and the rim cut into three equal parts. The flux valve sensor can be seen in figure 1-77. The excitation coil is in the center and the pick up coils or output coils are installed with one on each spoke of the flux valve core. The excitation coil is supplied with AC current with a frequency of 400 Hz. It is designed so that when the current flow in the excitation coil is at peak value, the core material is saturated. When the current falls below peak value, the earth's magnetic flux lines cut across the pick up coils and produce an output signal in each one. The excitation coil in effect alternately blocks out the earth's magnetic field and then allows it to move across the output coils. This produces an AC output signal from each of the three output coils. Since the angle of the earth's flux lines to

| FOR | | N 0 | 3 | 6 | E 9 | 12 | 15 | S 18 |
|---|---|---|---|---|---|---|---|---|
| STEER | RADIO | | | | | | | |
| | NO RADIO | | | | | | | |
| FOR | | | 21 | 24 | W 27 | 30 | 33 | |
| STEER | RADIO | | | | | | | |
| | NO RADIO | | | | | | | |

Figure 1-75. *The compass correction card is usually made up by the mechanic when he swings the compass to determine the deviation error.*

COMPASS CARD

LUBBER LINE

N-S ○ E-W

FIXED AIRCRAFT SYMBOL

CORRECTION SCREWS

Figure 1-76. *The vertical card compass displays a complete compass card and is easier to read than the older type. (Courtesy Canadair Group, Bombardier Inc.)*

the flux valve changes for each different heading, the relative values of the three output voltages will be different for each different heading. This is illustrated in figure 1-78. An electronic component measures the three output signals and derives the magnetic heading of the aircraft.

In order to give accurate readings, the flux gate sensor must normally be maintained in a level, horizontal position with respect to the Earth's surface. This leveling can be accomplished in one of two ways. In the first type of flux gate sensor found on aircraft, the sensor is suspended by a pendulous mechanism so that it can remain level when the aircraft attitude is changed. This type of flux gate has a housing filled with a light oil to dampen the motions of the moving parts. In the second type of flux gate compass system, the flux gate sensor is stabilized by a gyro system to keep it level. The output signals from a flux gate sensor are sent to an electronic unit which amplifies the signals and calculates magnetic heading. The output of this electronic unit is sent to cockpit indicators that require magnetic heading information and sometimes to navigational systems that require heading information. The two common cockpit instruments that receive signals from the flux gate system are the HSI and the RMI (radio magnetic indicator). The HSI and RMI can be seen in figure 1-79 which shows the flux gate compass system for a Challenger

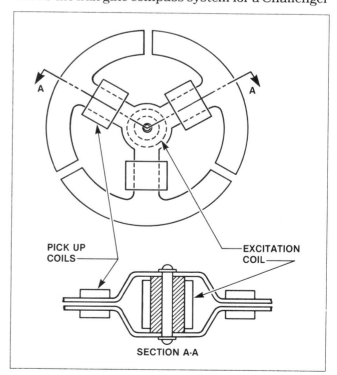

PICK UP COILS

EXCITATION COIL

SECTION A-A

Figure 1-77. *The flux valve sensor has an excitation coil in the center and three pick up coils on the spokes or arms.*

airplane. The flux valve sensors themselves are normally installed near the wing tips to keep them away from magnetic influences in the aircraft. The location of the vertical card magnetic compass is also shown in figure 1-79.

The HSI and the RMI both have a compass card which indicates the magnetic heading of the aircraft. The heading information comes from a flux gate compass system. The compass cards on both instruments are driven by a remote mounted directional gyro. The DG receives signals from the flux gate compass that automatically reset it to the correct magnetic heading. The remote DG is slaved to the flux gate compass and the compass cards on the instruments are slaved to the remote DG. The connections are shown in figure 1-80 which is a diagram of a flux gate compass system. In this system, the pilot never has to reset the instruments with his magnetic compass in the cockpit unless the flux gate compass system fails.

The face of an RMI is shown in figure 1-81. The compass card in this instrument indicates the magnetic heading of the aircraft as previously described. The RMI can be identified by the two pointers that have a common pivot point in the center of the instrument. These pointers are connected to radio navigation systems so that they point toward the location of the ground transmitter. The selector switches allow each pointer to be connected to an ADF or VOR radio receiver.

## 4. FARs for Compass Systems

There are a number of FARs that relate directly to compass systems.

### FAR 23.1327
**Magnetic Direction Indicator**

1. Must be installed to prevent influence by airplane vibrations or magnetic fields.
2. Maximum deviation in level flight is 10 degrees on any heading.
3. Magnetic non-stabilized may deviate more than 10 degrees due to electric heated windshield etc. if either a stabilized magnetic direction indicator or DG is installed. Deviation over 10 degrees requires a placard.

### FAR 23.1547
**Magnetic Direction Indicator Deviation Placard**

1. Placard must be installed on or near the MDI (compass).
2. Placard must list calibration for level flight with engines running.
3. Placard must state if calibration is for radios on or off.
4. Calibration increments must be 30 degrees maximum.

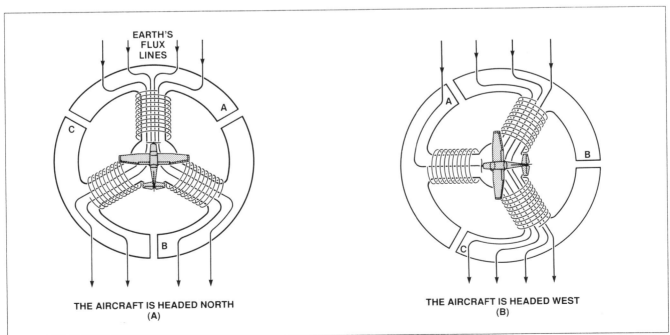

EARTH'S FLUX LINES

A
C
B

THE AIRCRAFT IS HEADED NORTH
(A)

A
B
C

THE AIRCRAFT IS HEADED WEST
(B)

*Figure 1-78. The changing angle of the earth's flux lines to the flux valve produces a different output signal for each different heading of the aircraft.*

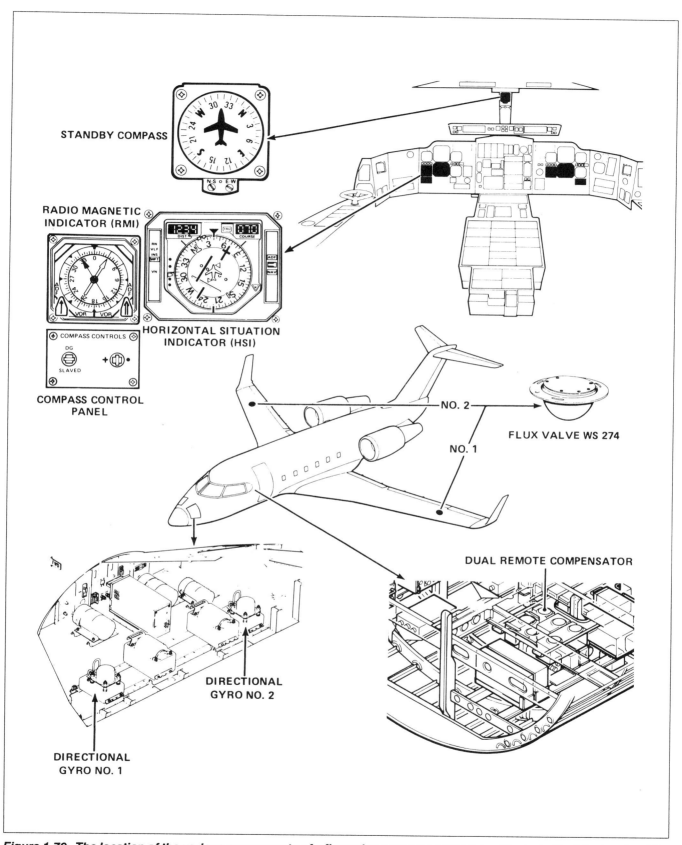

STANDBY COMPASS

RADIO MAGNETIC
INDICATOR (RMI)

HORIZONTAL SITUATION
INDICATOR (HSI)

COMPASS CONTROLS
DG
SLAVED

COMPASS CONTROL
PANEL

NO. 2

NO. 1

FLUX VALVE WS 274

DUAL REMOTE COMPENSATOR

DIRECTIONAL
GYRO NO. 2

DIRECTIONAL
GYRO NO. 1

**Figure 1-79. The location of the various components of a flux valve compass system are illustrated in this drawing. The standby magnetic compass is also shown. (Courtesy Canadair Group, Bombardier Inc.)**

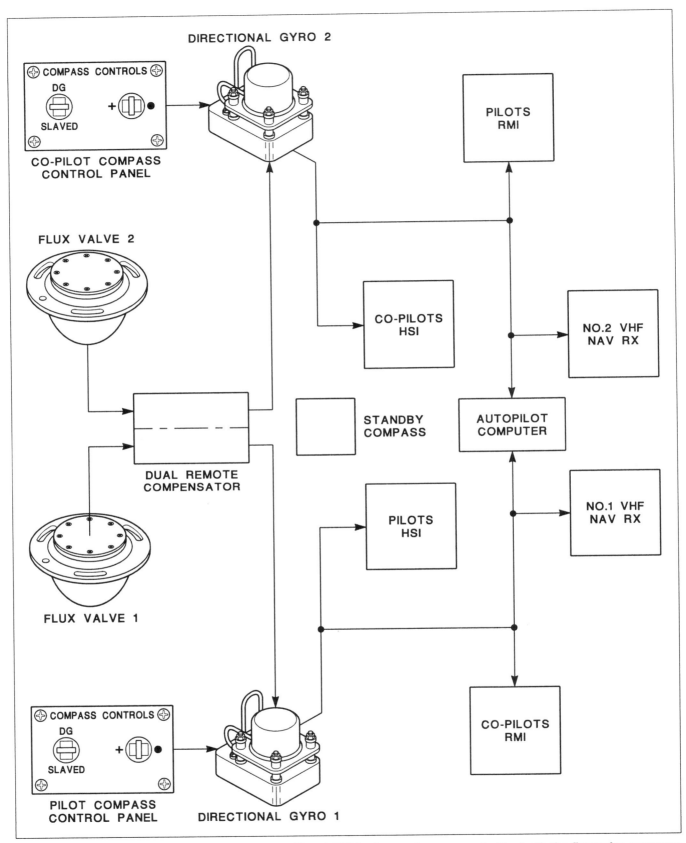

Figure 1-80. The compass cards in the aircraft HSI and RMI instruments are operated by both the flux valve compass system and the remote mounted directional gyros. (Courtesy Canadair Group, Bombardier Inc.)

5. More than 10 degrees deviation for electric heated windshield etc. must be placarded.

## F. Electronic Instruments

### 1. Basic Principles

The term "electronic instruments" is used to refer to the latest trend in aircraft instruments. This involves the use of CRTs (cathode ray tubes or TV screens) to display aircraft instrument information. Another common term for this system is the "glass cockpit". The use of CRTs permits a greater use of integrated instruments which display numerous types of information on one screen. It also permits greater flexibility because the method of displaying the information and the amount of information on each CRT can be changed in flight. It is also claimed that reliability is increased because complex electro-mechanical instruments are replaced by CRTs that have no moving parts. These CRTs are operated by a special type of computer control called a symbol generator. The latest generation of air carrier jets and bizjets was designed to use the glass cockpit displays. This group includes Boeing 757, 767 and 747-400; McDonnell Douglas MD-11 and Gulfstream G-IVs among others.

Other aircraft have been retrofitted with glass cockpit displays in their latest versions or as an option from the factory.

Some aircraft have only one or two CRTs, while others with a full glass cockpit system will use six or more CRTs. The electronic instruments that make up a full glass cockpit come in three types:

1. Electronic attitude director indicators (EADIs)
2. Electronic horizontal situation indicators (EHSIs)
3. Engine indication and crew alerting system (EICAS)

The appearance of the EADI and EHSI are very similar to the electro-mechanical versions that have been covered previously. The major difference is that the display is more versatile and the pilots can select what types of information they wish

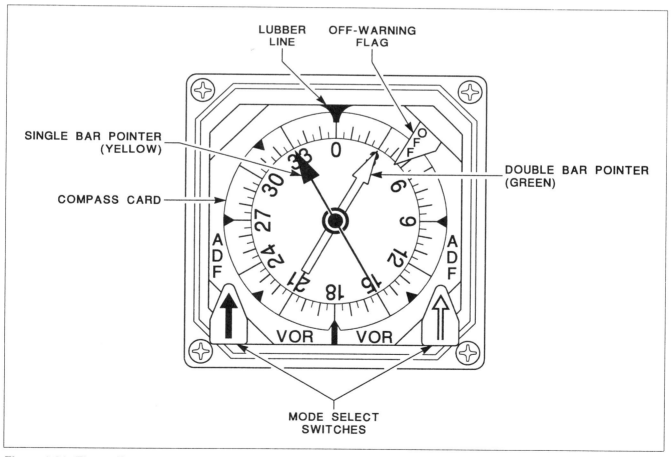

*Figure 1-81. The radio magnetic indicator (RMI) has a compass card which indicates the magnetic heading of the aircraft. (Courtesy Canadair Group, Bombardier Inc.)*

to see and much more information can be presented with the electronic version of the instrument. A typical EADI and EHSI are shown in figure 1-82. The EHSI can be set to a map mode which changes the appearance of the display to that of a map. An EHSI that is showing the map mode is found in figure 1-83. The map mode shows an airplane symbol along with navigational sites, airports and other features on the ground. The map mode presentation shows the aircraft moving across the map in correct relationship to locations on the ground. It is a very user friendly display which shows a large amount of information to the pilot in a way that makes it easier to read than more conventional displays.

## 2. EADI

Some of the information that can be presented on the EADI other than the basic pitch and roll data includes; radio glideslope data, radio localizer data,

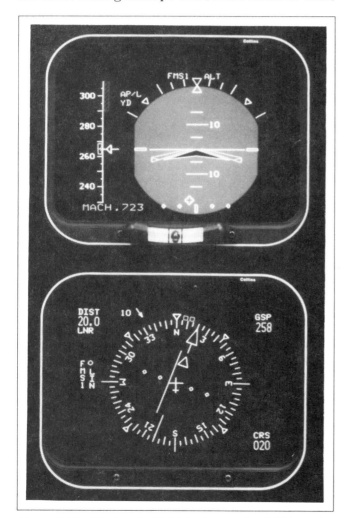

*Figure 1-82. Electronic flight instruments: EADI on the top and an EHSI below.*

radar altimeter data, autopilot status and aircraft indicated airspeed.

## 3. EHSI

Information displayed on the EHSI includes: magnetic heading, radio steering commands for VOR/INS, radio glideslope data, DME radio data and weather radar data. The EADI and EHSI are installed directly in front of the pilots to match the standard "T" configuration.

## 4. EICAS

The EICAS system usually consists of two large CRTs installed in the middle of the instrument panel. The two CRTs may be arranged vertically or horizontally depending on the particular aircraft involved. The EICAS display screens in figure 1-84 are positioned one above the other. The EICAS system has two main types of information that are displayed, as the name implies. The engine indication function displays numerous powerplant instruments in standard columns depending on how many engines the aircraft has. The crew alerting system function consists of many sensors located throughout the aircraft that monitor all the major systems such as engines, electrical, hydraulic, bleed air, pressurization, etc. These sensors are monitored by computer and any faults or abnormal readings are displayed to the flight crew. On many aircraft these sophisticated monitoring systems replace a human crew member, the flight engineer. This allows the aircraft manufacturer to design a large airplane like a 747-400 that only requires two flight crew members instead of three.

An EICAS system that uses two CRTs stacked vertically is probably the most common and will be described here. This system is shown in figure 1-84. The upper screen has a standard presentation which displays the primary engine parameters. These are the most important engine instruments that are used to set power and monitor the engines. Also on the upper screen is a list of alert and status messages concerning the aircraft systems.

During routine cruise flight conditions, the lower screen is very often blank. If a problem suddenly developed with the hydraulic pressure, for example, the EICAS computer would automatically put a message on the upper screen and show the hydraulic system instruments on the lower screen. The basic theory of this system is that normal readings on the instruments do not have to be displayed for the crew. When an abnormal reading occurs, then it will be displayed to the crew. This reduces the workload for the two-man cockpit.

The primary engine parameters on the upper screen are in two identical columns because the airplane has two engines. The instruments displayed are engine pressure ratio (EPR), N1 tachometer and exhaust gas temperature (EGT). During engine starts, the EICAS system will automatically display the secondary engine parameters as shown here. The EICAS screens can also display additional information such as check lists. If an engine flames out during flight, a checklist is automatically displayed which shows the acceptable altitudes and airspeeds for an attempted restart as well as the checklist to accomplish this task. The EICAS system is complex and expensive so it has been installed only on the more sophisticated aircraft. The EADI and EHSI can be found on all classes of aircraft including small single engine airplanes.

## 5. Heads Up Displays

The glass cockpit instruments were made possible by the rapid advances made in microprocessors and digital computer technology. An even newer item of advanced cockpit displays is the Heads Up Display. The use of a HUD system was developed by the military for combat aircraft. If information about important aircraft systems is displayed in the windshield area, the pilot does not have to shift his attention down to the instrument panel to get this information. The HUD allows the pilot to keep looking out the windshield of the aircraft (head up) and to see the information that is needed projected onto a special screen in the windshield area. A heads up display system for commercial jet airplanes has been developed and is installed in some aircraft at this time. This system is called the Heads Up Guidance System (HGS) and the display is shown in figure 1-85.

The HGS screen itself is a special type of glass plate which the pilot can look through even while information is being projected onto the screen. The images on the screen are focused at infinity so the pilot does not have to refocus his eyes to look at either the world outside the windshield or the

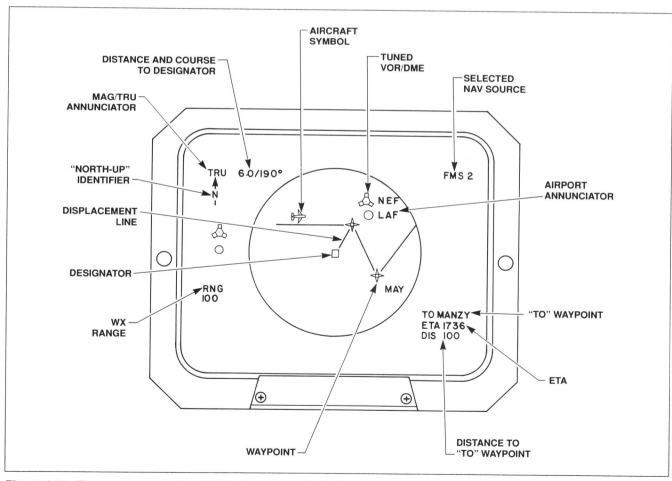

*Figure 1-83. The appearance of an EHSI when operating in MAP MODE.*

data on the HGS. The HGS screen is operated by a computer controlled system which has many sensors to display different information. On a civil aircraft the information displayed on the HGS is the same kind of information displayed on an EADI. The first airline to begin using an FAA-approved HGS system was Alaska Airlines. They retrofitted their Boeing 727s with HGS at a cost of about $200,000 for each aircraft. The use of the HGS enables the airline to operate in bad weather conditions that might ground aircraft of other airlines. The FAA has approved this operation because of the elimination of the need for the pilot to switch his attention from the instrument panel to the view out the windshield. The future will no doubt see an increasing use of HGS and other advanced display systems by many other airlines and aircraft operators. Versions of the heads up display designed for use in twin-engine turboprop aircraft are already being developed by several companies.

## G. Computers in Aircraft

The rapid advances in computer technology in recent years have been applied to many different aircraft systems such as cockpit displays, autopilots, navigational computers, engine controls

etc. The aviation maintenance technician that works on modern aircraft should have a basic understanding of computers in general and their application to aircraft systems. The modern digital computer is made possible by the rapid advances in integrated circuits that have taken place over the last twenty years. A modern microprocessor is in effect a computer on a small chip of silicon. This small and powerful chip makes possible the manufacture of small but powerful computers.

### 1. Basic Parts of a Computer

A computer is made up of three basic parts as related to their functions. The basic hardware consists of input devices, output devices and the CPU (central processing unit). Refer to figure 1-86.

Input devices are things like keyboards, mice, scanners etc. Output devices are CRTs, printers, plotters etc. The central processing unit contains the brains of the computer. The CPU can be divided into three different units by their function. The central control unit directs data from one place to another and maintains overall control of the

Figure 1-85. The display screen for a heads up guidance system (HGS) is a transparent plate that displays the same kinds of information as an ADI, but it allows the pilot to look out the windshield through the HGS display. (Courtesy Flight Dynamics, Inc.)

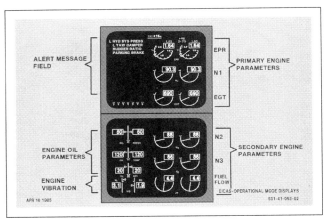

Figure 1-84. EICAS display screens. This system is used on the Boeing 757 and 767.

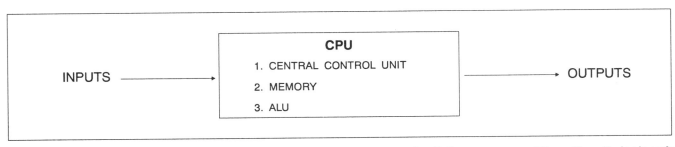

Figure 1-86. The basic parts of a computer. The CPU contains the control unit, the memory and the arithmetic logic unit which performs calculations.

52

operations. The memory stores information on special computer chips. The ALU is the arithmetic logic unit; it performs the mathematical calculations that are required. The term peripherals is often used in discussing computers. Peripherals are the various input and output devices, examples of which were given above.

The memory of a computer comes in two types that are known as RAM and ROM. The RAM or volatile memory temporarily holds data that is being acted upon by the computer. It is called volatile because it is lost each time the computer is switched off. The operator can change and manipulate the RAM memory with keyboard entries and other actions. The ROM or non-volatile memory is sometimes called hard-wired. The data in the ROM area will not be lost when the computer is switched off and cannot be altered by a simple keyboard entry. An example of ROM is the built-in startup test that most computers have. When the computer is first switched on, it tests itself for errors and checks to see what peripheral devices are connected to it. An example of RAM could be a term paper that you are typing into a computer using a word processor program. If you forget to save the document on a disk, it will be lost when the computer is switched off.

## 2. Some Applications of Computers in Aircraft

A modern jet airplane may have many different computers that perform a variety of functions. The use of digital systems on aircraft is becoming more and more common because it offers several advantages:

1. Increased reliability
2. Faster response
3. Reduced power consumption
4. Smaller and lighter weight equipment
5. Lower operating cost

Computers have become so common that they are now used in many different aircraft systems such as autopilot, engine controls, navigation, flight planning, etc.

## 3. BITE Systems

One of the features of the effort to reduce operating cost is the use of BITE (built-in test equipment). The latest types of aircraft electronic equipment and computers have special types of test equipment as a part of the major units. BITE systems often provide three different kinds of tests that can be used to identify and correct faults.

1. Fault Detection — continuous during equipment operation

2. Fault Isolation — faulty equipment can be isolated or bypassed
3. Operational Verification After Defect Repair

The last example is a type of BITE program that maintenance personnel would use most often. After changing a piece of equipment which is thought to be the cause of the problem, a verification test can be conducted to ensure that the system is now operating normally. Running this particular test usually involves just pushing the appropriate button.

To simplify the troubleshooting and repair of modern electronic equipment, it is installed in the aircraft in the form of LRUs. An LRU is a line replaceable unit which means a standard size container which slides easily in and out of a special mounting rack. A typical arrangement for LRUs and equipment installations is shown in figure 1-87. The LRUs use standard types of electrical connectors and mounting attachments; this makes it easy to locate and change one in a short period of time. The BITE systems in an aircraft are designed to identify faulty LRUs so that they can be changed quickly and easily.

## 5. Digital Data Transmission

The increasing use of computers and sophisticated electronic devices on modern aircraft requires that these devices be able to communicate with each other rapidly and efficiently. This rapid exchange of data is accomplished with digital data transmission using

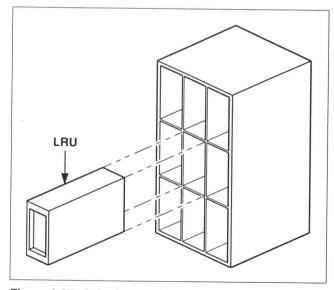

*Figure 1-87. Avionics equipment in modern aircraft is installed in special racks that accommodate standard sizes of line replaceable units or LRUs. This makes changing the LRUs a quick and simple procedure.*

digital data busses. Since the various pieces of equipment that use this data bus are manufactured by many different companies, a uniform standard for the method of data transmission is needed. The standard which is used by this type of equipment on modern air carrier jets and bizjets is ARINC 429.

The initials ARINC stand for Aeronautical Radio Incorporated. This organization has been in existence since the 1930s to provide certain services to the airline industry.

The members of ARINC include the major airlines, aircraft manufacturers and equipment manufacturers. They establish many study groups that investigate emerging technology and suggest standards that can be applied to new types of equipment. When these standards are approved, they will be followed by all the members of ARINC. In the case of ARINC 429, this means that computers and similar equipment that utilize digital signals will be compatible with each other. Since the airlines often lead the way in the development of new types of equipment, the manufacturers of equipment for smaller aircraft often use ARINC standards also— even if they are not members of ARINC. Unlike FAA and FCC regulations, ARINC standards are not laws; but anyone who wants to sell airplanes or equipment to the major airlines will comply with these accepted industry standards. ARINC 429 has been used as an example here because it applies to digital information transmission systems used on aircraft. Many of the newer types of equipment described earlier such as EADI, EHSI, EICAS, BITE, etc. will use digital data exchange systems that are designed in accordance with ARINC 429.

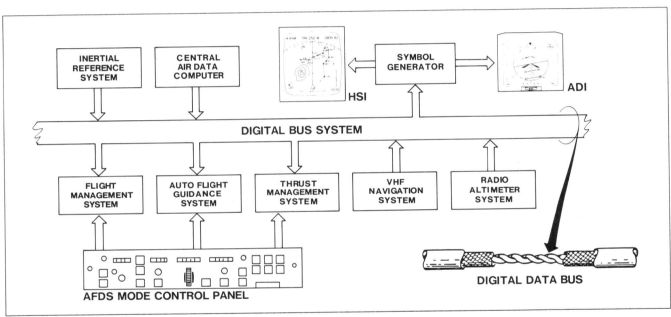

Figure 1-88. A digital data bus permits rapid transmission of data between the various electronic systems on the aircraft. The bus itself is a shielded twisted pair conductor which helps to prevent interference.

# CHAPTER II

# Powerplant Instruments and Logic Gates

The information presented in chapter 2 will be in three major topic areas: powerplant instruments, logic gates and binary numbers, and position indicating and annunciator systems.

## A. Liquid Quantity Measuring Systems

Depending on the type of aircraft involved, there may be just one or there may be many different liquids carried on the aircraft for which a quantity measurement is required. Most of the examples given here will be fuel quantity systems because they are the most common. It should be noted that for each type of system described, it could be used to measure fuel, oil, water, hydraulic fluid or some other liquid quantity.

Most small, single engine airplanes only have one liquid quantity indicating system in the cockpit and that is for fuel. The simplest types of fuel quantity systems are those that use mechanical systems and require no electrical power to give readings. These will be described first.

### 1. Sight Glass Gauges

The simplest kind of liquid quantity system is the sight glass gauge. In this system a small glass or plastic tube is connected into the tank so that the level of the liquid in the tube matches that in the tank. Markings on the tube itself or a plate behind it indicate the quantity. A sight glass gauge is shown in figure 2-1.

This type of quantity system has no moving parts, but the tank must be located in or near the cockpit area for it to be practical. It has been used on older aircraft for fuel and hydraulic fluid quantity systems.

### 2. Float-type Mechanical Gauges

A number of different kinds of mechanical float quantity systems have been used.

A very simple version utilized a float mounted on a metal rod which projected through a hole in the gas cap so that the rod would be visible from the cockpit. The fuel tank was located directly in front of the cockpit in the fuselage so that it could be easily seen. This type is illustrated by figure 2-2.

The float was often made of cork and it had to be coated with a special shellac or varnish so that it would not sink. Two disadvantages of this quantity system are that the rod tends to bounce up and down and there are no index markings at all. A variation of this system was used in many biplanes where the fuel tank was in the center section and the rod stuck down below the tank in a clear tube with an indicator fastened to it. This inverted float system with the indicator below the tank is shown in figure 2-3.

The gauge called the magnetic direct reading is a float-type gauge which uses a gear system to

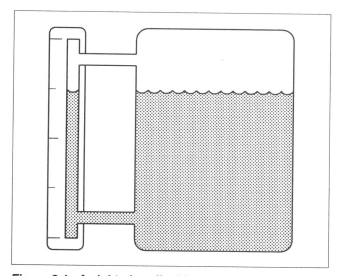

Figure 2-1. A sight glass liquid quantity gauge.

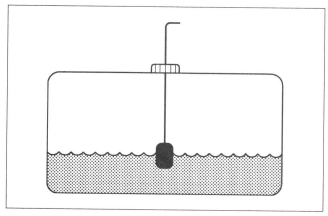

Figure 2-2. A mechanical float-type fuel quantity gauge for a fuselage tank.

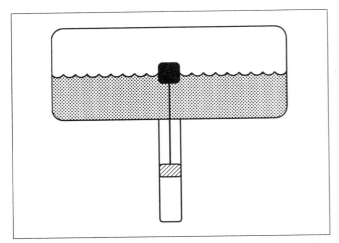

**Figure 2-3.** *A mechanical float fuel quantity gauge for the center section of a biplane.*

rotate a pointer in a round gauge and uses a magnetic principle to isolate the glass face cover and pointer from the fuel. This type of gauge was often used on high wing airplanes where the fuel tanks were in the butt end of the wing. The gauge was installed so that the float was inside the tank and the round face of the gauge was visible inside the cockpit. It is shown in figure 2-4.

The float rotated a shaft through a simple gearing system. On the end of the shaft was a U-shaped magnet which rotated along with the shaft. Separating the magnet and shaft from the pointer and

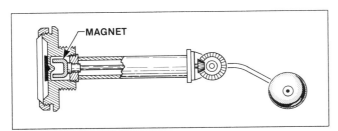

**Figure 2-4.** *Mechanical float-type gauge with a permanent magnet to isolate the fuel from the cover glass and pointer.*

the rest of the gauge in the cockpit was a piece of aluminum with sealing gaskets. The magnetic flux traveled through the aluminum and rotated a piece of ferrous metal that in turn rotated the pointer.

### 3. Resistance Gauges

The type of fuel quantity gauge most common on modern small airplanes is similar to the kind used in cars. It has a float in the tank that moves a variable resistor. The variable resistor alters the current flow in a DC circuit to operate a meter movement that is somewhat similar to those used in voltmeters and ammeters.

The gauge used with the float operated variable resistor is most often the ratiometer type seen in figure 2-5. This gauge uses two opposing magnetic fields so that the pointer reacts to the ratio of current flow in the two sections. In this way, it is less affected by fluctuations in system voltage caused by voltage regulator settings or a weak battery.

### 4. Underwing Fuel Quantity Indicators

Many large aircraft have two totally different types of fuel quantity measuring systems. One of these operates the cockpit gauges and the other is an underwing fuel quantity system. The underwing system can only be used on the ground and is most often employed by maintenance and service personnel rather than by the flight crew. There are three kinds of underwing fuel quantity systems, but they all share certain features in common. They all utilize a fuel quantity stick of some type which can be extended below the bottom surface of the wing. They measure the fuel quantity in terms of volume and not mass. These underwing quantity systems typically require no electrical power to obtain readings. This last characteristic would be an advantage if it was necessary to take fuel readings while working on the fuel system.

The oldest and simplest type of underwing fuel quantity system is called a drip stick. It uses a

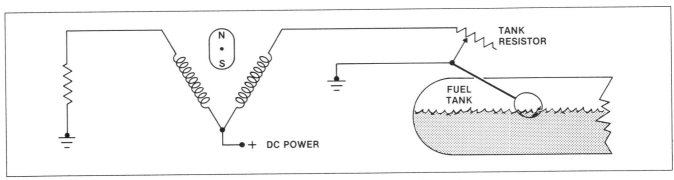

**Figure 2-5.** *Ratiometer fuel quantity system using a float-operated variable resistor.*

hollow tube which extends from the bottom of the wing up inside the fuel tank as illustrated in figure 2-6. The tube is normally stowed by being pushed up inside the tank until the bottom of the tube is flush with the bottom surface of the wing where it is latched in the closed position. In order to obtain a reading, the tube is unlatched and pulled down until the upper end reaches the top of the fuel level. When fuel begins to drip out the bottom of the tube, a reading is taken using the markings on the outside of the tube. This type of fuel quantity system is not used on modern aircraft because of the fire danger when fuel is allowed to drip on the ground or hangar floor.

Another type of underwing fuel quantity stick is the one which uses a clear Lucite® plastic rod. The main features of this device are shown in figure 2-7. The rod is made of clear plastic because it obtains readings by transmitting light along the rod. The principle involved is the refraction of light. Fuel and air have different light refraction characteristics and if a specially shaped quartz tip is installed on the top of the rod, it will produce a particular light pattern when it is positioned at the top of the fuel level. In order to take a reading, the tube is pulled down from the bottom of the wing until the light pattern on the bottom of the rod is focused to a point of light. The reading is then taken using the markings along the length of the rod.

The most common type of underwing fuel quantity stick on modern aircraft is the one which uses a float inside the tank that has a magnet fastened to it. The upper end of the stick has a magnet which will attract the float magnet when they are in alignment. This type of underwing fuel quantity stick is shown in figure 2-8.

A fuel reading is taken by unlatching the stick and pulling it down until the float and the top

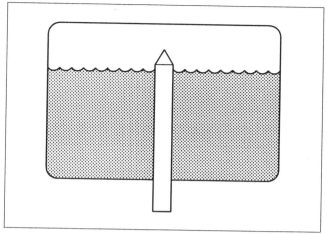

Figure 2-7.  *An underwing fuel quantity measuring stick that utilizes a clear Lucite rod.*

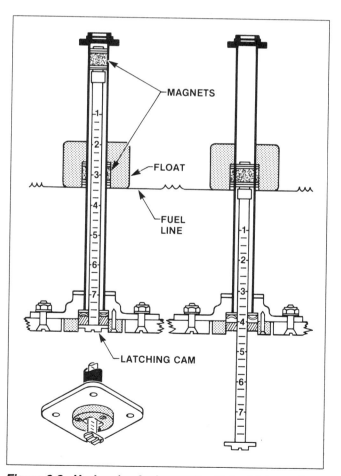

Figure 2-8.  *Underwing fuel quantity stick which employs a float and permanent magnets.*

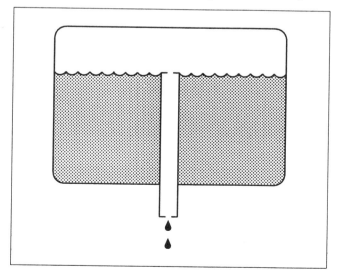

Figure 2-6.  *Older style drip stick underwing fuel quantity gauge.*

57

of the stick are held in position by magnetic attraction. The reading is then taken from the markings along the tube. The magnetic force is not strong enough to lift the float out of the fuel; so when the stick is pushed up, the magnetic attraction is broken and the stick can be pushed up and stowed.

These types of underwing fuel quantity systems are not usually as accurate as the cockpit fuel quantity system, but they can be used for maintenance and troubleshooting purposes.

### 5. Capacitance Quantity Indicators

The most common type of liquid quantity measuring system used on modern turbine engine aircraft is the capacitance type. It has the advantage over other quantity systems in that it can give accurate readings in very large or unusually shaped tanks. Another advantage is the fact that liquid quantity is measured in terms of mass or weight rather than in volume. Measuring fuel quantity in mass is especially useful with large turbine engine aircraft because the power produced by the engines is more a factor of the mass of fuel consumed rather than the volume. In very large fuel tanks, the volume of the fuel will vary considerably due to thermal expansion and contraction, but the mass would remain the same.

The capacitance liquid quantity system gets its name from the fact that the measuring probes located in the tank are capacitors. A simplified representation of this type of fuel quantity system is shown in figure 2-9. In the real system, the probe is usually constructed in the form of two concentric metal tubes which are the two plates of the capacitor. When this probe is located in a fuel tank, the two plates of the capacitor will be separated by fuel on the lower end and air on the upper end. Since fuel and air have different dielectric constant values, the amount of capacitance will change as the fuel level rises or falls. The dielectric constant for the fuel is also affected by density. Therefore any increase in density caused by thermal contraction will result in an increase in capacitance. The probes will automatically measure the mass or weight of the fuel. A small, symmetrical tank like an engine oil tank may only require one capacitance probe to give accurate readings. A large, tapered wing fuel tank might have 15 or more probes connected in parallel to ensure accurate readings. The capacitance fuel quantity system of figure 2-10 has a total of 17 capacitance probes. Electronic circuits measure the amount of capacitance in the probes, apply any needed corrections, and send electrical

signals to the cockpit gauges to indicate the fuel quantity in pounds. Capacitance fuel quantity systems usually include a totalizer. The totalizer gives a reading of the total fuel on board the aircraft. Some fuel systems will also give the fuel used since takeoff.

## B. Fuel Flow Indicators

There are a number of different gauges which might be used for aircraft fuel systems depending on the type and complexity of the particular kind of fuel system used. All powered aircraft will have a fuel quantity system. On small airplanes with gravity flow fuel systems, this would be the only type of fuel system instrument required. Aircraft with pump fed engines will need a fuel pressure gauge in addition to fuel quantity. Aircraft with fuel-injected or large radial piston engines and aircraft with turbine engines will usually have a fuel flow instrument. Some aircraft with turbine engines that operate in cold temperatures will also have a fuel temperature indicator to guard against the danger of ice crystals in the fuel. The various types of fuel flow indicator systems will be described in this section.

### 1. Fuel-injected Engine Flowmeters

The type of flowmeter commonly installed on aircraft with fuel-injected reciprocating engines is not a true flowmeter at all. The sensor used with this instrument system actually measures pressure not

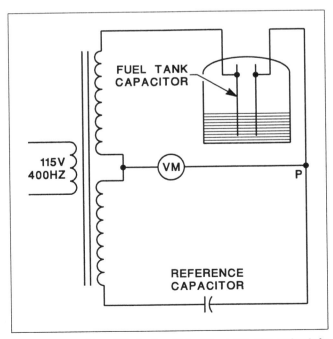

*Figure 2-9. Simplified circuit to illustrate the principle of operation for a capacitance liquid quantity system.*

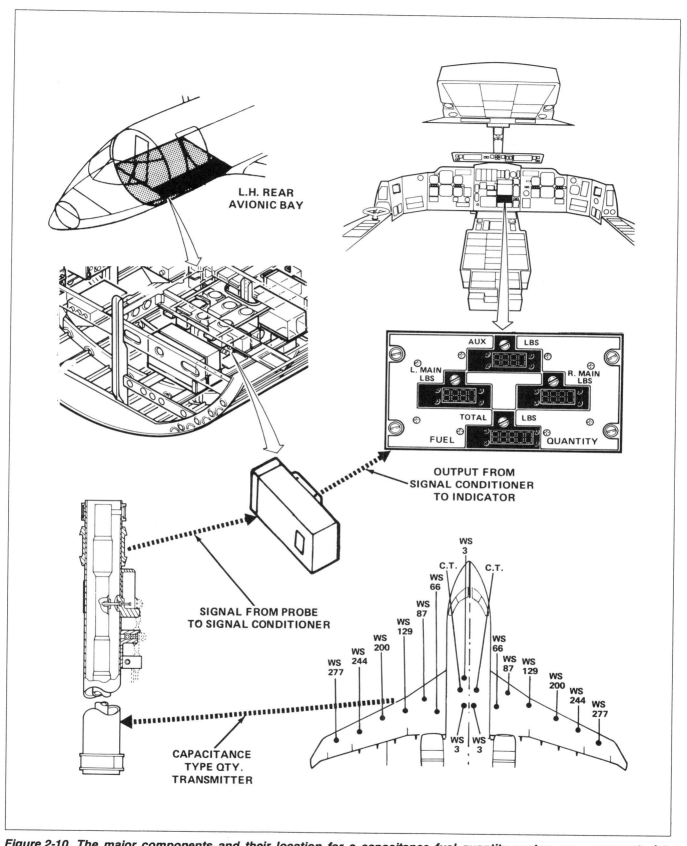

L.H. REAR
AVIONIC BAY

AUX LBS

L. MAIN
LBS

R. MAIN
LBS

TOTAL LBS

FUEL QUANTITY

OUTPUT FROM
SIGNAL CONDITIONER
TO INDICATOR

SIGNAL FROM PROBE
TO SIGNAL CONDITIONER

CAPACITANCE
TYPE QTY.
TRANSMITTER

WS
3

C.T. C.T.

WS
66

WS
87

WS
129

WS
200

WS
244

WS
277

WS
66

WS
87

WS
129

WS
200

WS
244

WS
277

WS
3

WS
3

Figure 2-10. *The major components and their location for a capacitance fuel quantity system on a corporate jet. (Courtesy Canadair Group, Bombardier Inc.)*

59

flow rate. Since the injector lines and nozzles have a certain restriction to flow, a given pressure supplied to the injection system will produce a given flow rate for normal operating conditions. This type of instrument uses a Bourdon tube in the gauge which is connected by tubing and hose to the fuel divider block on top of the engine. The line leading from the fuel distribution manifold on the engine can be seen in figure 2-11. The face of the instrument usually has three different units of measurement: PSI, gallons per hour (GPH) or pounds per hour and percent of cruise power. The instrument face shown in figure 2-12 has these three units. This instrument will give accurate readings for all three of these values as long as everything is operating normally. The pressure at the fuel distribution manifold will be proportional to the flow rate if the total restrictions to flow in the system are normal. If there is any fault in the system which causes the restriction to the flow of fuel to increase or decrease, the instrument can give erroneous readings. For example, if an injector nozzle was blocked this would cause a greater restriction to flow and an indication of increased fuel consumption when the actual fuel

flow rate would be decreased. A leak in an injector line would decrease the restriction to flow and decrease the indicated flow rate on the gauge but the fuel consumption would actually increase.

## 2. Vane-type Flowmeters

The vane-type flowmeter uses a sensor like that in figure 2-13 that is installed in the line that feeds fuel to the engine. The vane is mounted on a shaft so that it will rotate through an arc as the fuel pushes against it. The circular chamber that contains the vane has enough clearance between the cylinder walls and the vane that the flow of fuel is not retarded to any significant degree. The vane type sensor will measure the volumetric flow rate of the fuel.

The vane is rotated against a restraining spring so that the amount of rotation of the vane corresponds to the volumetric flow rate. The cockpit gauge is normally marked to show the flow rate in gallons per hour. The position of the vane in the sensor is transmitted electrically to the cockpit gauge where it rotates the pointer to the correct reading. The type of electrical system that transmits

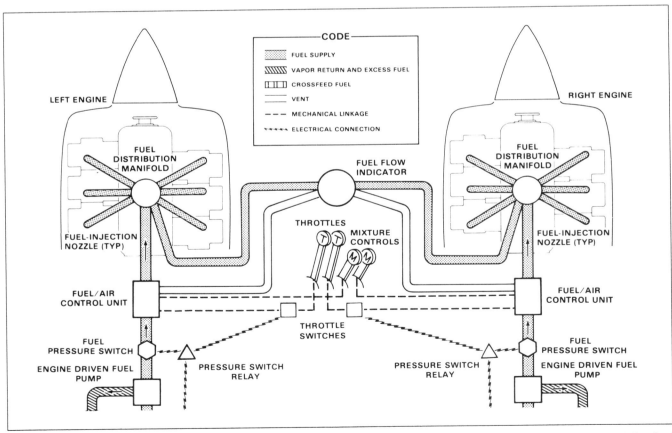

**Figure 2-11.** *The fuel flow indicator system for a fuel-injected reciprocating engine that measures pressure at the fuel distributor manifold. (Courtesy Cessna Aircraft Co.)*

this positional information concerning the vane is a type of synchro system. An example of a vane-type flowmeter with a synchro system is shown in figure 2-14. Since these synchro systems are used with many other types of aircraft instruments, they will be described next.

## 3. Synchro Systems

There are three types of synchro systems and they share the same basic features and are used for similar purposes. A synchro system consists of a transmitter unit and a receiver unit. The two are connected to each other by electrical wiring. The transmitter unit contains an input shaft and it can be connected to anything which will rotate

Figure 2-12. *Fuel flow indicator with three different measurement units: pounds per hour, PSI and percent of cruise power.*

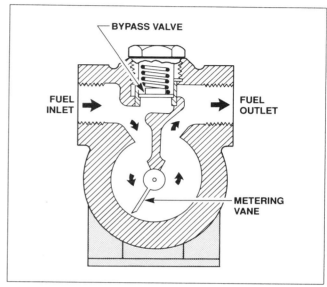

Figure 2-13. *A vane-type flow sensor that measures volumetric flow rate.*

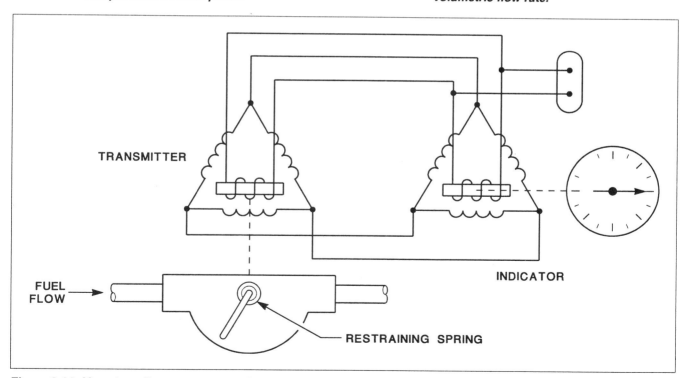

Figure 2-14. *Vane-type flowmeter system for a large airplane which includes a synchro system.*

this shaft through an arc. The receiver unit has a shaft which is connected to the pointer in the instrument. If the shaft in the transmitter unit is rotated 20° to the right, the shaft in the receiver will also rotate 20° to the right. The operation of a synchro system causes the receiver unit to move in synchronization with the transmitter unit. A large jet transport may have many different synchro systems for a variety of different instruments. The transmitter unit can be connected to anything which produces a rotation of the shaft through an arc. Figure 2-15 shows how the rotor in the receiver unit will position itself automatically based on the magnetic field created by the three outer magnets. The three different kinds of synchro systems will now be described. They do differ in details of construction, but the basic operation of all three is as described above.

## a. DC Selsyn® Synchro

The transmitter unit in the Selsyn synchro is a variable resistor with three sections as seen in figure 2-16. The shaft is connected to the wiper arm. The three sections of the variable resistor are connected by wires to the three coils in the receiver unit. The rotor of the receiver unit is a permanent magnet that is connected to the instrument pointer. The position of the wiper arm in the transmitter determines the voltages that are produced by the three sections of the resistor. The permanent magnet in the receiver unit will line up with the overall magnetic field produced by the three coils surrounding it. Any rotation of the shaft and wiper arm of the transmitter will cause different voltages to be applied to the receiver unit. A new orientation of the magnetic field in the receiver unit will pull the rotor into the correct alignment.

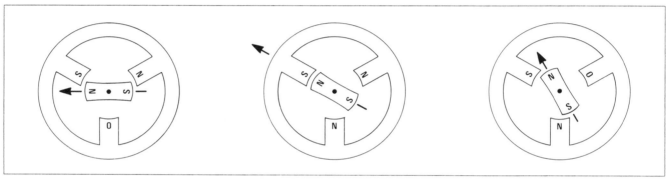

Figure 2-15. An illustration of the basic operation of a synchro receiver unit. The rotor will align itself with the resultant field of the three outer magnetic fields.

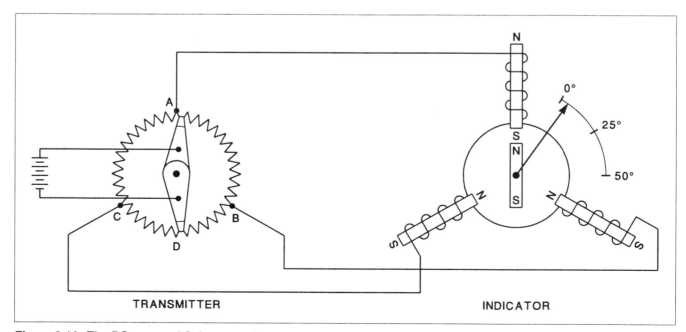

Figure 2-16. The DC-powered Selsyn synchro system.

### b. Magnesyn® Synchro

The Magnesyn synchro system uses AC power, most often 26 volts AC and 400 Hz. The use of AC power eliminates the need for a variable resistor and improves reliability because there are no brushes to wear or get out of adjustment. The construction features of the transmitter and receiver unit are similar, which can be seen in figure 2-17. The rotors are permanent magnets and the three section windings are connected together. The magnetic field produced in the receiver will pull the rotor into a position that corresponds to the rotor position in the transmitter unit.

### c. Autosyn® Synchro

The only difference between the Autosyn and Magnesyn synchros is that the Autosyn uses electromagnets instead of permanent magnets for the rotors. Figure 2-18 shows an Autosyn synchro system. It also uses AC power that is most often 26 volts AC at 400 Hz. Many pressure and flow type instruments on modern jet airplanes use a synchro system to transmit the information to the cockpit gauge.

### 4. Mass Flowmeters

The latest types of turbine engine aircraft use a flowmeter that gives a reading of the mass flow rate

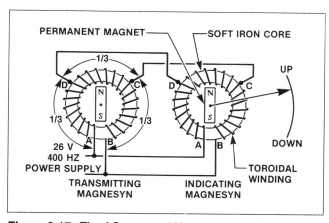

**Figure 2-17. The AC-powered Magnesyn synchro system.**

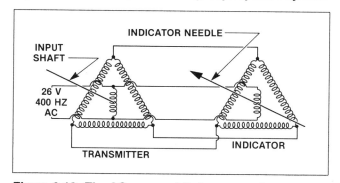

**Figure 2-18. The AC-powered Autosyn synchro system.**

in pounds per hour rather than a volumetric reading in gallons per hour. The mass flow rate is a more useful indication for this type of aircraft. Refer to figure 2-19 for a drawing of the mass flowmeter. The mass flowmeter consists of a motor-driven impeller, a turbine and a synchro system to transmit the data to a cockpit gauge. In order to give accurate readings, the impeller must be driven at a constant speed. This is accomplished with an AC synchronous motor or a similar device. As the fuel flows through the impeller, it is given a spin or rotation by the spinning impeller. When the fuel leaves the impeller, it strikes the turbine which is rotated against a restraining spring by the spin energy of the fuel. Because a denser fuel would impart more spin energy to the turbine, the degree of rotation of the turbine is a measure of mass flow rate. The turbine is connected to the transmitter rotor of a synchro system which will cause the pointer on the cockpit gauge to rotate to the proper position to indicate the correct mass flow rate. The sensor for this and other types of flowmeters is installed in the fuel system downstream of the fuel control device so that the flow rate represents the fuel consumption rate for that engine.

### 5. Computerized Fuel System

The computerized fuel system is a volumetric flow measuring system found on some fuel-injected reciprocating engines. The sensor is a small unit which is installed on top of the engine in the fuel line that feeds the fuel splitter or manifold. The sensor or transducer contains a small rotor that has the same density as the fuel to ensure accurate readings.

As the fuel flows past the rim of the rotor, it spins the rotor at a rate which is proportional to the volumetric flow rate of the fuel. The rotor has notches on its rim which interrupt a light beam from a light emitting diode (LED). This light beam falls on a phototransistor which produces an output signal with a frequency that matches the flicker rate of the light beam. The electrical output of the phototransistor is connected to the computer in the cockpit instrument which processes the data and displays information for the pilot. The input signal to the computer has a frequency which is an indication of flow rate, but the computer can calculate and display fuel flow, fuel used and fuel remaining in several different units of measurement. By including a computer to process the signal from the transducer, the computerized fuel system can give the pilot a number of different kinds of useful information. The cockpit indicator is usually a lighted display like that shown in figure 2-20. This is not a CRT but a digital lighted display. There are three common types of lighted digital displays available that use light emitting diodes (LEDs), liquid crystal displays (LCDs), or gas discharge tubes.

## 6. FARs for Fuel Systems

In chapter 1, the requirements for powerplant instruments were covered and it would be useful to look over that section again to review the information appropriate to the instruments covered in this section. Some additional FARs concerning fuel systems are given here.

### FAR 23.993
#### Fuel Systems

1. Each fuel line must be installed and supported to prevent vibration and to withstand fuel pressure and flight loads.

2. Where relative motion could exist, fuel lines must have provisions for flexibility.

3. Each flexible hose must be approved or shown to be suitable for the particular application.

4. No flexible hose that might be adversely affected by exposure to high temperatures may be used where excessive temperatures will exist during operation or after engine shutdown.

### FAR 23.1337
#### Powerplant Instruments

1. Each line carrying flammable fluids under pressure must:

   a. Have restricting orifices or other safety devices at the source of pressure to prevent the escape of excessive fluid if a line fails; and

   b. Be installed and located so that the escape of fluids would not create a hazard.

2. Each powerplant instrument that utilizes flammable fluids must be installed and located so that the escape of fluid would not create a hazard.

3. Fuel Quantity Indicator — There must be a means to indicate to the flight crew members the quantity of fuel in each tank during flight. An indicator, calibrated in either gallons or pounds, and clearly marked to indicate which scale is used, may be used. In addition:

   a. Each fuel quantity indicator must be calibrated to read zero during level flight when the quantity of fuel remaining in the tank is equal to the unusable fuel supply.

   b. Each exposed sight gauge used as a fuel quantity indicator must be protected against damage.

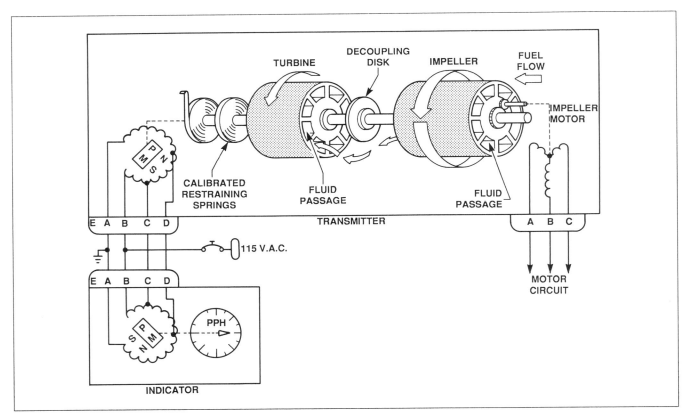

*Figure 2-19. A fuel flowmeter system that measures the mass flow rate of fuel for a turbine engine.*

c. Each sight gauge that can collect water and freeze must have a means to allow drainage on the ground.

d. Tanks with interconnected outlets and airspaces may be considered as one tank and need not have separate indicators.

4. Fuel Flowmeter System — Each metering component must have a means to bypass fuel if a malfunction of that component severely restricts fuel flow.

## FAR 23.1553
### Fuel Quantity Indicator

If the unusable fuel supply for any tank exceeds one gallon, or five percent of tank capacity, whichever is greater, a red arc must be marked on its indicator extending from the calibrated zero reading to the lowest reading obtainable in level flight.

## FAR 23.1557
### Miscellaneous Markings and Placards

1. Fuel and oil filler openings.
   a. Each fuel filler opening must be marked on or near the filler cover with the word "fuel" and the acceptable fuel grades.
   b. For pressure fueling systems, the maximum permissible fueling and defueling pressures must be indicated.

c. Oil filler openings must be marked at or near the filler cover with the word "oil".

## C. Temperature Measuring Systems

There are a number of common methods of measuring temperatures on an aircraft. All of them will have a limit as to how high a temperature they can be used to measure. The common types of temperature measuring systems will be described, but not all of the possible applications can be included. Aircraft temperature indicators may give readings in degrees Fahrenheit or in degrees Celsius. Most of the temperatures given here will be in degrees Fahrenheit for ease of comparison.

### 1. Bimetallic

The bimetallic temperature system is limited to measuring temperatures up to a maximum of 140°F. The outside air temperature gauge (OAT) or free air temperature gauge is an example of the bimetallic system. The device that reacts to changes in temperature is a bimetallic sensor that consists of two thin strips of metal joined together. The strips are made of different metals that have different coefficients of expansion. The metals iron and brass are often used.

As the temperature changes, one of the metal strips will expand or contract more than the other causing the device to bend and move the indicator pointer. The basic principle of a bimetallic temperature sensor is shown in figure 2-21. The two metal strips are

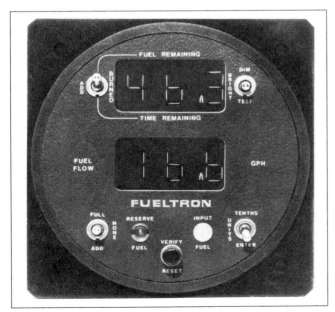

*Figure 2-20. The lighted digital display instrument for a computerized fuel flow system.*

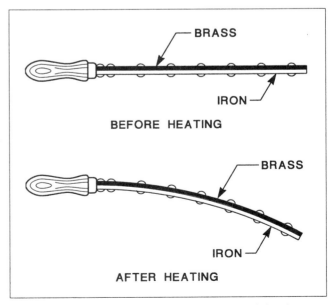

*Figure 2-21. An illustration of the basic principle of operation for a bimetallic temperature sensor.*

often formed into a spiral shape so that a temperature change will cause a rotating motion of the sensor strips. A typical bimetallic outside air temperature gauge is shown in figure 2-22. This type is often installed through the windshield.

## 2. Mechanical Bulb

The mechanical bulb utilizes the principle of the increase in pressure of a confined gas with temperature increases to measure temperatures. As shown in figure 2-23, the mechanical bulb system consists of a bourdon tube gauge to measure pressure, a thin-walled bulb which is at the point of measurement and a thin tube (capillary tube) to connect them together.

The system is filled with a chemical such as methyl chloride which will be part liquid and part gas. The system is sealed with the proper amount of the chemical so that the change in pressure with temperature changes will give an accurate reading on the bourdon tube gauge. The mechanical bulb system is found as an oil temperature indicator system on many smaller airplanes that don't have an electrical system. A mechanical bulb is also found on some jet engines where it transmits compressor inlet temperature (CIT) data to the fuel control unit. The maximum temperature for this type of system is about 300°F.

**Figure 2-22. An outside air temperature gauge for a small airplane. This gauge uses the bimetallic principle.**

## 3. Wheatstone Bridge

This method of measuring temperature is powered by electricity and limited to about 300°F. The Wheatstone bridge system is illustrated in figure 2-24. The bridge circuit consists of three fixed resistors

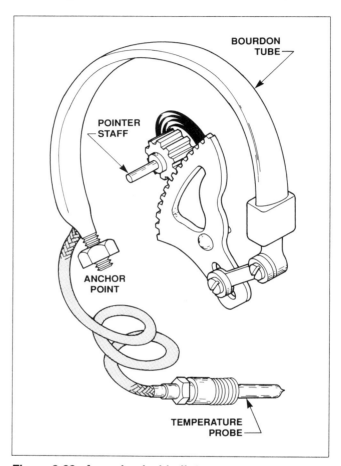

**Figure 2-23. A mechanical bulb temperature measuring system which measures the vapor pressure of a special chemical.**

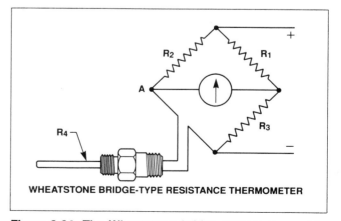

WHEATSTONE BRIDGE-TYPE RESISTANCE THERMOMETER

**Figure 2-24. The Wheatstone bridge system is used to measure temperatures with a variable resistance probe.**

and one variable resistor. The variable resistor is the temperature probe which contains a coil of fine nickel wire. As the coil of wire is heated, its resistance increases and alters the current flow in the bridge which moves the needle in the gauge. Electromagnetic attraction and repulsion will move the pointer whenever the current flow through the meter changes. A disadvantage of the Wheatstone bridge is that any added resistance due to bad connections or any fluctuations in the system voltage can cause inaccurate readings. For this reason, it has been largely replaced by the ratiometer.

## 4. Ratiometer

The ratiometer uses the same kind of electrical power and the same kind of probe that the Wheatstone bridge uses. The difference is in the meter movement that moves the indicator pointer. The ratiometer has two opposing magnetic fields that combine to produce a resultant field that moves the pointer. The resultant field is a ratio of the two opposing fields so that a lower voltage applied to the system will not cause inaccurate readings. The ratiometer can measure temperatures up to 300°F. and is used for oil temperature indicators and other similar requirements. The schematic for a ratiometer is shown in figure 2-25.

## 5. Thermocouples

When it becomes necessary to measure temperatures of about 500°F or more the thermocouple is most often used. The principle of the thermocouple is shown in figure 2-26. When a junction of two dissimilar metals is heated, it will produce a difference of potential or voltage. The amount of voltage produced is proportional to the temperature. The terms "hot junction" and "cold junction" are used with thermocouples. The hot junction is where the temperature measurement is being taken, while the cold junction is at the opposite end of the wires in the instrument. The voltage output of the thermocouple is a result of the temperature difference between the hot junction and the cold junction. It sometimes is necessary to compensate

for any temperature variances at the cold junction in order to obtain accurate readings. Only a few combinations of metals are used for thermocouple hot junctions. The metals must not only withstand the high temperature being measured, but they must produce a usable amount of voltage. The chart in figure 2-27 shows the three commonly used pairs of metals and their voltage output at various temperatures. The actual voltages produced are very low, particularly at lower temperatures. This is why the thermocouple system is not usually used for temperatures below about 400°F. The three types of thermocouples are the iron-constantan, the copper-constantan and the chromel-alumel. Notice that the chromel-alumel can measure much higher temperatures than the other two types. Thermocouple leads are available in standard lengths with specific values of resistance. The length of a thermocouple lead should not be altered in the field.

An application of the thermocouple on piston engines is the cylinder head temperature (CHT) gauge. This gauge is used to monitor the cooling of an air-cooled engine. If only one probe is used, it will be installed in the hottest running cylinder. This would usually be a rear cylinder on a horizontally opposed engine. One type of CHT probe is a gasket that goes under the spark plug, another type fits in a special fitting in the cylinder head. These two types are shown in figures 2-28 and 2-29 respectively. It is better to install CHT probes in all the cylinders. In addition to monitoring all the cylinders, it can be used to troubleshoot some types of engine problems. Another application for the thermocouple is as an exhaust gas temperature (EGT) gauge. All turbine engines have an

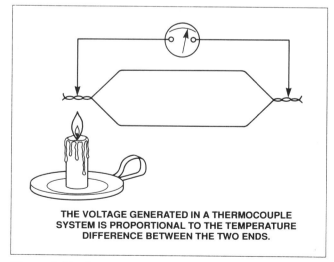

THE VOLTAGE GENERATED IN A THERMOCOUPLE SYSTEM IS PROPORTIONAL TO THE TEMPERATURE DIFFERENCE BETWEEN THE TWO ENDS.

*Figure 2-26. An example of a simple thermocouple system showing the hot junction and cold junction.*

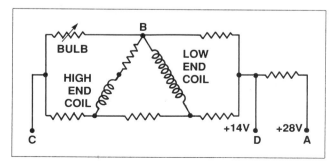

*Figure 2-25. The circuit for a ratiometer temperature system that can operate on 14 or 28 volts DC.*

EGT gauge or gas temperature gauge because turbine engines can be severely damaged by high temperatures in the turbine sections. A number of terms and abbreviations are used for the gas temperature gauge on turbine engines. Turbine inlet temperature (TIT) refers to a system where the probes are installed ahead of the turbine stages. Inter turbine temperature (ITT) means the probes are located between the different sections of the turbine. Turbine outlet temperature (TOT) and EGT refer to measurements that have the probes installed downstream of all the turbine stages. These locations and abbreviations are shown in figure 2-30. Turbine engines use multiple thermocouple probes that are connected in parallel to give an average temperature as seen in figures 2-31 and 2-32.

Some aircraft use the term measured gas temperature (MGT) for the required gas temperature indicator. An MGT gauge for a turbine engine helicopter is shown in figure 2-33.

On reciprocating engine aircraft, the EGT gauge has a different purpose. It is used to manually lean the fuel-air mixture for better economy. The thermocouple probe is installed in an exhaust pipe and connected to a simple gauge in the cockpit. The actual procedure for leaning the engine will vary from one aircraft to another, the example given here

is for purposes of illustration. When ready to set the fuel-air mixture, the pilot watches the EGT gauge as the mixture control knob is pulled back. The temperature will rise as the mixture is leaned because more efficient combustion is taking place. When the EGT reaches a peak, the proper mixture for maximum economy has been reached. If only one probe is installed for the EGT system, the indication is really the average EGT for all the cylinders and they can vary. It is best to have an EGT probe for each cylinder as this gives more information and permits the use of EGT for troubleshooting engine faults. When the EGT gauge is used for leaning, there is usually no redline at all on the gauge. This can be seen on the gauge in figure 2-34 which is an EGT system for a reciprocating engine airplane. However, a turbo-supercharged reciprocating engine will have a redline because the turbo-supercharger can be damaged by high temperatures.

In aircraft schematics, the thermocouple wires are given standard color codes for ease of identification. The standard colors for the wires are:

1. IRON — Black
2. CONSTANTAN — Yellow
3. COPPER — Red
4. CHROMEL — White
5. ALUMEL — Green

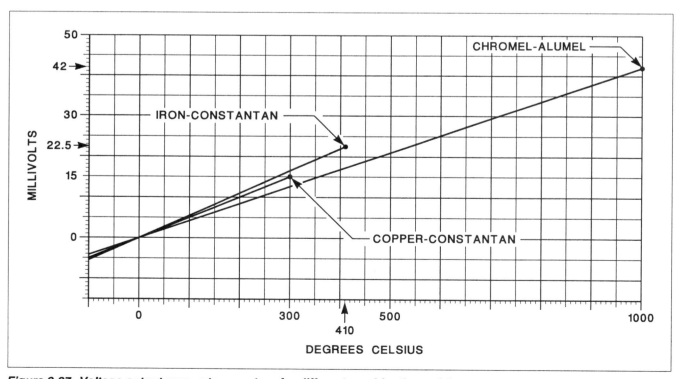

*Figure 2-27. Voltage output versus temperature for different combinations of thermocouple metals.*

# D. Position Indicating Systems

There are many different components and systems on aircraft that might have a position indicating system. There are a relatively small number of different methods that are used to obtain these indications. The basic operation of common types of position indicating systems will be explained and some specific applications will be discussed.

Some of the different methods used to operate position indicating systems are:

1. Mechanical — Rods, levers, cables, etc.
2. Microswitches — Sometimes called limit switches (figure 2-35).
3. Variable Resistance — Wheatstone bridge and ratiometer.
4. Proximity sensors — Mainly on larger, more modern aircraft.
5. Synchro Systems — Selsyn, Magnesyn and Autosyn.

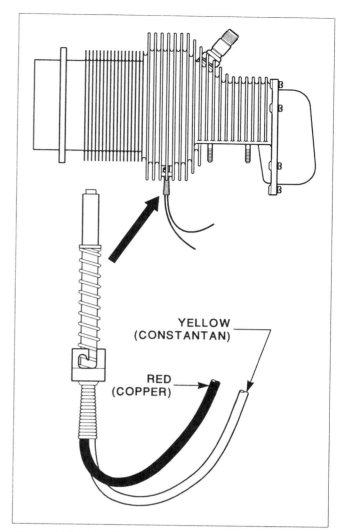

Figure 2-29. A cylinder head temperature system that uses a bayonet-type probe which fits into a special recess in the cylinder head.

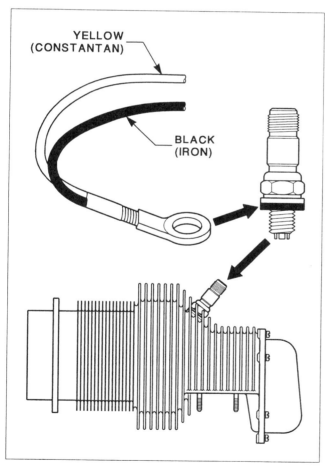

Figure 2-28. A cylinder head temperature (CHT) system for a small reciprocating engine. The thermocouple probe is in the form of a spark plug gasket.

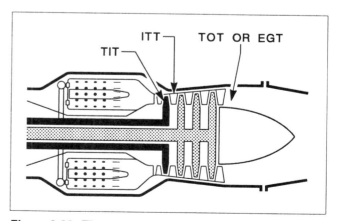

Figure 2-30. The measurement points in the turbine section for turbine inlet temperature, inter-turbine temperature, turbine outlet temperature and exhaust gas temperature.

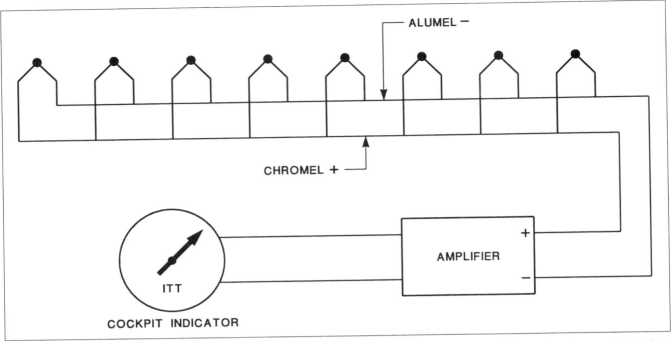

Figure 2-31. *Turbine engine gas temperature systems such as the ITT gauge use multiple probes in parallel and an amplifier to supply signals to the cockpit indicator.*

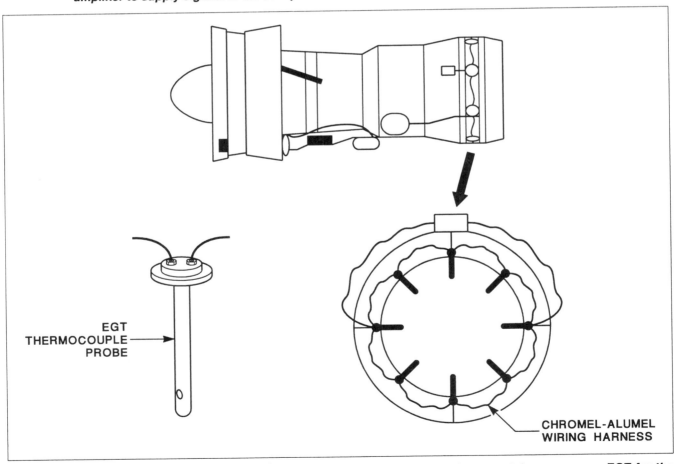

Figure 2-32. *Turbine engines use multiple EGT probes of the chromel / alumel type to take an average EGT for the exhaust section of the tailpipe.*

All the systems and components in an aircraft that might have a position indicating system can be divided into two categories: those that only have two operating positions and those that have many or an infinite number of different operating positions. Some examples follow:

1. Landing Gear — 2 Positions
2. Cabin and Cargo Doors — 2 Positions
3. Thrust Reversers — 2 Positions
4. Ground Spoilers — 2 Positions
5. Trailing Edge Flaps — Many Positions
6. Flight Control Surfaces — Infinite Positions
7. Trim Tabs — Infinite Positions

On smaller aircraft, the systems that only have two operating positions most often use microswitches. Landing gear position indicators are usually lights that are operated by microswitches on the landing gear. This type is shown in figure 2-36. A problem with microswitches is that they are prone to damage from rocks, sand, water, etc. that are thrown up onto the landing gear in service. They also have problems with arcing and burning of the small contact points. For these reasons, most larger aircraft employ proximity sensors instead of microswitches. Figure 2-37 illustrates the operation of one type of proximity sensor. The proximity sensor is a sealed unit that operates in conjunction with a metal target. The proximity sensor produces an electromagnetic field that is distorted when the target piece of metal moves close to it. This change is detected by an electronic circuit to give an indication of gear-up, gear-down etc. The target never touches the proximity sensor and there are no small contacts to cause problems. About the only disadvantages of the proximity sensor systems are that they cost more and since they use electronic circuits, adjustment is more complicated than for a simple microswitch.

On simple aircraft, the systems that have many or an infinite number of operating positions will use mechanical or variable resistance position indicating systems. An example of a mechanical trim tab position indicator is shown in figure 2-38. The wheel that the pilot rotates to move the trim tab contains a spiral groove which moves a small wire pointer to show the position of the trim tab. The ratiometer type variable resistance system is used as a flap position indicator on small airplanes. It works like the ratiometer system already described except that the variable resistor is moved by a part of the flap mechanism.

On the more sophisticated aircraft, the systems that have many or an infinite number of operating positions use synchros. Surface position indicators are usually found on bizjets and air carrier jets to show the flight crew the position of the flight control surfaces. These use a synchro system with the transmitter unit attached to the mechanical linkage of the flight control surface and the receiver unit in the cockpit gauge or indicator. This type of system is shown in figure 2-39.

## E. Tachometers

Most types of aircraft have at least one tachometer to indicate the rotational speed of the engine. Aircraft with reciprocating engines have tachometers that indicate the crankshaft RPM. This is true for engines with reduction gearing also; the tachometer gives engine crankshaft RPM, not propeller RPM. Helicopters have a tachometer for the main rotor or rotors to enable the pilot to maintain a safe rotor RPM. Turbine engines use tachometers that give readings in percent of RPM rather than actual revolutions per minute.

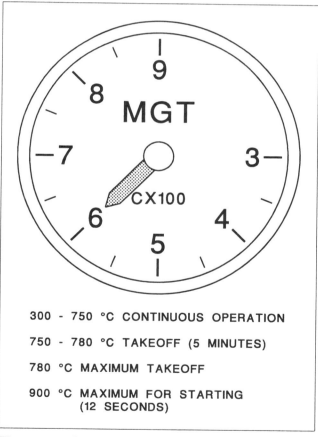

300 - 750 °C CONTINUOUS OPERATION

750 - 780 °C TAKEOFF (5 MINUTES)

780 °C MAXIMUM TAKEOFF

900 °C MAXIMUM FOR STARTING (12 SECONDS)

*Figure 2-33. Some gas temperature gauges are labeled MGT for measured gas temperature. The maximum operating temperatures are often time limited for specific operations.*

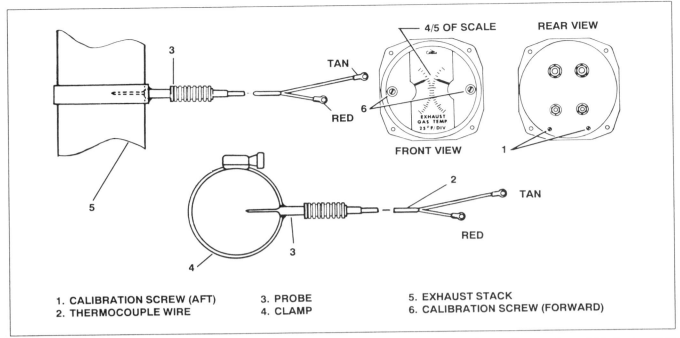

1. CALIBRATION SCREW (AFT)     3. PROBE          5. EXHAUST STACK
2. THERMOCOUPLE WIRE           4. CLAMP          6. CALIBRATION SCREW (FORWARD)

*Figure 2-34. The components in an EGT system for a twin-engine airplane with reciprocating engines. This instrument is sometimes referred to as a mixture indicator. (Courtesy Cessna Aircraft Co.)*

Split spool turbine engines contain more than one main shaft in the engine. They usually have two spools or shafts, but there are some turbine engines with three. The split spool engines will have a tachometer for each main shaft. In the case of turbojet and turbofan engines, these are referred to as the $N_1$ and $N_2$ tachometers. The $N_1$ tach is the low pressure compressor tach and $N_2$ is the high pressure compressor tach. The low pressure compressor and high pressure compressor sections can be seen in the drawing of a twin-spool turbojet engine in figure 2-40. Turboprop and turboshaft engines may use different designations for the tachometers such as gas producer tach and power section tach. The gas producer tach for a turbine engine helicopter shown in figure 2-41 shows some time limited permissible readings above 100%. All tachometers have a red radial line to indicate the maximum permissible RPM. On turbine engines this redline is not necessarily at 100%; it could be above or below the 100% reading. The turbine engine manufacturer will establish what engine section RPM is equal to 100%. On one particular model of CF34 turbofan engine, a reading of 100% $N_2$ is equal to 17,820 RPM. Some reciprocating engine tachometers will have a red arc which denotes a range of engine speeds that is prohibited due to vibration problems at those rotational speeds. A triple tach for a twin-engine helicopter is shown in figure 2-42. It is three tachometers in one to give readings for the power sections of both engines and the main rotor.

## 1. Mechanical Tachometers

Most small general aviation aircraft use simple mechanical tachometers that utilize a flexible drive cable similar to the speedometer drive cable in a car. This flexible drive cable is connected to a drive gear in the engine accessory section and the other end is connected to the tachometer in the cockpit. Older style tachometers used rotating flyweights to move the pointer in the tachometer instrument as illustrated in figure 2-43. Later mechanical tachometers use a rotating permanent magnet and a drag cup to move the pointer. A tachometer drag cup is shown in figure 2-44. The small permanent

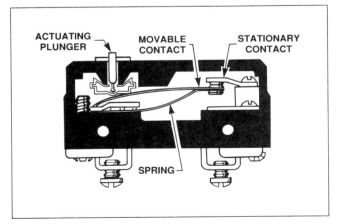

*Figure 2-35. A microswitch is designed so that the contact points open and close with a very small motion of the plunger.*

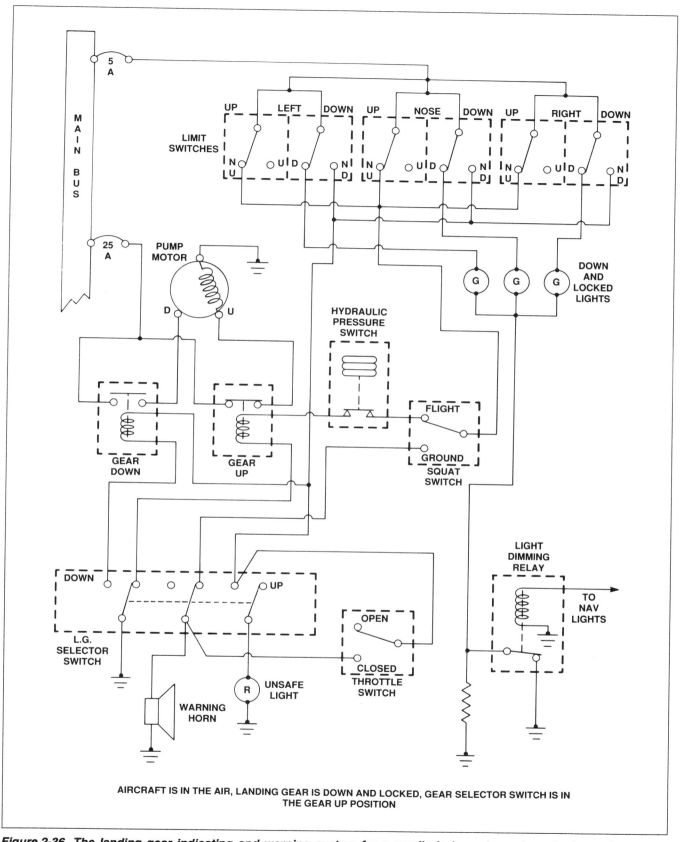

Figure 2-36. *The landing gear indicating and warning system for a small airplane. A number of microswitches are utilized.*

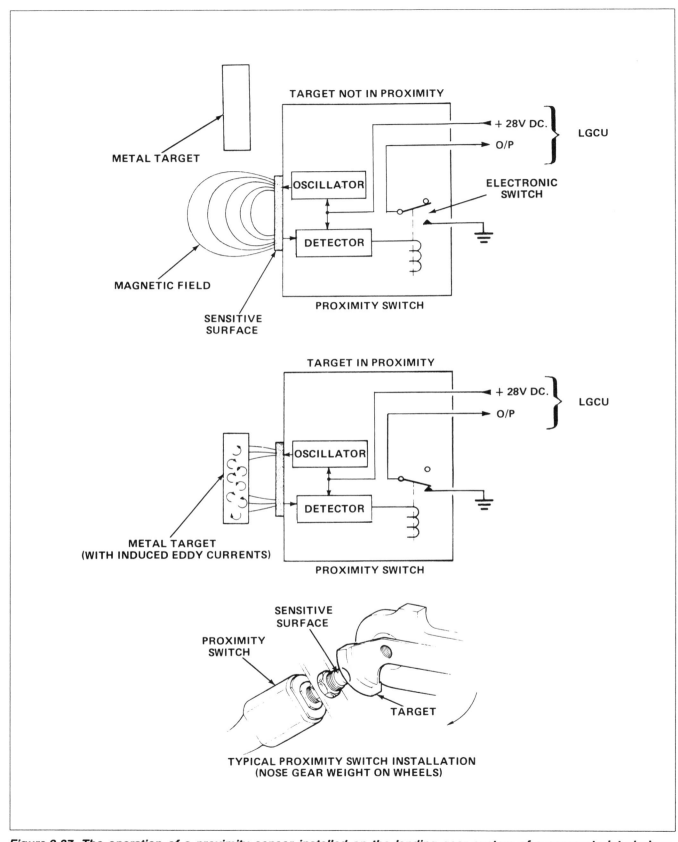

**Figure 2-37.** *The operation of a proximity sensor installed on the landing gear system of a corporate jet airplane. (Courtesy Canadair Group, Bombardier Inc.)*

74

magnet is fastened to the end of the drive mechanism so that it produces a rotating magnetic field. Surrounding the magnet is a drag cup made of aluminum. As the magnet rotates, it sets up eddy currents in the aluminum drag cup and the magnetic fields of the eddy currents interact with the rotating field of the permanent magnet. The interaction of the two fields causes a torque force or drag force to be applied to the drag cup which rotates it against spring tension to move the pointer. The main advantage of the drag cup tachometer is that there is no direct mechanical connection between the drive cable and the pointer mechanism. This makes it smoother in operation and less likely to break if some minor binding occurs.

## 2. Tachometer Generators

This type of tachometer system uses an electrical generator that is mechanically driven by gears at the engine and which transmits electrical energy to the cockpit instrument to give an indication of RPM. There are both AC and DC tach generator systems, but the DC type is not found on modern aircraft. The DC type had a small DC generator on the engine and a cockpit gauge which indicated the voltage output of the generator as RPM. The major disadvantage of this type of tach generator is that any fault which caused a lower than normal voltage would result in an error in the indicated RPM. The AC tach generator eliminates that problem by using an AC generator on the engine and an AC synchronous motor in the indicator. An AC tach generator system is shown in figure 2-45. The primary determining factor in the motor RPM is the frequency of the AC that powers

it. A lower voltage caused by loose connections for example would not have much affect on the indicated RPM. Both types of tach generator systems use permanent magnets so that they are totally independent of the electrical systems of the aircraft.

## 3. Electronic Tachometers

There are several different types of electronic tachometers used on aircraft. The kind used on some reciprocating engines is operated by a special set of points in the engine magneto. This set of contact points opens and closes like the normal points, but only supplies signals for the tach system.

The points in the magneto are connected by wiring to the cockpit instrument. Since the frequency of opening of the points is proportional to the engine RPM, an electronic circuit measures the frequency at which the points open and close and moves the pointer to indicate the proper RPM of the engine.

Two slightly different kinds of electronic tachometers are found on turbine engines. The first type is often used as a fan speed sensor to measure the RPM of the fan section of a turbofan engine. Figure 2-46 shows this type. It uses a sensor which contains a coil of wire that generates a magnetic field. The sensor is mounted in the shroud around the fan. As each fan blade goes by, it cuts the field of the coil and this is sensed and measured by an electronic circuit. The frequency at which the fan blades cut across the field of the sensor is directly proportional to the fan RPM.

Another type of electronic tach used on turbine engines has a gear driven shaft on the engine which turns a rotor with a permanent magnet embedded in its rim. The sensor contains a coil which is located close to the rotating magnet. Each time the field of the rotating permanent magnet cuts across the coil, it induces a voltage. The frequency of this signal is measured by an electronic circuit and used to position the pointer for the correct RPM indication. This type of tachometer is used in figure 2-47 for the $N_2$ indication for a large turbofan engine.

## F. Oil Pressure Indicators

The oil pressure gauges on small aircraft are usually the direct reading type. The oil pressure line is connected into an oil passage in the engine and transmits that pressure through tubing and hose to the cockpit instrument which contains a bourdon tube to move the pointer. Larger aircraft such as corporate turboprops, bizjets and air carrier jets will use instruments that do not rely on having fluids under pressure in the cockpit area. These aircraft may use a bourdon tube or similar pressure sensor, but it will be installed

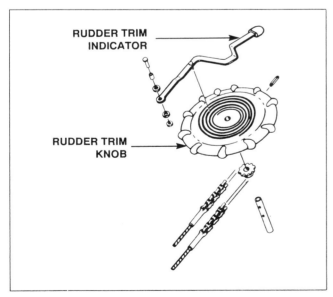

*Figure 2-38. A mechanical position indicator for the rudder trim on a twin-engine airplane. (Courtesy Cessna Aircraft Co.)*

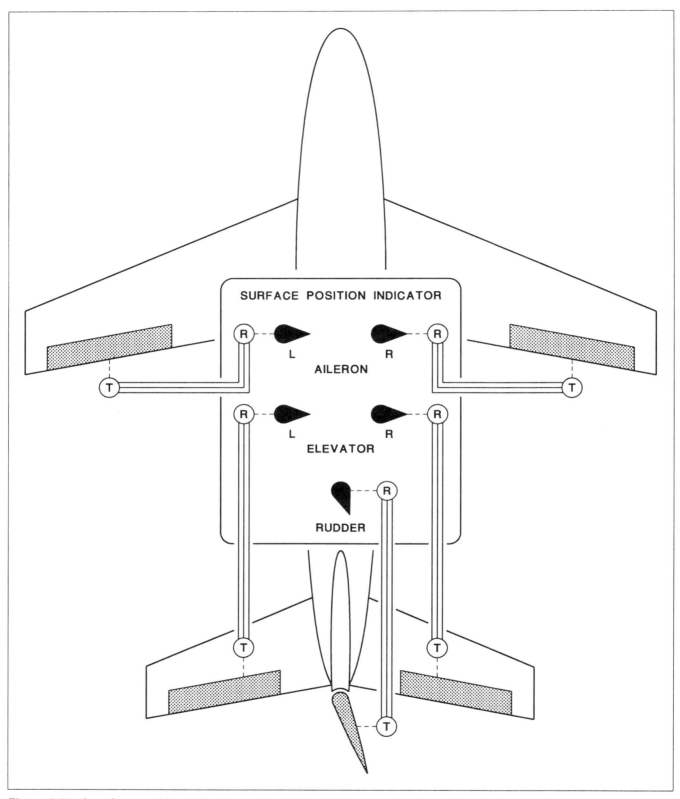

*Figure 2-39. A surface position indicator system for the flight control surfaces. Synchro transmitters and receivers are used to transmit the information from the control surfaces to the cockpit indicator.*

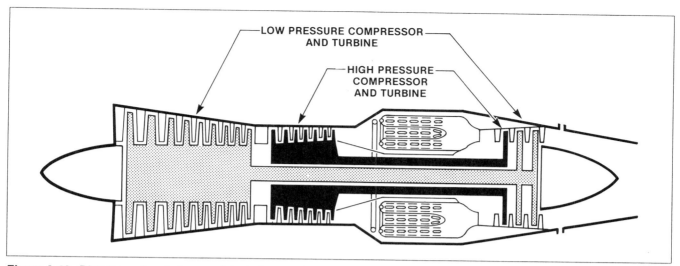

*Figure 2-40. Diagram of a twin-spool turbojet engine showing the low pressure compressor and high pressure compressor.*

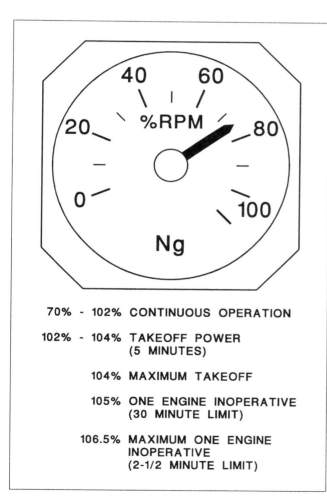

70% - 102% CONTINUOUS OPERATION

102% - 104% TAKEOFF POWER
(5 MINUTES)

104% MAXIMUM TAKEOFF

105% ONE ENGINE INOPERATIVE
(30 MINUTE LIMIT)

106.5% MAXIMUM ONE ENGINE
INOPERATIVE
(2-1/2 MINUTE LIMIT)

*Figure 2-41. The label Ng is commonly applied to the gas producer tachometer for turboprop and tur- boshaft engines. Some maximum values are time limited and some only apply when one engine has failed on a twin engine aircraft.*

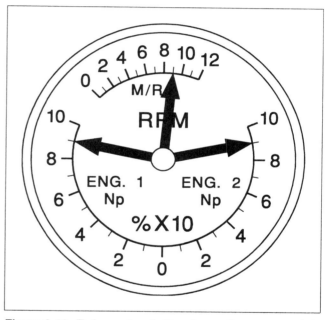

*Figure 2-42. Twin-engine helicopters often use a triple tachometer that provides indications for both engines and the main rotor. The engine RPM is Np for twin spool engines since the indication is for the power turbine section.*

on the engine or wherever the pressure source is located. The information will be transmitted to the cockpit gauges by electrical signals from a synchro transmitter or similar device that is located at the sensor end of the system. Figure 2-48 illustrates an oil pressure system with an Autosyn synchro. The same basic principle of operation would apply to fuel pressure gauges, hydraulic pressure gauges, and similar instruments.

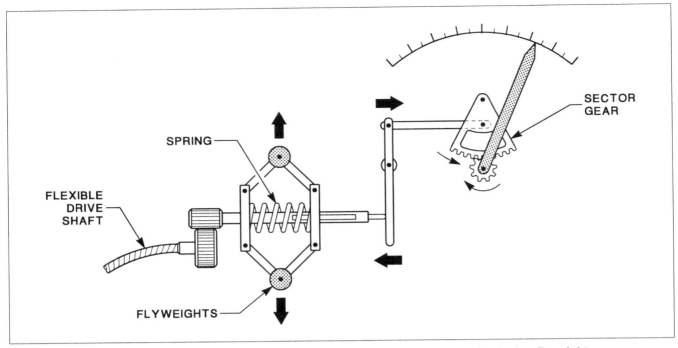

*Figure 2-43. Older type of mechanical tachometer that used the centrifugal force of spinning flyweights.*

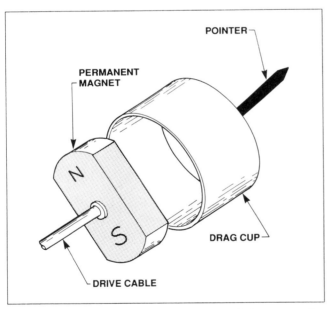

*Figure 2-44. The permanent magnet and drag cup of a modern mechanical tachometer.*

## G. Torquemeters

Torquemeters are used to give an indication of the torque being produced by an engine or the torque being delivered to the main rotor drive of a helicopter. Turboprop airplanes and aircraft with turboshaft engines will have a torquemeter installed because it is the best way to measure the power being produced by these types of turbine engines. Figure

2-49 is a triple torquemeter for a twin engine helicopter. It supplies readings of the torque for each engine and the main rotor drive.

Helicopters often have a torquemeter that is located at the rotor drive gearbox to indicate the torque that is driving the main rotor. Large radial reciprocating engines like those found in DC-6s and Convair 240s also had torquemeters to accurately measure the power developed by the engines.

There are several techniques used to measure torque for an aircraft torquemeter instrument. One technique is to put sensors on a driveshaft, like the main rotor drive shaft of a helicopter. The sensors can be seen at the bottom of the main rotor drive shaft in figure 2-50 which illustrates this principle. The sensors measure the amount of twist in the shaft which is caused by the torque force. The electrical signals from the sensors are processed and used to position the cockpit indicator. Another technique which is used relies on a measurement of torque pressure. The sensor for this type of system is a small oil filled cylinder with a piston in it. The sensor would be located in the reduction gearbox. The reduction gearbox for a turboprop engine is shown in figure 2-51. The sensor is installed in the reduction gearbox so that the torque reaction force is applied to the piston and creates a build-up of pressure that is proportional to the torque force. Figure 2-52 shows another example of this type of torque sensor. The torque pressure is measured and causes the instrument pointer to show the corresponding torque reading. The cockpit indicator for a torquemeter system may use a number of different units of measure. Those units of measure most often seen are horsepower, PSI, foot-pounds and percent.

## H. Engine Pressure Ratio Indicators

This type of instrument is used on some kinds of turbojet and turbofan airplane engines. Those engines built by Pratt & Whitney and Rolls Royce use an engine pressure ratio gauge (EPR) as a primary engine instrument. Jet engines built by GE and Garrett usually do not have an EPR gauge, but use the $N_1$ tachometer in its place. As its name implies, the engine pressure ratio gauge indicates the ratio of two different pressures measured on the engine. The two pressures are most often called $Pt_2$ and $Pt_7$. The total inlet pressure at the front of the engine is $Pt_2$. The total outlet pressure at the aft end of the engine is $Pt_7$. Figure 2-53 illustrates the location of the probes and the differential pressure transducer. These pressures are called total pressures because the probes measure both static and dynamic pressure. The probes

operate like pitot tubes since they measure ram pressure or total pressure in the airstream. The two probes are connected by tubing to a transducer mounted on the engine. The transducer is a differential pressure device that produces an electrical output related to the ratio of $Pt_7/Pt_2$. The transducer may use a synchro transmitter that is connected to the synchro receiver in the cockpit instrument. The $Pt_2$ probe in the front of the engine is prone to icing so it includes a heating system to prevent blockage by ice. The transducer and cockpit gauge for a typical EPR system is shown in figure 2-54. Engine pressure ratio gauges often include an index mark which can be set manually by the pilot. When the correct power setting for takeoff has been determined, a knob is used to set the bug or index mark to the correct value on the face of the instrument. During takeoff, the power is set by lining up the EPR gauge pointer with the bug. This makes it easier to set the correct level of engine power for takeoff.

## I. Manifold Pressure Gauges

Manifold pressure gauges are only found on certain reciprocating engines where they are required to

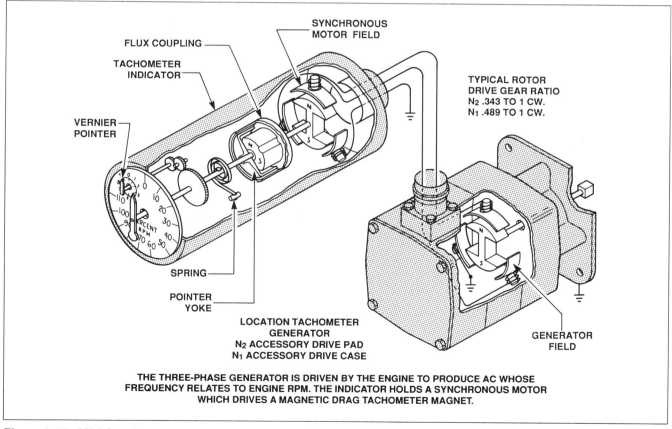

*Figure 2-45. AN AC tach generator system.*

79

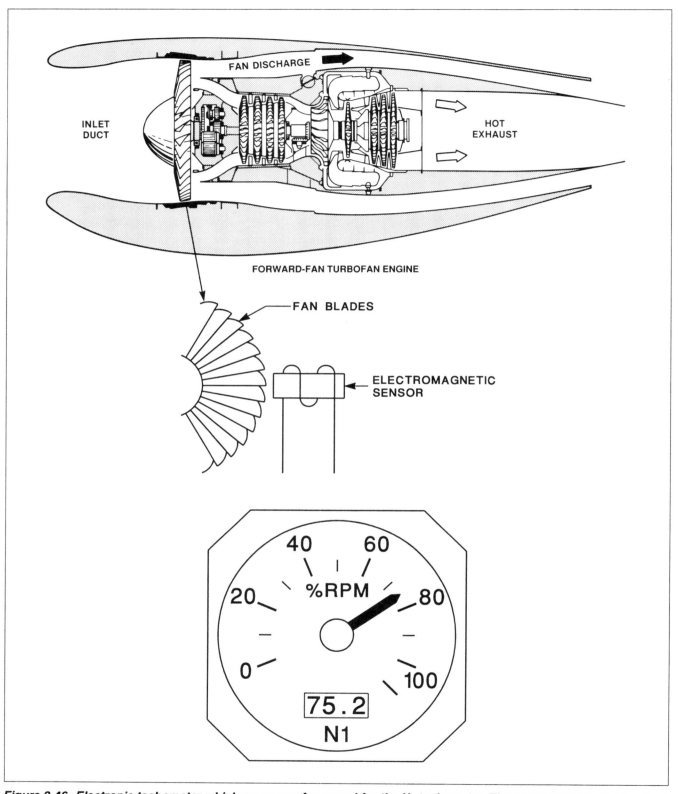

*Figure 2-46. Electronic tachometer which measures fan speed for the N₁ tachometer. The sensors produce an output signal each time a fan blade cuts through the magnetic field. The frequency of this output signal is measured to provide indications of N₁ RPM.*

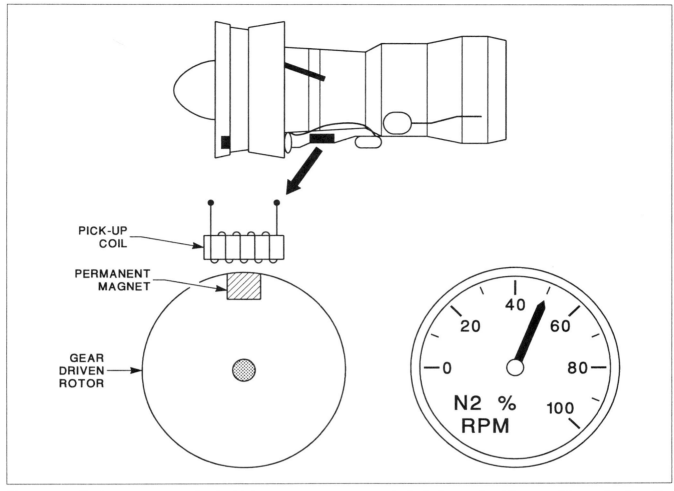

**Figure 2-47. Tachometer system for the high pressure compressor of a turbofan engine. The gear-driven rotor from the accessory section has a permanent magnet which induces signals in a pick-up coil.**

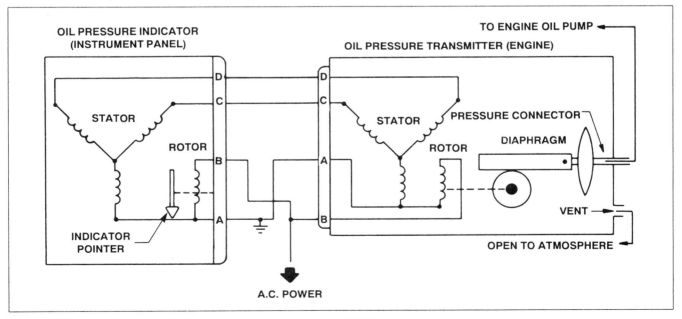

**Figure 2-48. An oil pressure indicating system for a large airplane.**

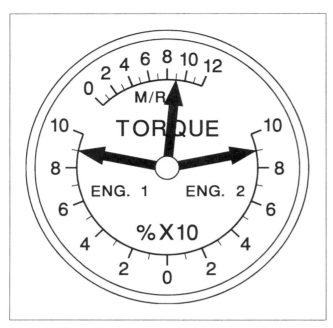

Figure 2-49. *A triple torquemeter for a twin-engine helicopter. The torque for both engines and the main rotor is given on the same instrument with readings in percent.*

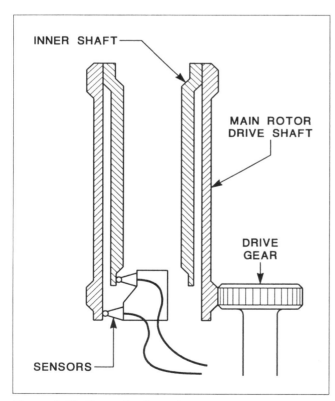

Figure 2-50. *Example of a main rotor mast torque system for a helicopter. The two sensors measure the amount of twist in the main rotor drive shaft as an indication of torque.*

accurately set engine power. Aircraft with supercharged engines and aircraft with constant-speed propellers will have manifold pressure gauges. The manifold pressure gauge measures the absolute pressure in inches of mercury at a specific point in the induction system of the engine. Figure 2-55 shows the location of the manifold pressure (MAP) measurement for a radial supercharged engine. Figure 2-56 shows the location of the MAP connection in the induction system of a turbocharged horizontally opposed reciprocating engine. The pressure is measured downstream of the carburetor or fuel control unit and downstream of the supercharger if so equipped. The pressure measuring port in the induction system is connected by tubing and hose to a bellows or diaphragm in the instrument. Since the pressure in the induction system is below ambient pressure at idle or low power settings, the use of absolute pressure eliminates the confusion of having both positive and negative numbers on the gauge. At idle, the reading on the MAP gauge will be about 10 in. Hg. At full throttle with an unsupercharged engine at sea level, the reading will be about 28 in. Hg. With an unsupercharged engine the full throttle reading will always be below ambient pressure because of friction and pressure

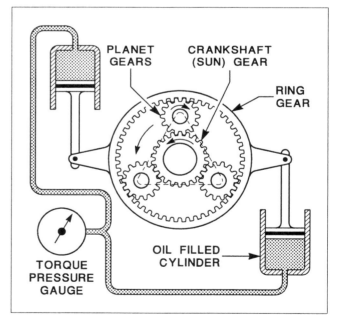

Figure 2-51. *An illustration of the basic operating principles of a torque pressure gauge. The planetary reduction gears have a ring gear which is prevented from rotating by the pistons in the oil filled cylinders. The torque force on the ring gear causes pressure to be applied to the oil in the cylinders. This pressure is a measurement of torque.*

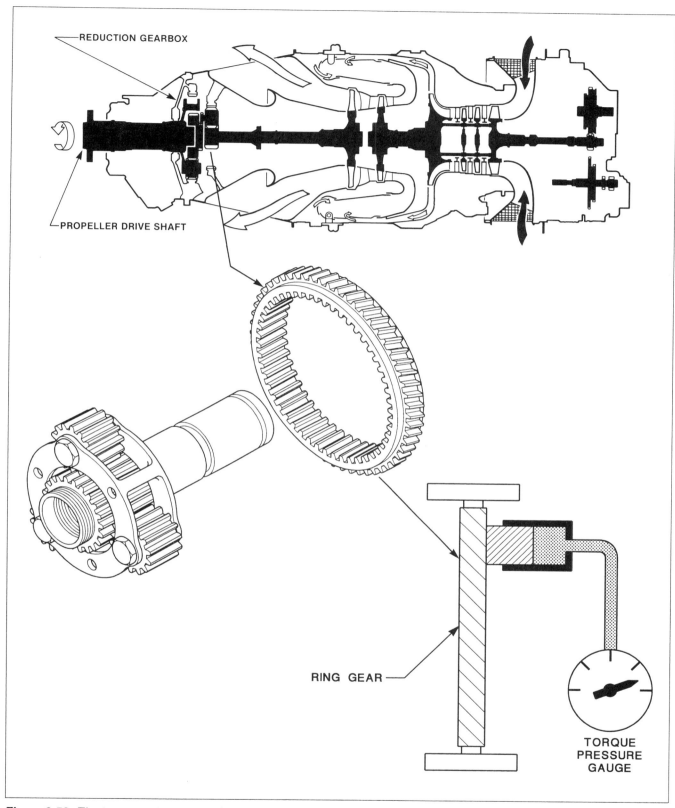

*Figure 2-52. The torquemeter system for a turboprop engine. The ring gear of the planetary gear set is prevented from rotating by the helical splines on the outer circumference that mesh with splines in the outer housing. Torque force causes the ring gear to more rearward and push against the small piston. The piston applies pressure to the oil in the cylinder and this pressure is a measure of the torque produced.*

loss in the induction system. A supercharged engine will have a redline on the MAP gauge to indicate the maximum permissible manifold pressure. The redline might range from 35–75 in. Hg depending on the type of engine.

## J. Primary Power Setting Instruments

The specific powerplant instruments installed in a particular aircraft will vary considerably depending on the type of powerplants it has and what kinds of information the pilot needs to operate the engines properly. The most important kinds of powerplant instruments have been described and some information has been given concerning what types of powerplants would use each kind of instrument. In order to gain a better understanding of the application of powerplant instruments to different powerplants, the primary power setting instruments used with various types of engines will be described.

A reciprocating engine with a fixed-pitch propeller uses the engine tachometer as the primary power setting instrument. This is normally the only instrument available on aircraft with this engine and propeller combination that can be used to determine the power setting. The fixed-pitch blade angle for the propeller is chosen so that full throttle can be used for takeoff without over-speeding the engine.

When a constant-speed propeller is fitted on a reciprocating engine, the tachometer alone cannot be used to accurately set engine power. The constant-speed propeller will automatically vary the blade angle to maintain a selected RPM.

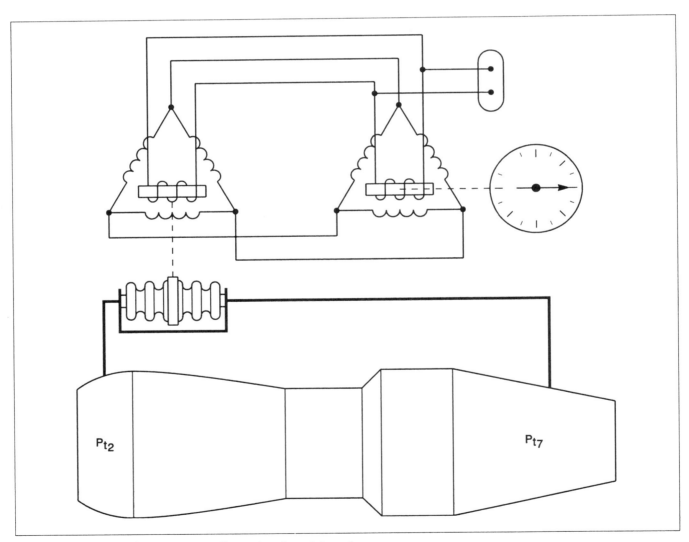

*Figure 2-53. The engine pressure ratio system for a jet engine.*

Fairly large movements of the throttle lever can be made without affecting the engine RPM, so that the tachometer by itself cannot be used to set engine power. The primary power setting instrument for this type of aircraft is the manifold pressure gauge. A cruise power setting would be made by first setting the desired engine RPM with the propeller control and then adjusting the manifold pressure gauge to the desired power setting. Information is available in the Pilot's Operating Handbook so the pilot can determine what settings will produce a given percent of power for cruise. Common cruise settings would be 55, 65 or 75 percent of maximum engine power. Supercharged reciprocating engines also use the manifold pressure gauge as the primary power setting instrument.

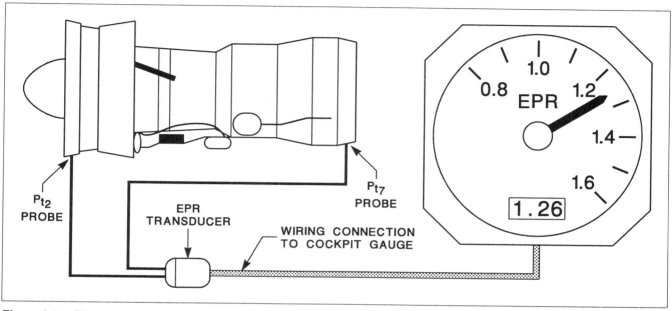

Figure 2-54. *The EPR gauge measures engine pressure ratio which is the ratio of $Pt_7$ / $Pt_2$. It provides indications of the thrust being produced by a turbojet or turbofan engine.*

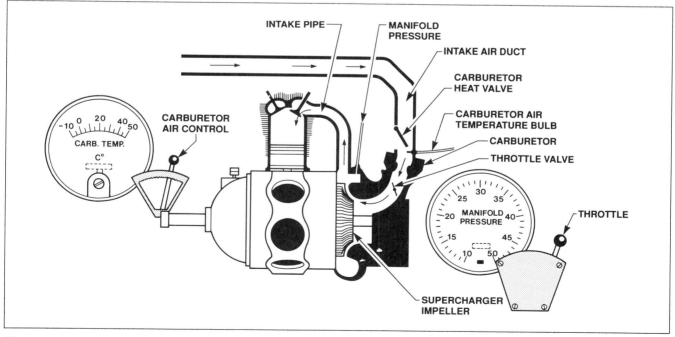

Figure 2-55. *The measurement point for manifold pressure is downstream of the carburetor and downstream of the supercharger in this radial engine.*

The primary power setting instrument for aircraft with turboshaft and turboprop engines is the torquemeter. Engine RPM is not a good measure of engine power because of the way these engines operate. The gas temperature gauge is a very important instrument for these types of engines. The pilot needs to monitor the gas temperature reading to prevent damage to the engine by excessive heat. Turboshaft and turboprop engines are often given a flat rating for the maximum permissible engine power. For example, an engine might be rated at 575 SHP (shaft horsepower) from sea level to 20,000 ft. This is in effect a derating of the engine at lower altitudes. The maximum power the engine can safely produce at low altitudes is limited by the strength of the reduction gearbox. At higher altitudes, the engine is less efficient and must work harder to produce horsepower. This results in higher engine temperatures; therefore, at higher altitudes, the maximum safe throttle setting is determined by the redline on the gas temperature gauge. The torquemeter is the primary power setting instrument because it has a direct relationship to engine horsepower. The

maximum power setting that can be safely used is determined by the strength of the gearbox at low altitudes and the gas temperature at higher altitudes.

The primary power setting instrument for turbojet and turbofan engines depends on who manufactured the engine. Some of these engines use the EPR gauge and others use the $N_1$ tachometer as the primary power setting instrument. There are some advantages and disadvantages to each method and the choice of which one to use is based on conventional usage.

Turbojet and turbofan engines made by Pratt & Whitney and Rolls Royce use the EPR gauge as the primary power setting instrument. Those engines made by GE and a few other companies use the $N_1$ tach as the primary power setting instrument. There is a standard placement of primary engine instruments for virtually all air carrier jet airplanes.

The most important engine instruments are installed in the center of the instrument panel, toward the top. The primary power setting instrument will

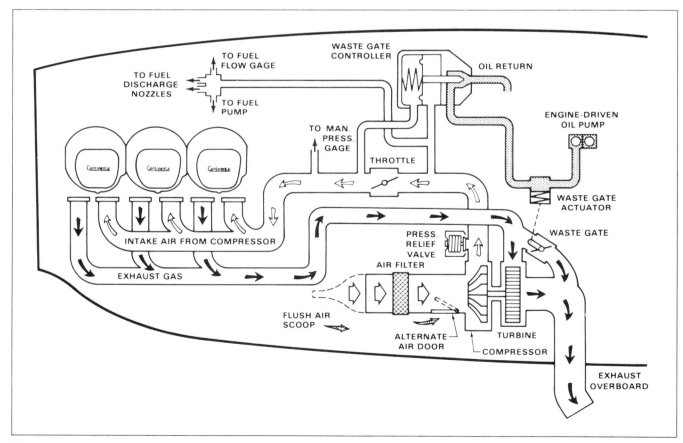

**Figure 2-56. Manifold pressure is measured downstream of the supercharger and downstream of the throttle plate in the fuel-air control unit for a turbo-supercharged, fuel-injected reciprocating engine. (Courtesy Cessna Aircraft Co.)**

be the one at the top of this stack of engine instruments. The EPR gauge will be at the top of the stack on some air carrier jets, and the $N_1$ tach on other airplanes. Figure 2-57 shows the primary engine instruments for an air carrier jet with Pratt & Whitney engines. Figure 2-58 shows the primary engine instruments for an air carrier jet with GE engines.

## K. Vibration Indicators

Aircraft with turbine engines often have a vibration indicator system which monitors vibration from the engines. Any significant imbalance in a turbine engine can cause serious damage due to the very high rotational speeds of the rotors. Vibration caused by an imbalance or other factors is indicated to the crew in the cockpit so that they can take appropriate action. The vibration indicator system shown in figure 2-59 is typical of the type found on modern jet airplanes. The sensor is a piezoelectric crystal which produces an electrical signal when it is vibrated. This signal is sent to a signal conditioner and then to the cockpit instrument to provide an indication of the amount of vibration at the sensor location on the side of the engine.

## L. Logic Circuits and Digital Systems

Logic circuits and microprocessors have made possible some of the very sophisticated electronic instruments and similar systems on modern aircraft. They are used for many different applications from relatively simple switching functions to complex computer systems. Certain basic principles are involved in these advanced systems, and these will be covered first.

### 1. Binary Numbers

The binary number system and binary codes are the method used by logic gates to transmit and process information. The word digital refers to the use of binary numbers and codes. A simple example of the concept of digital and analog type signals is shown in figure 2-60. The values of voltage and current in the circuits represent the digital and analog systems. In a circuit with a variable resistor, there are an infinite number of different values for current flow. Another example of this would be a simple fuel quantity system that uses a float operated variable resistor. The resistor moves in very small increments so that there are an infinite number of different current flows that can occur in the circuit. The circuit with the switch illustrates the concept of digital values. The switch is either

on or off with no in-between settings. This follows the binary or digital signal system because only two different values are used. The two conditions in a binary or digital circuit are called 1 and 0, or high and low, or on and off.

The binary number system is a base 2 number system. The decimal number system that we are more familiar with is a base 10 system. The decimal system uses 10 different digits to make up numbers. The 10 numbers are 0 through 9. By showing some examples of converting numbers from binary to decimal and vice versa, the binary system will be better understood.

The procedure for converting a number from binary to decimal is illustrated in figure 2-61. We start by writing down the binary number as shown by row (A). Then just above each binary digit, the base 2 equivalent for that digit is written as shown by row (B). In row (C), the decimal equivalents are entered starting at the right and working back to the left. Notice that the decimal equivalents start with 1 at the right and are doubled each digit as you move toward the left. Next you look at the binary digits in row (A) and wherever there is a binary 1 you bring down the decimal equivalent as shown in row (D). Where there is a binary zero in row (A), you do not bring down any decimal equivalent since binary zero and decimal zero have the same value. Finally, the decimal equivalents are added up to produce the decimal equivalent of 77.

The procedure for converting a decimal number to binary will be illustrated by converting the decimal number 77 to its binary equivalent. The technique for converting from decimal to binary consists of a series of divisions by the number two. We start by setting up a table with three columns as shown in figure 2-62. The first step is to divide 77 by 2 and enter the quotient and remainder in the proper column. The quotient is then brought down each time and divided by 2 and the values recorded. The process is repeated until the quotient is zero. The digits in the remainder column are read from the bottom up and this will be the binary equivalent.

There are some terms used with binary numbers that refer to how the binary digits are grouped. For example, in the binary number [ 101 110 ], there are two sets of three digits each. In digital or binary terminology, we would say that there are three bits in each byte. A bit is a binary digit, while a byte is a group of bits together. As an analogy, we might compare them to letters and words. The previous example would be like a group of words with three letters in each word. This is what is meant by binary codes, how the binary digits are grouped.

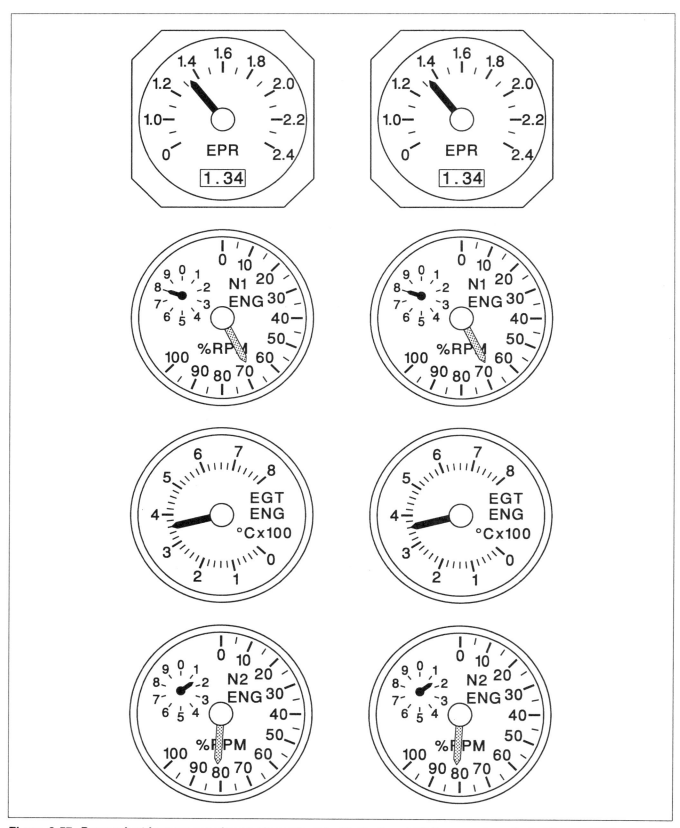

*Figure 2-57. Powerplant instruments for an air carrier jet with Pratt and Whitney engines that utilize an EPR gauge.*

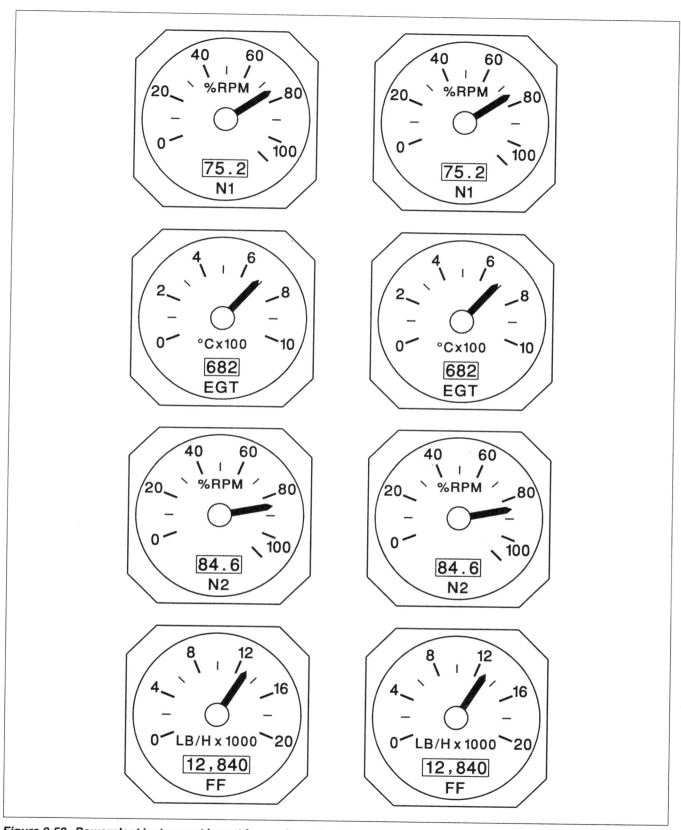

Figure 2-58. *Powerplant instrument layout for an air carrier jet with G.E. engines and the N₁ tachs at the top of the stack.*

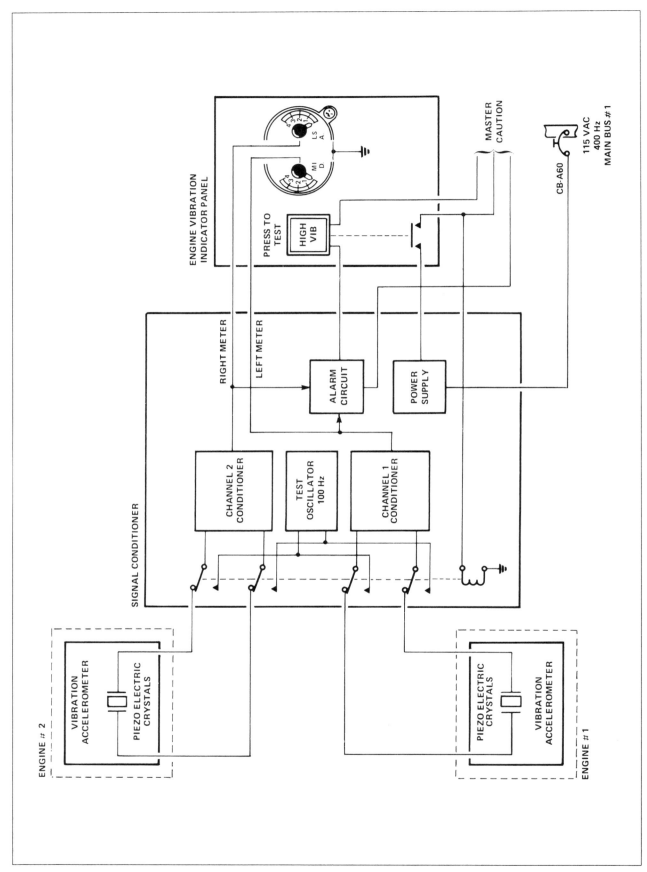

*Figure 2-59. Engine vibration monitoring system for a corporate jet airplane that employs piezoelectric crystals as sensors. (Courtesy Canadair Group, Bombardier Inc.)*

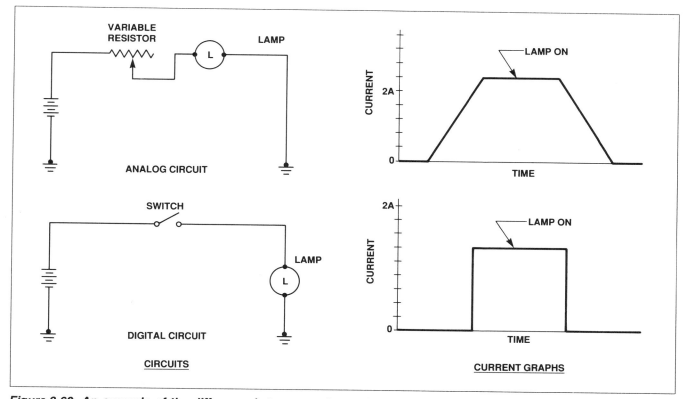

*Figure 2-60. An example of the difference between analog and digital. The circuit with the switch represents digital because it has two conditions: on and off. The circuit with the variable resistor is analog because it can have an infinite number of different current flows between maximum and minimum.*

| (c) | 64 | 32 | 16 | 8 | 4 | 2 | 1 | | |
|-----|----|----|----|----|----|----|----|----|----|
| (b) | $2^6$ | $2^5$ | $2^4$ | $2^3$ | $2^2$ | $2^1$ | $2^0$ | | |
| (a) | 1 | 0 | 0 | 1 | 1 | 0 | 1 | | |
| (d) | 64 | 0 + | 0 + | 8 + | 4 + | 0 + | 1 | = | 77 |

*Figure 2-61. An example of the method for converting a number from binary to decimal notation.*

| division | quotient | remainder |
|----------|----------|-----------|
| 77/2 | 38 | 1 |
| 38/2 | 19 | 0 |
| 19/2 | 9 | 1 |
| 9/2 | 4 | 1 |
| 4/2 | 2 | 0 |
| 2/2 | 1 | 0 |
| 1/2 | 0 | 1 |

*Figure 2-62. An example of converting a number from decimal to binary notation.*

Two common types of binary codes that are used with logic circuits are Binary Coded Decimal (BCD) and Octal. An example of BCD coding would be [ 1001 1101 1110 ]. The rule for BCD is that there are four bits in each byte. An example of Octal coding is [ 100 111 101 ]. This is the same as an earlier example. There are three bits in each byte. The reason that standard coding systems such as these are used is that it is more efficient than having a variable number of bits in each byte. The Octal code gets its name from the fact that there are eight different decimal equivalent numbers that can be encoded in a three bit byte. For example, 000 is equal to decimal 0 and 111 is equal to decimal 7.

## 2. Logic Gates

Logic gates can be thought of as the most simple and basic building blocks for digital control systems.

A logic gate uses binary signals as its inputs and outputs. It is a semi-conductor device which is manufactured using techniques similar to those used to produce diodes and transistors. Since logic gates are found in all types of systems on modern aircraft, it is useful to know something about them so that their function in a circuit can be understood. There are six basic kinds of logic gates that can be identified by their standard schematic symbols. All of them have certain things in common: they may have different numbers of inputs, but each logic gate has just one output. Logic gates can be thought of as special types of electronic switches, in fact, they are often used to perform switching functions. For simplicity, logic gates with no more than two inputs will be described here.

### a. AND Gate

The AND gate is shown in figure 2-63 along with its truth table. The truth table shows all the possible combinations of inputs and the output that will be produced for each set of inputs. The truth table can be explained with a statement: the AND gate produces a binary 1 output only when all inputs are binary 1. The name of this logic gate can make it easier to remember the truth table.

### b. OR Gate

The OR gate is shown in figure 2-64. The statement which describes the truth table is: the OR gate produces a 1 output when any input is 1. Notice that in the truth table for the OR gate, the input combinations are listed in the same order as they were for the AND gate. This makes it easier to remember the truth tables. All logic gates with two inputs have the inputs listed in the same order.

### c. INVERT Gate

The Invert gate is shown in figure 2-65. This is a very simple logic gate, it only has one input and the output is always the opposite of the input. The Invert gate simply inverts any signal that is applied to it. Notice the small open circle on the output side of the Invert gate symbol. This will be used in combination with the basic shapes already covered to identify other kinds of logic gates.

### d. NAND Gate

The NAND gate is shown in figure 2-66. Notice the small open circle on the output side. This distinguishes it from the AND gate and also tells how it works. The NAND gate is just an AND gate with the ouputs inverted. This can be stated as: the NAND gate produces a 0 output only when all the inputs are 1.

### e. NOR Gate

The NOR gate is shown in figure 2-67. The NOR gate is an OR gate with the outputs inverted. The truth table can be described as: the NOR gate produces a 0 output when any input is 1. Notice the small open circle on the output side which distinguishes it from the OR gate.

### f. EXCLUSIVE OR Gate

The Exclusive OR gate is shown in figure 2-68. The truth table can be explained by the statement: the Exclusive OR gate produces a 1 output whenever the inputs are dissimilar. It is the only logic gate with two inputs that has equal numbers of ones and zeros in the outputs column.

An aircraft schematic using logic gates is shown in figure 2-75. It is evident that in order to

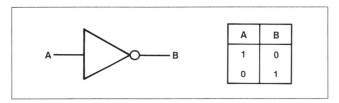

*Figure 2-65. The INVERT gate and its truth table.*

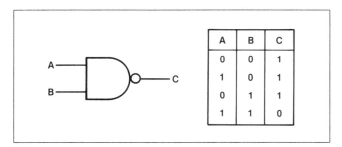

*Figure 2-66. The NAND gate and its truth table.*

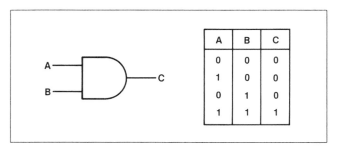

*Figure 2-63. The AND gate and its truth table.*

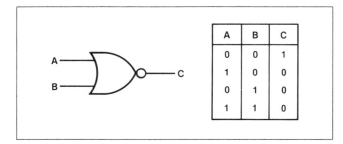

*Figure 2-67. The NOR gate and its truth table.*

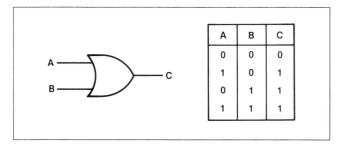

*Figure 2-64. The OR gate and its truth table.*

92

understand and troubleshoot this aircraft system, the technician should be familiar with logic gates and their truth tables.

### g. Amplifier or Buffer

The buffer or amplifier is shown in figure 2-69. It produces no change in the logic state of the input signal. It is used to amplify or increase signal strength. It can also be used to isolate one part of a circuit from another part of the same circuit or from some other unit.

### h. Positive and Negative Logic

Logic gates use different values of voltage to represent binary ones and zeros. The terms positive and negative logic refer to whether the voltage value for a binary 1 is more positive or more negative than the voltage value for binary 0. Figure 2-70(A) shows examples of positive logic. The voltage value for binary 1 is more positive (or less negative) than the value for binary 0. Figure 2-70(B) shows examples of negative logic which is the opposite situation.

## 3. Integrated Circuits

The evolution of electronic circuit technology is shown in figure 2-71(A) and figure 2-71(B). For many years, the vacuum tube represented the state of the art in delicate control of electron flow for radios and early computers. The development of the transistor in the 1960s allowed much smaller and more efficient electronic components to be made.

The transistor was made from a semi-conductor material like silicon or germanium. In the 1970s, the integrated circuit was invented. An integrated circuit is a small chip of semi-conductor material with the equivalent of many transistors on it. It was no longer necessary to manufacture transistors one at a time in individual units. Since the invention of the integrated circuit, the technology has advanced rapidly by crowding more and more transistors onto this small chip of silicon or germanium.

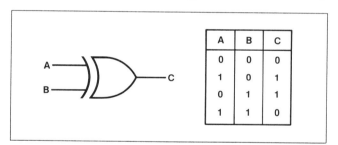

| A | B | C |
|---|---|---|
| 0 | 0 | 0 |
| 1 | 0 | 1 |
| 0 | 1 | 1 |
| 1 | 1 | 0 |

*Figure 2-68. The EXCLUSIVE OR gate and its truth table.*

| A | B |
|---|---|
| 0 | 0 |
| 1 | 1 |

*Figure 2-69. The AMPLIFIER and its truth table.*

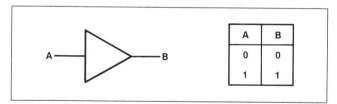

| A | Binary 1 | +5V | +2V | +10V | 0V | −5V |
|---|---|---|---|---|---|---|
|   | Binary 0 | 0V | −2V | +5V | −5V | −10V |
| B | Binary 1 | 0V | −2V | +5V | −5V | −10V |
|   | Binary 0 | +5V | +2V | +10V | 0V | −5V |

*Figure 2-70.*
*(A) Example of positive logic.*
*(B) Example of negative logic.*

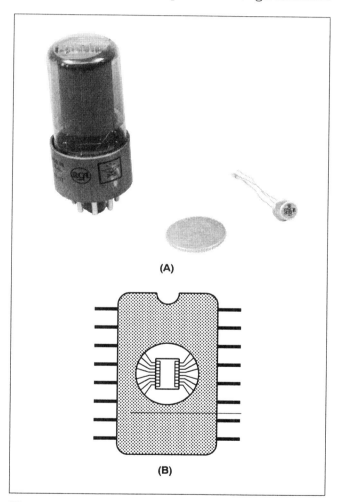

*Figure 2-71*
*(A) In the 1960s, transistors began to replace vacuum tubes as a means to provide precise control of electrical signals for amplifiers and other electronic devices including computers.*
*(B) An integrated circuit contains the equivalent of many transistors on a small chip of silicon. Very fine wires connect the chip to the outer pins.*

The term microprocessor refers to an integrated circuit that has the equivalent of thousands of transistors on one tiny chip of silicon. The microprocessor has made possible the widespread use of computer controls for cars, radios, and in airplanes as well. The logic gates that we have been discussing are not manufactured one at a time. Logic gates are contained within integrated circuits. Integrated circuits vary considerably in complexity. Simple integrated circuits that contain 6 or 8 logic gates can be purchased for about 25 cents. The most complex integrated circuits are those called microprocessors, which would have the equivalent of thousands of logic gates on one chip. A schematic representation of the logic gates in a simple integrated circuit is shown in figure 2-72.

Integrated circuits are manufactured from silicon that has been specially processed. The circuit that will be placed onto the silicon is drawn with great accuracy. The circuit drawing is then shrunk to a small size using techniques similar to those for reducing a photograph. The circuit tracings are transferred to the chip of silicon by etching them into the chip. The small chip of silicon is then sealed in a housing of plastic or ceramic. The integrated circuit has connector pins along the sides to carry signals to and from the small chip of silicon within. Figure 2-71(B) shows these features of an integrated circuit with very fine wires connecting the chip to the outer contact pins along the sides.

One of the goals when designing integrated circuits is to make the chip as small as possible. On a very high speed microprocessor, the time it takes electrons to move the width of the chip limits the speed of computation.

Integrated circuits are divided into categories based on their complexity. The four categories normally referred to are:

1. Small scale integration (SSI)
2. Medium scale integration (MSI)
3. Large scale integration (LSI)
4. Very Large scale integration (VLSI)

If a digital system has many different integrated circuits that are connected to each other, they must be compatible with each other. Integrated circuits that use the same values of voltage for binary ones and zeros and operate at similar speeds are said to be in the same family. Two of the more common families are TTL (transistor-transistor logic) and CMOS (complimentary metal oxide semi-conductor). The TTL family, for instance, uses positive logic with binary 1 = +5V and binary 0 = 0V.

## 4. Dip Standards

Integrated circuits (ICs) are manufactured in standard sizes and shapes. This means that ICs made by different companies can be installed in the same way and simplifies replacement. The DIP (dual inline package) standard concerns the numbering of the connector pins and the shape and size of the integrated circuit. A typical DIP integrated circuit is shown in figure 2-72. With the notch at the top, the connector pins are numbered down the left side and then up the right side. The spacing of the pins fits the standard pattern. The total number of pins varies from about 8 to more than 40 depending on the complexity of the integrated circuit. Logic gates can be used for many different purposes. The smaller ones can be used as high speed switches. Adders and subtractors are used in a computer to perform mathematical calculations. Clocks are logic gates that supply a set frequency to synchronize the operation of different units. Latches and flip-flops are used for memory functions. A typical computer contains many integrated circuits that perform a variety of functions such as those mentioned here.

## 5. ARINC 429 Digital Standards

The latest air carrier jets have many different computers and digital systems on board the aircraft. These many digital systems must have a rapid and efficient way to communicate using binary coded signals. ARINC 429 is the standard for Digital Information Transfer Systems that is used on these airplanes. This standard specifies the use of a dual digital data bus where the various units connected will receive messages on both sections of the bus

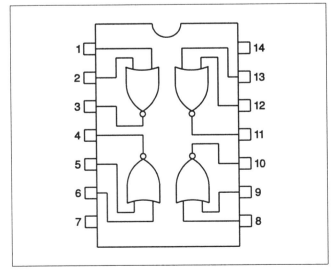

*Figure 2-72. An example of a relatively simple integrated circuit (IC) showing logic gate functions and pin connections.*

but only transmit on one of them. The type of message transmission is serial which means different messages are sent in a series one after the other. The messages are separated by time intervals. This industry standard also specifies what coding systems will be used such as binary, binary coded decimal and discrete. The standard length of an ARINC 429 word is 32 bits as shown in figure 2-73. The use of ARINC 429 by the equipment manufacturers permits the airlines and other users to purchase electronic equipment from different sources and know that the different units will be compatible with each other.

## 6. Digital Aircraft Systems

The trend in the design of modern aircraft and aircraft systems is to make greater use of digital circuits and digital signals because of the advantages they have over older style analog systems. This follows another trend which is the use of more automated monitoring and control systems.

Some of the fundamental concepts involved in the design of electronic systems for current production aircraft are:

1. The use of proximity sensors to replace microswitches.
2. The use of transistors to replace potentiometers, relays etc.
3. Designing equipment to fit in standard size LRUs (line replaceable units).
4. Increased use of BITE (built-in test equipment).
5. Computer controls for navigation, engines, systems instruments, etc.
6. Electronic instruments (CRTs) to replace electro-mechanical instruments and displays.
7. LEDs and LCDs employed for lighted displays that replace older style displays and controls.

The use of computer monitoring systems like EICAS has permitted the elimination of a flight crew member on many aircraft. The flight engineer is replaced by the sophisticated computer monitoring systems and automatic control systems to create what is called the two-man cockpit in aircraft such as the Boeing 747-400 and McDonnell Douglas MD-11.

The use of ARINC 600 standard LRUs permits more efficient installation and maintenance of aircraft equipment. Many of the LRUs contain BITE systems which can be used to troubleshoot problems and identify faulty LRUs for replacement. Maintenance technicians still need to be very familiar with the aircraft systems so that they can do a better job of troubleshooting and repair, and so that the number of false removals of good LRUs can be reduced.

## M. Takeoff Warning Systems

A takeoff warning system is designed to sound a warning if the flight crew tries to takeoff in an airplane with the flaps or other important systems in an incorrect position for a safe takeoff. Air carrier jets will have takeoff warning systems while most simpler aircraft will not. The critical items that are monitored by the takeoff warning system are:

1. Pitch trim or stabilizer trim
2. Speed brake
3. Leading edge flaps and slats
4. Trailing edge flaps

A schematic of a typical takeoff warning system is shown in figure 2-74. The two series switches are on the throttles and landing gear. When there is weight on the wheels and the throttles are advanced for takeoff, both of these switches will be

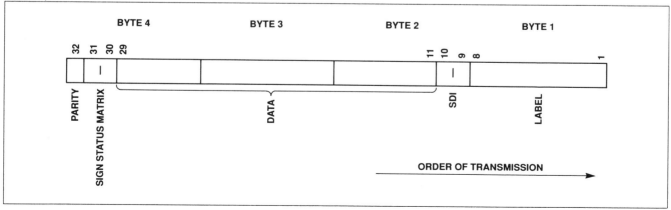

*Figure 2-73. ARINC 429 is the industry standard for digital information transmission systems. An ARINC 429 standard word contains 32 bits.*

closed. If any of the parallel switches is closed, a takeoff warning will be initiated.

A more detailed schematic of a takeoff warning system is shown in figure 2-75. Notice the use of logic gate symbols on this relatively simple aircraft system.

There have been aircraft accidents caused by the failure of the takeoff warning system and an attempted takeoff with one of the critical systems set improperly. It is an important system that should

be inspected regularly and maintained properly to give warnings when needed.

## N. Angle of Attack Indicators

The angle of attack indicator is a system that gives an instrument indication in the cockpit of the angle of attack for the wings of the airplane. Angle of attack is the angle between the chord line of an airfoil and the relative wind. The angle of attack instrument

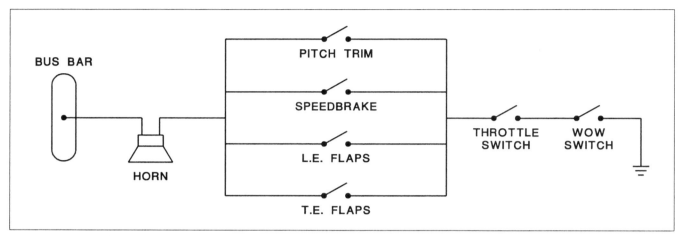

Figure 2-74. A simplified schematic of a takeoff warning system.

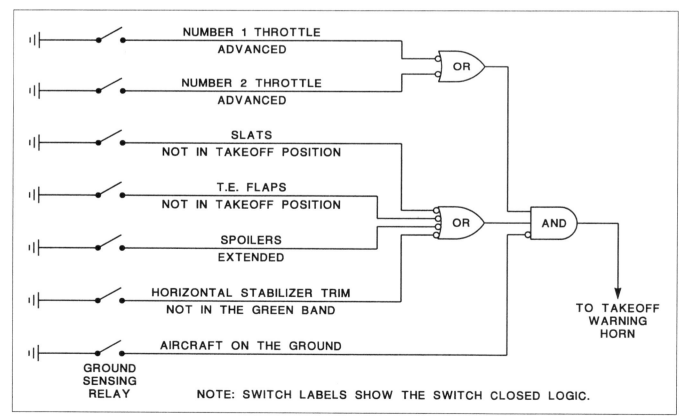

Figure 2-75. The takeoff warning system for an air carrier jet airplane. Logic gate symbols are often found on aircraft schematics.

can be very useful in critical flight conditions where maximum performance must be employed. During landing and takeoff from short runways and in an encounter with wind shear, the angle of attack instrument can allow more precise control of the airplane. There are two common types of sensors used for AOA systems. The first type is a small vane on a pivot that is installed on the forward fuselage of the airplane. This type can be seen as a part of the stall warning system shown in figure 2-76. Angle of attack sensors can be used with a stall warning system, an AOA gauge, or both. The vane rotates to align itself with the relative wind and this information is transmitted to the cockpit with a synchro system where it moves a pointer on the AOA instrument. The second type uses a sensor which is a tube with two slots that projects out into the airstream, normally from the forward fuselage. This

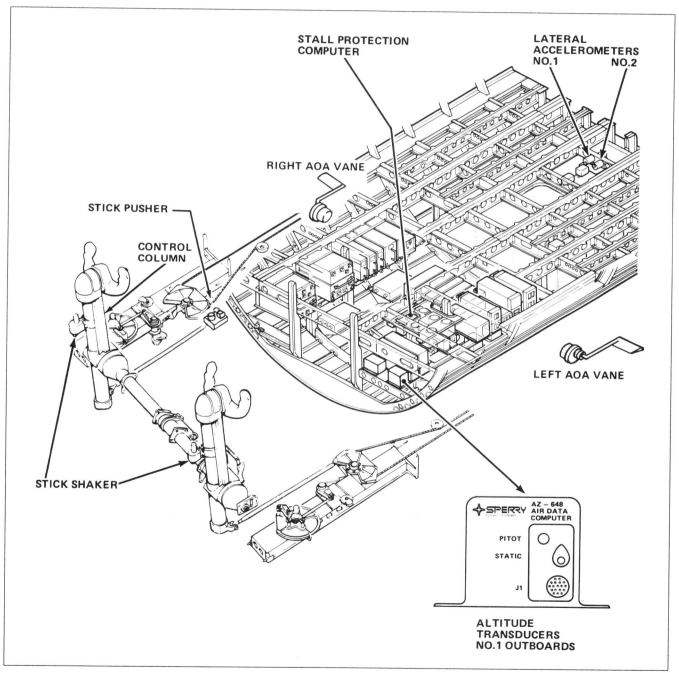

*Figure 2-76. The stall warning system for a corporate jet airplane that employs vane-type angle-of-attack sensors. (Courtesy Canadair Group, Bombardier Inc.)*

type of probe, along with the AOA indicator, is shown in figure 2-77. The two slots in the probe are connected to two chambers. As the angle of attack changes, the relative pressure in the two slots changes along with the pressures in the air chambers. The difference in air pressure rotates a vane in the unit inside the fuselage which is connected by synchro to the cockpit instrument. The units displayed on the cockpit instrument face can be a percent or decimal numbers that indicate the angle of attack. The reading of 100% or 1.0 would indicate a stall angle of attack, so the pilot can readily determine if a safe margin is being maintained from the stall angle-of-attack.

## O. Stall Warning Systems

A stall warning system is required for all modern airplanes. Several of the common types will be described, but they all rely on some measurement of angle of attack to activate the stall warning system. The airspeed of the airplane cannot be used to operate a stall warning system because the airplane can stall at many different airspeeds. An airplane will stall at a higher airspeed in a steep bank than it will in level flight because some of the wing lift is being used to make the airplane turn. The airplane will stall at the same angle of attack in both straight and turning flight, so AOA is a better indicator for stall warning than airspeed.

The stall warning system found on many older airplanes used a vibrating reed and required no outside power source. Figure 2-78 shows this type of system. A small hole in the leading edge of the wing is connected by tubing to a reed and horn near the cockpit. At high angles of attack close to a stall, a low pressure or suction is produced at the opening in the leading edge and this pulls air through the reed to make it vibrate and produce a noise.

On later small airplanes, a vane operated switch is located on the leading edge and this switch is closed by the upward movement of the vane at high angles of attack. This system uses DC power to operate the stall warning horn. Figure 2-79 shows this type of stall warning sensor.

Modern high performance airplanes use an AOA probe as previously described which is connected to a stall warning circuit. These airplanes usually have several other sensors connected to the stall warning circuit or computer. Sensors for flap and slat position are used to give an accurate stall warning for any flight condition. Most jet airplanes have a stick shaker as part of the stall warning system. This device actually shakes or vibrates the control column to warn the pilot of an approaching stall. The stick shaker can be seen at the left side of figure 2-76.

## P. Annunciators

Other than simple single-engine airplanes, most aircraft have an annunciator panel which groups together a number of different indicator lights for a variety of aircraft systems and equipment. There

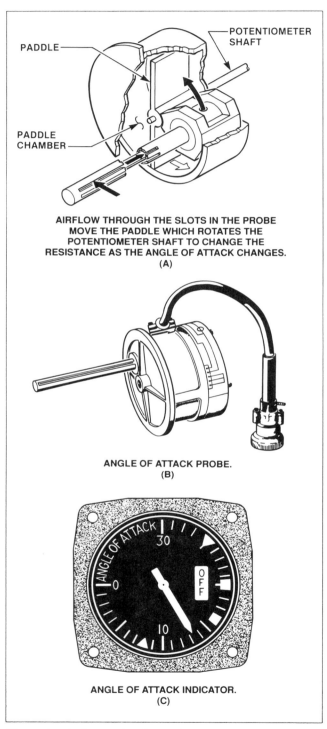

AIRFLOW THROUGH THE SLOTS IN THE PROBE MOVE THE PADDLE WHICH ROTATES THE POTENTIOMETER SHAFT TO CHANGE THE RESISTANCE AS THE ANGLE OF ATTACK CHANGES.
(A)

ANGLE OF ATTACK PROBE.
(B)

ANGLE OF ATTACK INDICATOR.
(C)

**Figure 2-77 An angle-of-attack indicating system that uses the air pressure type of AOA probe.**

are usually three categories of annunciator indications based on how important the information is to the flight crew. Warnings are the most serious and normally activate a red light. For very serious conditions · like fires, a sound warning is also given. Caution annunciators are usually amber in color. Status or special purpose annunciators may be white or some other color lights. If the airplane has a large number of annunciators and the panel must be located overhead or some other location which is not in front of the crew, master caution and warning lights are employed. With this system, there is one red light and one amber light in plain view in front of the pilot and/or copilot. When any warning light on the main panel is illuminated, the master warning light also comes on. The crew is alerted to look up at the main annunciator panel to find the source of the warning. The master warning light is then reset so it will be available to give any additional warnings

that might be needed. The master caution light works in a similar manner. Some of the typical indications for an annunciator panel for a small twin-engine airplane are shown in figure 2-80

## Q. FARs for Warning Systems and Annunciators

Some of the FAA requirements for warning systems and annunciators are given below to familiarize the reader with the kinds of rules that apply to these systems.

**FAR 23.207**
**Stall Warning**

A. There must be a clear and distinctive stall warning with flaps and landing gear in any normal position in straight and turning flight.

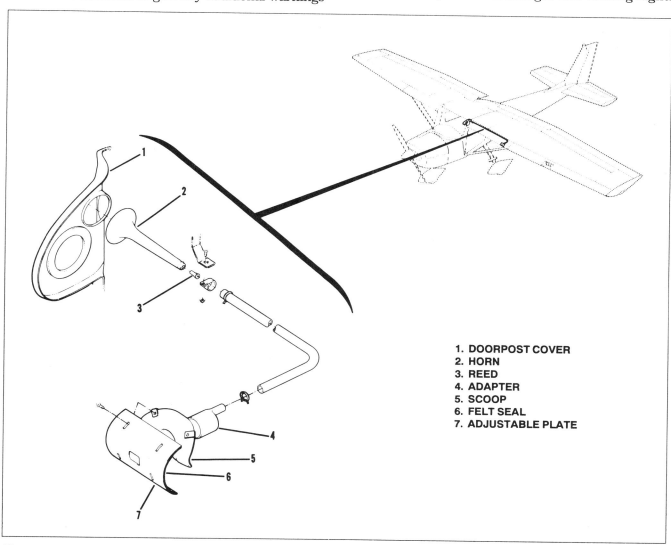

1. DOORPOST COVER
2. HORN
3. REED
4. ADAPTER
5. SCOOP
6. FELT SEAL
7. ADJUSTABLE PLATE

*Figure 2-78. The components in a vibrating reed stall warning system. (Courtesy Cessna Aircraft Co.)*

B. The stall warning may be inherent buffet or a device. If a device is used, visual indications by themselves that require the pilot's attention to be directed in the cockpit are not acceptable.

C. The stall warning must begin not less than 5 knots above stall speed; but not more than 10 knots or 15% above stall speed, whichever is greater. The stall warning must continue to the stall.

## FAR 23.729
### Retractable Landing Gear

A. There must be a position indicating system for extended and retracted.

B. Warning system.

1. There must be a warning if one or more throttles are retarded and the landing gear is not down and locked.

2. There must be a warning when the flaps are extended to or beyond the approach flap setting and the landing gear is not down and locked.

## FAR 23.1203
### Fire Detector System

For multi-engine, turbine-powered airplanes, multi-engine reciprocating engine airplanes incorporating turbosuperchargers and all commuter category airplanes:

A. There must be a means which ensures the prompt detection of a fire in an engine compartment.

## FAR 23.1303
### Flight and Navigation Instruments

The following are required flight and navigation instruments:

E. A speed warning device for:

1. Turbine engine powered airplanes

2. Other airplanes for which Vmo/Mmo and Vd/Md are established under FAR 23 if Vmo/Mmo is greater than 0.8 Vd/Md.

## FAR 23.1353
### Storage Battery Design and Installation

g. Nickel cadmium battery installations capable of being used to start an engine or auxiliary power unit must have:

1. A system to control the charging rate of the battery automatically so as to prevent battery overheating.

2. A battery temperature sensing and over-temperature warning system with a means for disconnecting the battery from its charging source in the event of an over-temperature condition.

3. A battery failure sensing and warning system with a means for disconnecting the battery from its charging source in the event of a battery failure.

## FAR 91.219
### Altitude Alerting System or Device Turbojet-Powered Civil Airplanes:

1. No person may operate a turbojet powered civil airplane unless it is equipped with an altitude alerting system or device that:

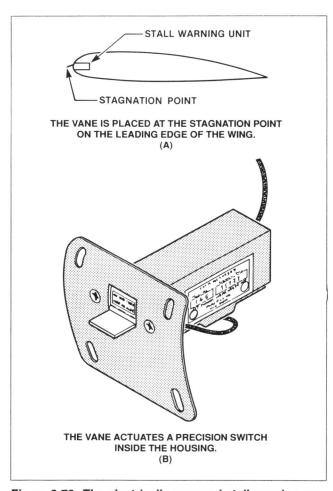

STALL WARNING UNIT

STAGNATION POINT

THE VANE IS PLACED AT THE STAGNATION POINT ON THE LEADING EDGE OF THE WING.
(A)

THE VANE ACTUATES A PRECISION SWITCH INSIDE THE HOUSING.
(B)

*Figure 2-79. The electrically powered stall warning system for a small airplane that uses a vane operated switch.*

2. Will alert the pilot upon approaching a pre-selected altitude in either ascent or descent, by a sequence of both aural and visual signals in sufficient time to establish level flight at the preselected altitude.

The control and operation of a typical altitude alerting system are shown in figure 2-81.

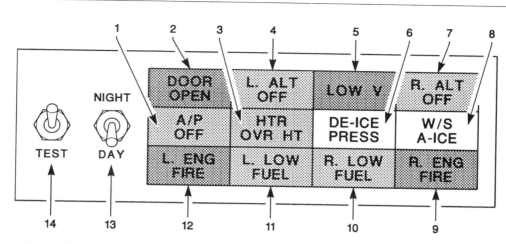

1. AUTOPILOT OFF LIGHT (AMBER) — Indicates the autopilot has disengaged.
2. DOOR OPEN LIGHT (RED) — Indicates that the forward baggage compartment door, the cabin entry doors and/or the emergency exit door are not secured safely for flight.
3. HEATER OVERHEAT LIGHT (AMBER) — Indicates an abnormally high temperature has occurred in the combustion heater and it has been automatically shut off. Once the light illuminates, the heater will not operate until the overheat switch in the right forward nose section (accessible in nosewheel well) has been reset.
4. LEFT ALTERNATOR OFF LIGHT (AMBER) — Indicates the left alternator is not supplying electrical current.
5. LOW VOLTAGE LIGHT (RED) — Indicates electrical system bus voltage is less than 24.5 volts.
6. WING AND STABILIZER DEICE SYSTEM PRESSURE LIGHT (GREEN) — Indicates pressure is being applied to the surface deice boots to inflate them.
7. RIGHT ALTERNATOR OFF LIGHT (AMBER) — Indicates the right alternator is not supplying electrical current.
8. WINDSHIELD ANTI-ICE SYSTEM LIGHT (GREEN) — Indicates that heating elements in the windshield anti-ice system are operating.
9. RIGHT ENGINE FIRE LIGHT (RED) — Indicates an excessive temperature condition or possible fire has occurred in the right engine compartment.
10. RIGHT LOW FUEL LIGHT (AMBER) — Indicates fuel quantity in right main fuel tank is 60 lbs. or less.
11. LEFT LOW FUEL LIGHT (AMBER) — Indicaties fuel quantity in left main fuel tank is 60 lbs. or less.
12. LEFT ENGINE FIRE LIGHT (RED) — Indicates an excessive temperature condition or possible fire has occurred in the left engine compartment.
13. DAY/NIGHT SWITCH — Sets brightness level of annunciator panel indicator lamps for either day or night operation.
14. TEST SWITCH — Tests operation of annunciator panel lamps, landing gear system position indicator lights, and aural warning tones of landing gear, fire detection and stall warning systems. Also, switch can be used to silence an activated engine fire detection warning tone.

Note: For illustration only. Not to be used for operational purposes.

*Figure 2-80. (Courtesy Cessna Aircraft Co.)*
*(A) The annunciator panel for a small twin-engine airplane.*
*(B) The meanings for the various annunciator lights*

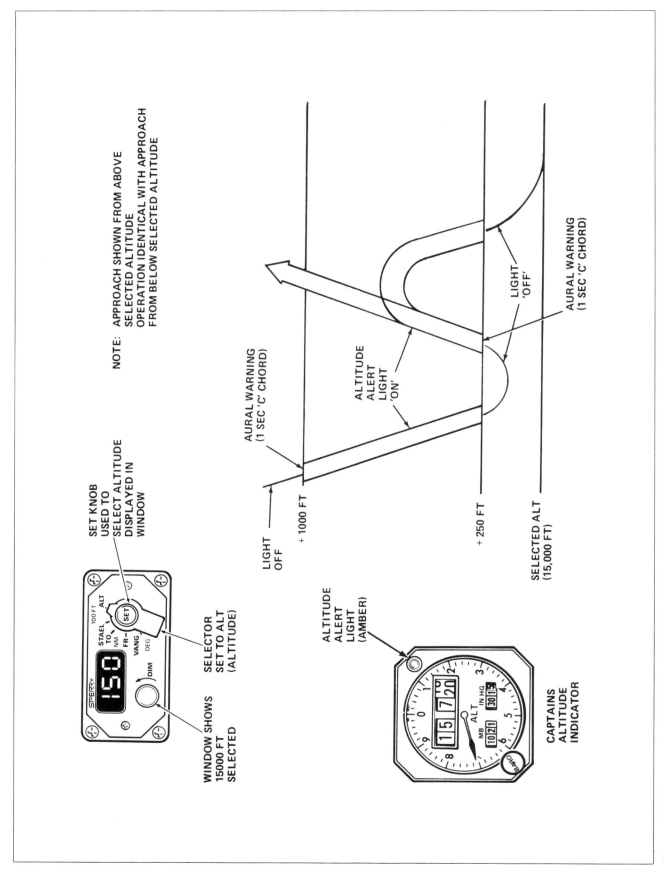

NOTE: APPROACH SHOWN FROM ABOVE SELECTED ALTITUDE OPERATION IDENTICAL WITH APPROACH FROM BELOW SELECTED ALTITUDE

SET KNOB USED TO SELECT ALTITUDE DISPLAYED IN WINDOW

AURAL WARNING (1 SEC 'C' CHORD)

AURAL WARNING (1 SEC 'C' CHORD)

LIGHT 'OFF'

ALTITUDE ALERT LIGHT 'ON'

LIGHT OFF

+ 1000 FT

+ 250 FT

SELECTED ALT (15,000 FT)

SELECTOR SET TO ALT (ALTITUDE)

WINDOW SHOWS 15000 FT SELECTED

ALTITUDE ALERT LIGHT (AMBER)

CAPTAINS ALTITUDE INDICATOR

*Figure 2-81. The visual and aural warnings associated with a typical altitude alerting system. (Courtesy Canadair Group, Bombardier Inc.)*

# CHAPTER III

# Communication and Navigation Systems

The avionics and radio equipment found in aircraft has seen more change and advancement in recent years than any other part of the aircraft. Most of these changes have resulted from the same technology that has produced personal computers and a world wide telecommunications industry. Although early radios were in use prior to World War I, it is only since the 1940s that extensive use has been made of radios for communication and navigation in all types of aircraft. The basic VHF communications and navigation systems that are used in aviation were developed in the 1940s, but the introduction of newer systems has been increasing dramatically in recent years. This chapter will cover the types of avionics equipment that are already in widespread use and the latest developments that are only beginning to be installed on airplanes. Most of the systems described utilize radio waves, so we will begin with the fundamentals of radio systems.

## A. Radio Fundamentals

The basic components found in radios and the operating principles involved will be explained here so that the specific aircraft avionics systems described later can be understood more easily.

### 1. Types of Aircraft Radio Systems

The first radios installed in airplanes were used for communications and it was only much later that navigational radio systems were developed. Radio systems for other purposes have also been developed, especially in the last 20 to 30 years. Some of the uses for radio in modern aircraft can be categorized as follows.

1. Communications — Both voice and data.
2. Navigation — Many different systems are in use today.
3. ATC Radar — The Air Traffic Control system relies on radar.
4. Weather Avoidance — Used to avoid areas of adverse weather.
5. Approach Aids — A specialized type of navigation to guide an aircraft down to the runway in bad weather.
6. Altitude Measurement — Gives precise altitude above ground level.
7. Airborne Collision Avoidance — Warns the pilot of nearby aircraft.

All of these examples use radio waves, but there are other avionics systems that do not rely on the use of radio waves.

### 2. Electromagnetic Waves

#### a. Frequency Bands

The range and diversity of electromagnetic waves, or EM waves, is very broad. The entire spectrum of EM waves includes not only radio waves but visible light, gamma rays, infrared, etc. The range of radio wave frequencies that we will be involved with is illustrated in figure 3-1. The frequencies are divided into bands which, starting at the low end, are: very low frequency (VLF), low frequency (LF), medium frequency (MF), high frequency (HF), very high frequency (VHF), ultra high frequency (UHF), super high frequency (SHF) and extremely high frequency (EHF). Common aircraft radio systems are included on the right side in figure 3-1. Notice that there is an aviation application for all of the bands except EHF. The two common radio broadcast bands are also listed for purposes of comparison.

All EM waves consist of two different invisible energy fields that travel through space. The electric field and the magnetic field are at right angles to each other and to the direction of propagation or travel. Figure 3-2 shows the two fields and the direction of propagation. Radio waves are produced when a radio frequency electrical signal is sent down a conductor to an antenna. The antenna transforms the electrical signal into EM waves which propagate outward from the antenna through space. The EM waves travel through space at the velocity of light, which is 186,284 miles per second or 300,000,000 meters per second. When the EM waves strike a receive antenna, they induce voltage and current to produce an electrical signal that matches the one applied to the transmit antenna, but of course the signal is much weaker. The basic operating frequency of a radio is called the carrier frequency, because this is the signal that carries the data or information that needs to be transmitted from one place to another.

The wavelength of EM waves is often used in describing antennas and other radio components. The

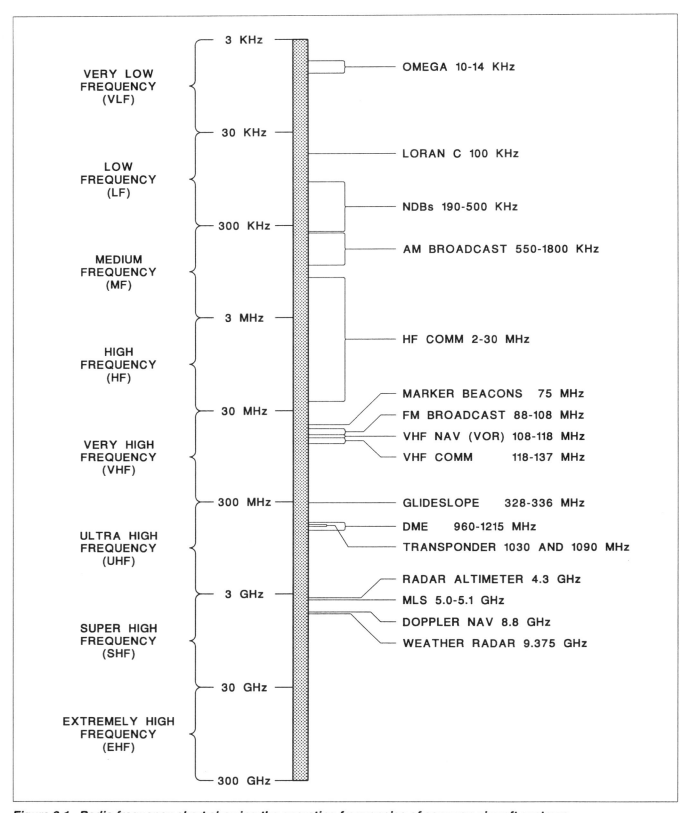

**Figure 3-1. Radio frequency chart showing the operating frequencies of common aircraft systems.**

104

wavelength of an EM wave is the distance from peak to peak for the invisible waves in the electric and magnetic fields. Wavelength is measured in meters and it is inversely proportional to the frequency. The wavelength in meters can be found by dividing the constant 300,000,000 by the frequency in hertz. At higher frequencies, it is easier to use 300 divided by the frequency in MHz to obtain the wavelength.

### b. Modulation

If we design a radio transmitter that sends out a steady carrier wave, we would not be able to transmit

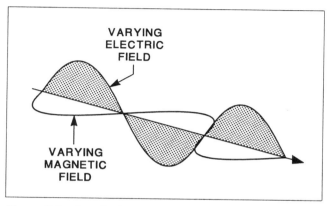

Figure 3-2. *An electromagnetic wave with the electric field and magnetic field at right angles to each other and the direction of propagation.*

any data or information. The receiver would only produce a steady hum or nothing at all depending on the design of the receiver. In order to transmit any data or intelligence, it is necessary to vary or alter the carrier wave in some way. The process of changing or varying the carrier wave is called modulation. When the Italian inventor Guglielmo Marconi was developing the first practical radio system in 1896, there was no way to modulate the radio wave in order to transmit voice, so he used a method of switching the transmitter on and off to transmit Morse code signals. This simplest form of modulation is called CW or radio telegraphy since it borrowed the Morse code from the telegraph industry. Figure 3-3 shows a radio carrier wave which uses CW to send Morse code dots and dashes. Within ten years, new inventions permitted voice and music to be transmitted by radio using improved types of modulation. Figure 3-4 illustrates the principles

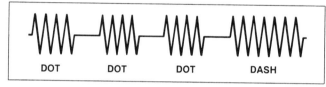

Figure 3-3. *The simplest form of transmitting data with radio waves is with Morse code dots and dashes or CW.*

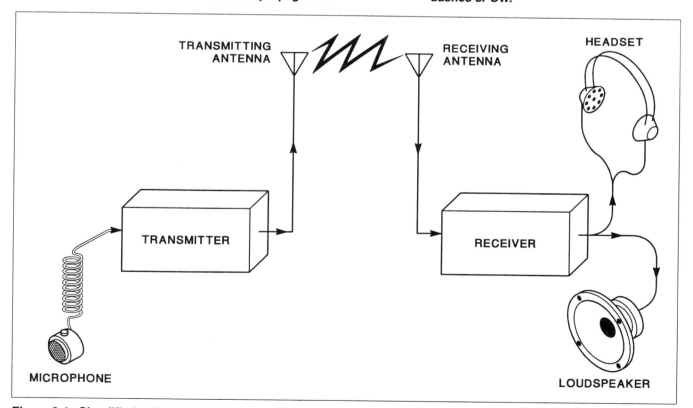

Figure 3-4. *Simplified voice radio system.*

of a simple voice radio system. A microphone converts sound waves to electrical signals that are combined with the carrier wave using AM or FM modulation. The receiver picks up the modulated carrier wave and then separates out the audio frequency using a demodulator. The audio output of the demodulator drives a speaker or headset to reproduce the sound waves that were picked up by the microphone in the transmitter. Current radio systems use a number of different types of modulation, the two most common being amplitude modulation (AM) and frequency modulation (FM). When amplitude modulation is used, the intensity or amplitude of the carrier wave signal is varied up and down as shown in figure 3-5. The frequency of the carrier wave is changed when frequency modulation is used. Figure 3-6 shows a carrier wave with this type of modulation. The two commercial broadcast radio bands are a good example here since one uses AM and the other FM. One of the advantages of FM is that it is less affected by atmospheric noise from thunderstorms and other disturbances.

### c. Audio and Radio Frequencies

Two terms that are often used in discussions about radio systems are audio frequency (AF) and radio frequency (RF). Audio frequencies are those of 20,000 Hz or less. They are called audio because

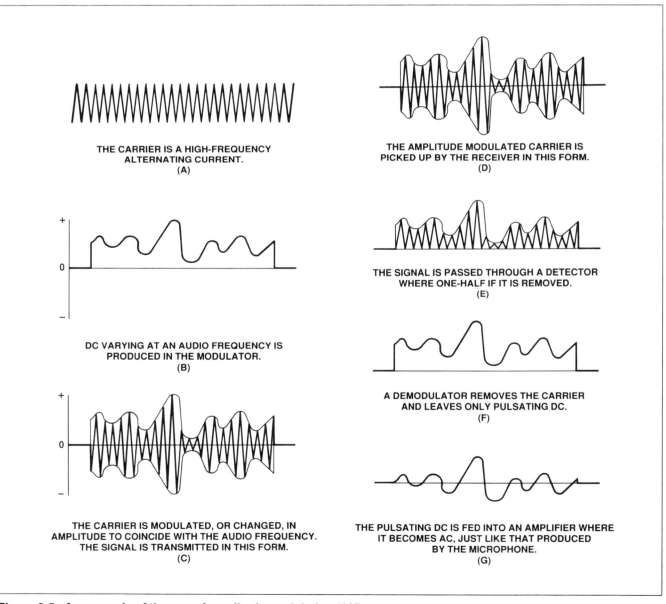

THE CARRIER IS A HIGH-FREQUENCY
ALTERNATING CURRENT.
(A)

DC VARYING AT AN AUDIO FREQUENCY IS
PRODUCED IN THE MODULATOR.
(B)

THE CARRIER IS MODULATED, OR CHANGED, IN
AMPLITUDE TO COINCIDE WITH THE AUDIO FREQUENCY.
THE SIGNAL IS TRANSMITTED IN THIS FORM.
(C)

THE AMPLITUDE MODULATED CARRIER IS
PICKED UP BY THE RECEIVER IN THIS FORM.
(D)

THE SIGNAL IS PASSED THROUGH A DETECTOR
WHERE ONE-HALF IF IT IS REMOVED.
(E)

A DEMODULATOR REMOVES THE CARRIER
AND LEAVES ONLY PULSATING DC.
(F)

THE PULSATING DC IS FED INTO AN AMPLIFIER WHERE
IT BECOMES AC, JUST LIKE THAT PRODUCED
BY THE MICROPHONE.
(G)

*Figure 3-5. An example of the use of amplitude modulation (AM).*

these are approximately the frequencies of sound waves that can be heard by the human ear. Radio frequencies are those above 20,000 Hz. These terms are most often used when discussing the electrical signals that are produced and used by radio receivers and transmitters.

#### d. Ground, Sky and Space Waves

The behavior of radio waves as they travel through the earth's atmosphere and beyond are classified by the terms ground, space and sky waves. The propagation characteristics of ground waves, sky waves and space waves are illustrated in figure 3-7. Radio waves at frequencies below the HF band (below 3 MHz) are called ground waves because they will follow the curvature of the earth and bend. Radio waves that operate in the HF band from 3 MHz to 30 MHz are called sky waves. They tend to travel in straight lines and will not follow the curvature of the earth. Sky waves will bounce or refract off the ionosphere. The ionosphere is made up of layers of ionized particles from about 60–200 miles high. When sky waves strike a layer of the ionosphere in the right way, they will be refracted so that they will come back to earth hundreds of miles away. This characteristic of sky waves can be used to achieve long range transmission of radio signals. Space waves are the result of transmissions of radio waves at frequencies above 30 MHz or above the HF band. Space waves travel in straight lines, but they will not bounce off the ionosphere. The radio signals used to communicate with orbiting satellites are above 30 MHz. A good example can be given here for those who are familiar with AM

and FM radio receivers. The commercial broadcast stations known as AM broadcast in the MF band so that the EM waves behave as ground waves. At night, it is not unusual to pick up an AM station that is hundreds of miles away because the signal has followed the curvature of the earth. Commercial FM stations operate in the VHF band and the reception range is limited to line-of-sight or straight lines because they are space waves. The maximum reception range for these stations is usually about 60 miles because they are blocked by the earth's surface at greater distances.

### 3. Basic Radio Components

#### a. Amplifiers

An amplifier is a device that increases the strength of a signal. They are found in both transmitters and receivers. A transmitter must increase the strength of the signal sent to the antenna so that the EM waves will travel a useful distance outward from the antenna. A receiver needs amplifiers because the strength of the signal from the antenna is very low and must be increased to enable the signal to be heard. Up until the 1960s, most amplifiers relied on vacuum tubes to increase the strength of signals. The transistor has replaced the vacuum tube for most amplifier applications. Amplifiers can be categorized as Class A, Class B and Class C. The difference between these is the shape of the output waveform. Figure 3-8 shows the output of a Class A amplifier, it is complete sine waves just like the input. The Class B amplifier has an output which shows only half of each sine wave as shown in figure 3-8. The Class C amplifier

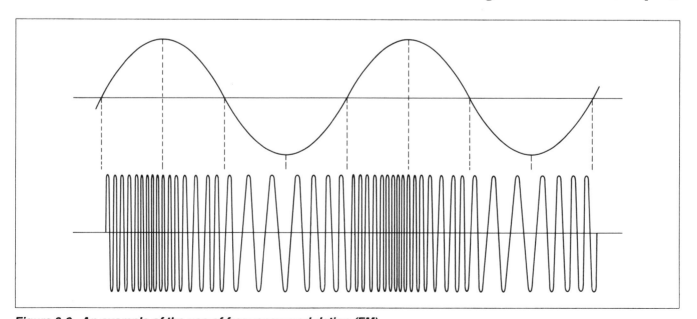

*Figure 3-6. An example of the use of frequency modulation (FM).*

has an output waveform which is less than half of the sine wave as shown at the bottom in figure 3-8. The Class C amplifier is often used as a power amplifier because of its higher efficiency. The output of the Class C amplifier can be sent through an LC circuit or other device to restore the complete sine wave shape.

### b. Oscillators

An oscillator is a device that produces the frequencies needed by both receivers and transmitters. A simple oscillator is an LC circuit or tank circuit made up of a capacitor and inductor in parallel. The LC circuit will have a resonant frequency which matches the desired frequency. An LC circuit by itself will not continue to oscillate because of resistance in the components and wires. Figure 3-9 shows an LC tank circuit which can be connected to a battery to produce oscillations. If the switch in figure 3-9 is moved to position A, the capacitor will be charged by the battery. If the switch is then moved to position C, the tank circuit will start to oscillate as energy is transferred rapidly back and forth between the capacitor and inductor. The oscillations will become weaker and die out because of the resistance in the circuit. In order to maintain oscillations, some energy must be fed back into

the tank circuit. In earlier radios a vacuum tube was used to supply the needed feedback. A transistor is used instead of a vacuum tube in newer radio designs as shown in figure 3-10. The resonant frequency or oscillation frequency is determined by the values of capacitance and inductance in the tank circuit. The LC circuit will not be stable over a period of time and may drift off the correct frequency. A common technique to stabilize the oscillator and produce a more accurate frequency is to use a crystal as shown in figure 3-11. The piezoelectric effect of the crystal will produce a more accurate and consistent output frequency from the oscillator.

### c. Modulators and Demodulators

We will use a voice communications radio as an example of the purpose and function of modulators and demodulators. In the radio transmitter, a device is needed which will combine the AF signal with the RF carrier wave signal before it is sent to the antenna. This is the function of a modulator, it combines the AF and RF signals so that information can be transmitted. The output of the modulator is called modulated RF. The signal produced by the antenna in a receiver will be modulated RF. In order to hear the voice as an output of the

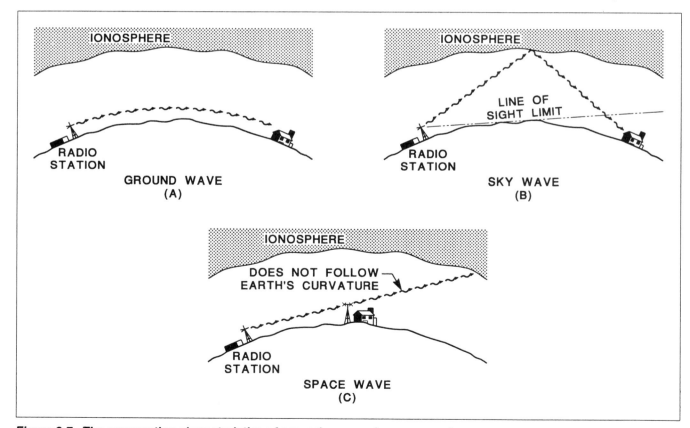

*Figure 3-7. The propagation characteristics of ground waves, sky waves and space waves.*

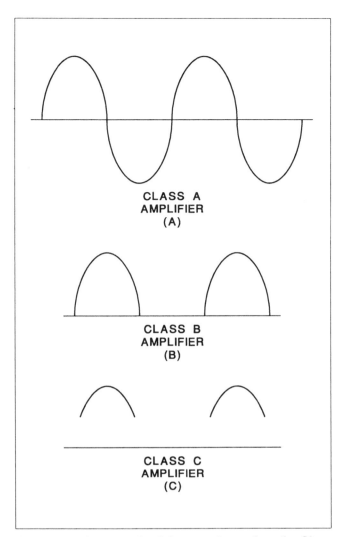

Figure 3-8. An example of the output waveform for Class A, B and C amplifiers.

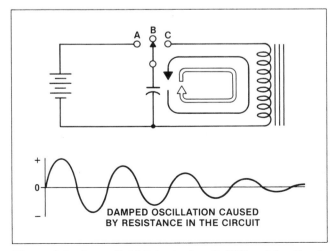

Figure 3-9. A parallel LC tank circuit. Without feedback, the oscillations will be weakened by resistance in the circuit and die out.

receiver, the AF component must be separated out. The demodulator removes the RF component of the modulated RF signal and produces an AF output.

When the AF and RF signals are combined in the modulator, they must have the proper relative

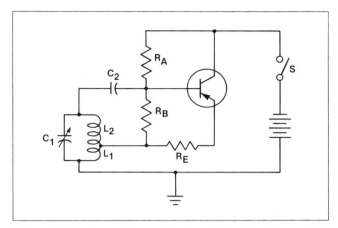

Figure 3-10. An oscillator circuit with feedback supplied by a transistor.

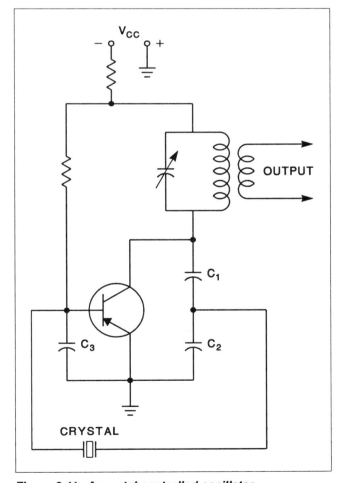

Figure 3-11. A crystal controlled oscillator.

109

strengths for maximum efficiency. The amount of modulation is called the modulation rate. If the AF signal is too weak compared to the RF signal, the modulation rate will be low and the efficiency will also be low. If the modulation rate is over 100%, there will be distortion in the signal due to the gaps created. Figure 3-12 gives examples of 50%, 100% and more than 100% modulation rates with

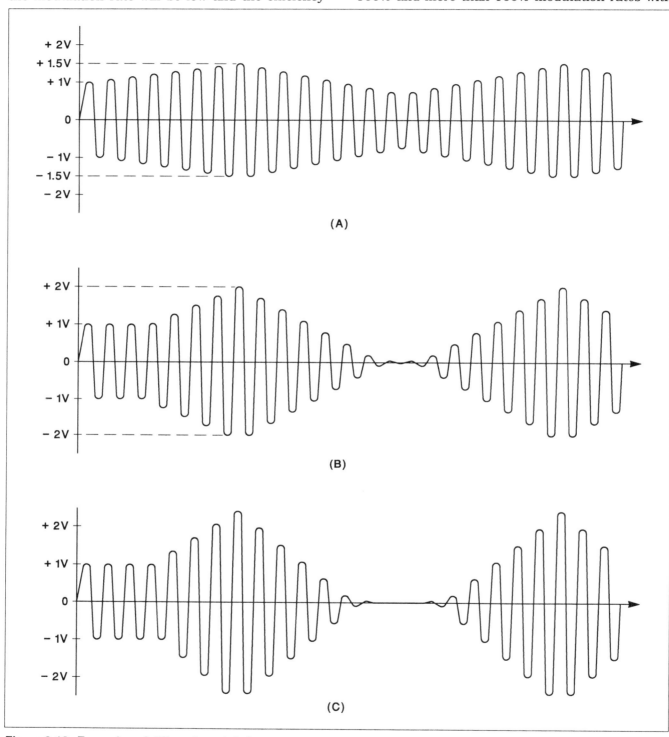

Figure 3-12. Examples of different modulation rates.
(A) 50%
(B) 100%
(C) Over 100%

AM modulation. Most radio transmitters are adjusted to about 90–95% modulation to provide a little margin to prevent distortion. Shouting into a microphone when using a radio can cause over-modulation and should be avoided.

### d. Filters

A filter is used in a radio circuit to remove or filter out unwanted frequencies. The signals that are processed by the circuits in a radio often have additional frequencies present that are not needed. If the proper filter is installed, it will filter out the frequency or frequencies that are not wanted. A filter is usually made up of an arrangement of inductors and capacitors as shown in figure 3-13. A low pass filter will remove all frequencies above a certain value and pass the low ones. A high pass filter does the opposite. If a range of frequencies must be blocked, a band reject filter will be used. A bandpass filter will allow a certain band of frequencies to go through and block frequencies either above or below that range.

### e. Antennas

An antenna is a device that transforms electrical signals into EM waves in the case of a transmit antenna, or transforms EM waves into electrical signals in the case of a receive antenna. Depending on the particular radio system involved, an antenna may be used for transmit only, receive only, or both. The maintenance, inspection and installation of antennas is usually the responsibility of the airframe technician since they are attached to the structure or skin of the aircraft. Antennas often have general names that describe some of their

basic characteristics. Two of the more common types are the Hertz dipole antenna and the Marconi monopole antenna. The Hertz dipole antenna has two metal conductors in a straight line with the connection in the middle. It is called a half-wave antenna because the overall length is equal to one half the wavelength of the EM wave it is designed to be used with. Figure 3-14 is an example of a Hertz dipole antenna. The Marconi antenna is a single metal conductor with a length of ¼ wavelength as illustrated in figure 3-15. In order to work properly, the Marconi antenna must have metal surrounding the mounting base. The metal at the base is needed for efficient operation of the antenna. The necessary metal at the base is called the groundplane or counterpoise. In figure 3-15, the groundplane is the four metal rods at the base of the antenna; the metal skin of an aircraft is used as a groundplane for most aircraft antennas. Most antennas must be installed with the correct

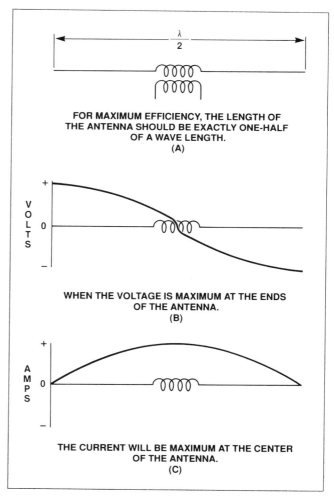

**Figure 3-14. The Hertz dipole antenna is a half-wave antenna.**

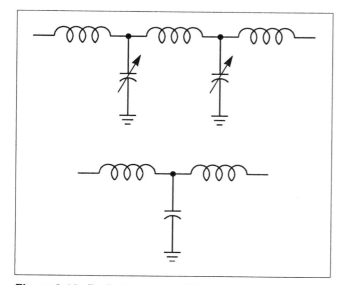

*Figure 3-13. Radio frequency filters are combinations of inductors and capacitors.*

polarization. Polarization refers to the orientation of the electric field relative to the earth. If the electric field is vertical, it has vertical polarization.

The Marconi antenna will produce a vertically polarized radiation pattern as shown in figure 3-16. Horizontal polarization means that the electric field will be parallel to the earth's surface. The horizontally polarized pattern of a Hertz dipole antenna is shown in figure 3-17. Another way to understand polarization is that the polarization of the aircraft antenna should normally match the polarization of the ground based antenna and the EM waves it will utilize. An aircraft VHF communications antenna is an example of a Marconi antenna with vertical polarization. The common example of a Hertz antenna is the VHF navigation antenna found on small airplanes. It is a V-shaped dipole antenna with horizontal polarization.

Antennas must not only be matched to the proper radio, but the conductor that connects the radio and antenna is very critical. A special type of conductor used to connect radios and antennas is called a coaxial cable or coax. Figure 3-18 shows the basic parts of a coaxial cable designed to carry RF signals. It consists of a center conductor covered by a special kind of insulation and an outer conductor around the insulation. Plain wires cannot be used for radio frequency signals because the energy loss would be too great at these frequencies. The antennas and coaxial cables must be maintained in good condition to ensure proper performance from the radio system.

The connection between an antenna and a radio normally requires a coupler in order to give the best transfer of energy between the two of them. Two common types of antenna couplers are the LC circuit and the transformer types. A transformer type of antenna coupler is shown in the antenna connection in figure 3-19. The use of an LC circuit as a coupler between the coax and antenna is shown in figure 3-20. Most aircraft antennas are speed-rated. For example, an antenna rated at 250 mph should not be installed on an aircraft with a higher Vne speed.

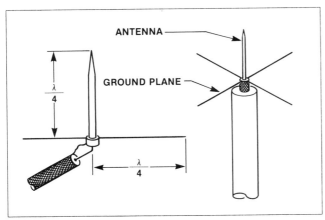

Figure 3-15. *The Marconi antenna is a ¼-wave monopole antenna that requires a groundplane.*

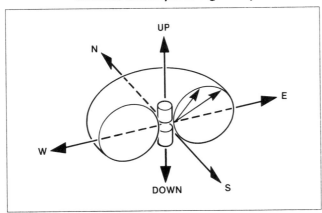

Figure 3-16. *A vertically polarized marconi antenna will produce this type of radiation pattern.*

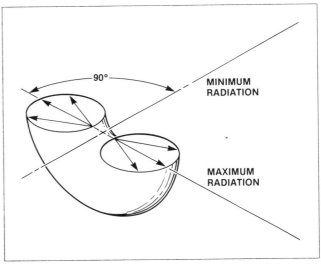

Figure 3-17. *A horizontally polarized Hertz antenna will produce this type of radiation pattern.*

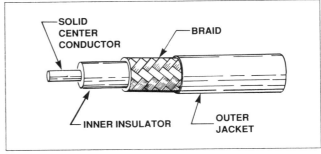

Figure 3-18. *Coaxial cable is used to carry radio frequency electrical signals between radios and antennas.*

## f. Tuning Circuits

An antenna will intercept many different EM waves of different frequencies so some method must be used to separate out the desired frequency. The tuning circuit performs this function. A simple tuning circuit is shown in figure 3-21, it consists of a variable capacitor and an inductor in parallel. As the tuning knob is rotated on the radio, it moves the variable capacitor until the resonant frequency of the circuit matches the frequency of the desired station. This signal is passed into the radio and the other frequencies are blocked out. A better type of tuner which is found on most modern radios uses a frequency synthesizer which contains a number of crystals that can be combined to match the desired frequency. The basic operation of a frequency synthesizer is shown in figure 3-22. Each crystal has a particular frequency and by using switches the crystals can be combined to produce many additional frequencies. When two frequencies are combined, two new frequencies are created that are equal to the sum and the difference of the two frequencies. By using this technique, hundreds of frequencies can be created using a relatively small number of fixed frequency crystals.

## g. Transmitters

The components that have been described will be combined in a block diagram to see how they work together. A voice radio transmitter is shown in figure 3-23. The microphone changes the sound waves of a human voice into AF signals that are amplified and then sent to the modulator. The oscillator in this radio operates at one half the carrier frequency, so its output is amplified and then doubled. The modulator combines the AF and RF signals which are then amplified in the power amp before being sent down the coax to the antenna.

## h. Receivers

In the 1920s, a new type of radio receiver was invented that produced better sound quality. It was called the superheterodyne or superhet radio. The only major difference between the superhet and earlier radios was that it reduced the modulated RF signal from the antenna to an AF signal in more than one jump or stage. Since modern radio components are much smaller and more efficient than in the 1920s, virtually all modern radio receivers are superhet. Figure 3-24 shows a block diagram of a VHF superhet aircraft receiver. The RF signal from the antenna is combined with a local oscillator frequency to produce a lower IF frequency. The intermediate frequencies found in a superhet radio are abbreviated as IF. The basic principle of the mixer is that when two different frequencies are combined, two new frequencies are created; the sum and the difference of the two combined frequencies. In this example, the output of the mixer is the difference between the RF frequency and the local oscillator frequency. The IF signal is amplified and then sent to the detector and demodulator. The detector chops off half of each sine wave to produce a varying DC signal from an AC signal. The AF signal is amplified and used to drive the speaker.

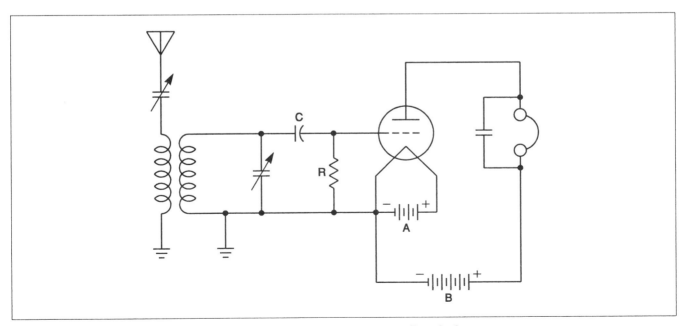

*Figure 3-19. An isolation transformer can be used as an antenna coupling device.*

### i. Speakers and Microphones

Aircraft radios often supply an audio output for the pilot and voice transmitters require an audio input from a microphone. A speaker is a device that transforms electrical signals into sound waves. A dynamic speaker is shown in figure 3-25.

When the audio frequency signal is applied to the windings in the speaker, it sets up a magnetic field that expands and contracts at an audio rate. This field causes the metal diaphragm to vibrate at a corresponding rate to produce the movement of air that generates sound waves. Dynamic microphones are available which operate in the opposite way. Many newer and more efficient types of microphones are now being manufactured, but they all work by transforming the vibrations of sound waves into varying electrical signals.

### j. Audio Control Panels

When an aircraft has more than one radio, an efficient means of switching the microphone and speaker connections from one radio to another is needed.

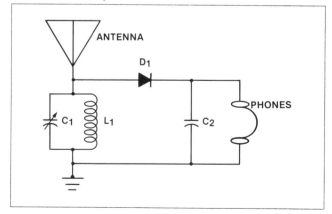

**Figure 3-20. An LC circuit can be used as an antenna coupler.**

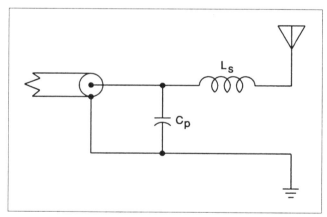

**Figure 3-21. This simple radio receiver uses a variable capacitor to tune in different frequencies by changing the resonant frequency of the tank circuit.**

The audio control panel performs this function. A typical audio control panel is shown in figure 3-26. An audio control panel is not a radio because it only uses audio frequencies, but it is associated with the radios in the aircraft. This audio control panel has a row of toggle switches that can be used to connect the audio output of the various radios to the speaker or headphones. It also has a rotary selector switch to connect the microphone audio output to the different radio transmitters and intercom systems available for the aircraft. The audio control panel illustrated also has three lights that are the indicators for the marker beacon system on the aircraft. The marker beacon system will be described later.

## B. Regulations and Standards for Radios

Aircraft avionics equipment might have to comply with a number of different regulations and standards depending on the type of equipment and the type of aircraft in which it is installed. Regulations from the FAA and the FCC apply to the manufacture and use of most types of equipment and carry the force of law. FAA standards for equipment are usually in the form of TSO (Technical Standard Order) approvals. FCC rules generally apply to equipment which produces radio waves. An FCC Station License is required for aircraft

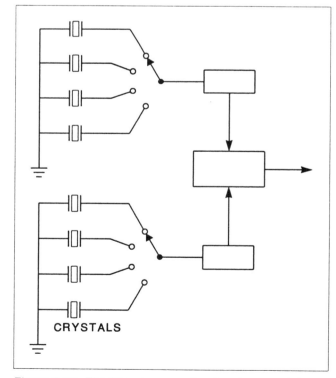

**Figure 3-22. The frequency synthesizer is a crystal controlled tuning device found on many modern radios and other electronic units.**

that have radio transmitters other than ELT. Each different type of transmitter must be listed on the license that is displayed in the cockpit. The role of ARINC in established standards has been described earlier. These standards apply to the equipment in air carrier jets and bizjets primarily. In addition to the rules for the equipment itself, there are some FAA Regulations concerning the use of radio equipment in flight. Some of these FAA rules

are given here. Others will be covered later when the specific types of equipment to which the rules apply are discussed.

## FAR 91.130 (c)

No person may operate an aircraft in an Airport Radar Service Area (ARSA) unless two-way radio communication is established and maintained with

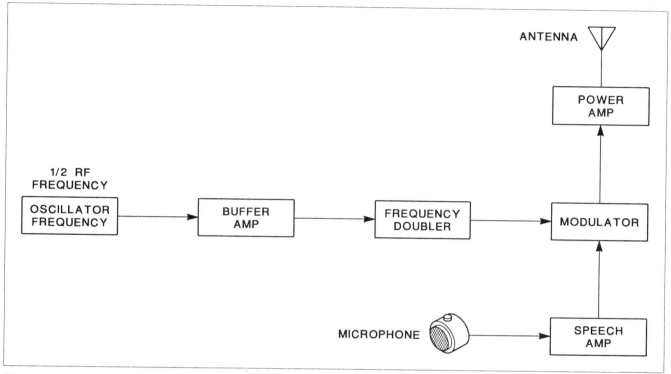

*Figure 3-23. Simplified block diagram of a VHF voice radio transmitter.*

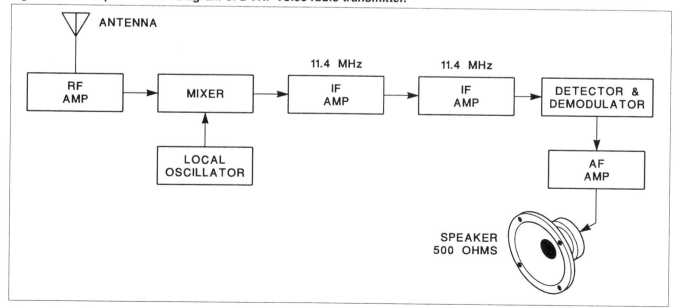

*Figure 3-24. Simplified block diagram of a superheterodyne VHF voice radio receiver.*

115

ATC. A transponder with Mode C automatic reporting of aircraft pressure altitude is also required in all ARSAs.

## FAR 91.131 (c) and (d)

No person may operate an aircraft in a Terminal Control Area (TCA) unless it has:

1. A two-way radio with appropriate frequencies available.

2. An operable transponder with Mode C altitude reporting.

## FAR 91.205 (d) and (e)
### Minimum Equipment Requirements for IFR

1. Two-way radio communications and navigation equipment appropriate to the ground facilities that will be used.

2. At and above 24,000 ft. MSL; approved DME (distance measuring equipment).

## FAR 91.511

Large and turbine-powered, multi-engine airplanes, if operating over water more than 30

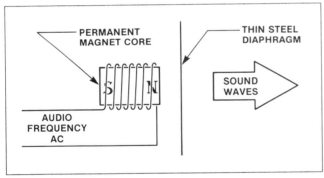

*Figure 3-25. A dynamic speaker produces a magnetic field that varies at an audio rate, causing the diaphragm to vibrate and produce sound waves.*

minutes or 100 nautical miles from the nearest shoreline, must have:

1. Radio communication equipment appropriate to the ground facilities.

2. Two transmitters.

3. Two microphones.

4. Two headsets (or headset and speaker).

5. Two independent receivers.

6. If needed, one HF transceiver.

## C. Intercom and Interphone Systems

Intercom and interphone systems are not radio systems, they use audio signals to permit communication between various points in and around the aircraft. The two systems operate in a similar manner, the difference is who uses the systems and where the phone jacks are located. The intercom system is used for voice communications from one point to another within the aircraft. Large aircraft have intercom systems so that the cockpit crew can communicate with the cabin crew and vice versa. On small airplanes, the intercom is used to communicate within the cockpit area and is needed because of noise in the cockpit area. The interphone system permits conversation between the cockpit and someone outside the aircraft, usually maintenance or service personnel. The operation of intercom and interphone systems is the same. Phone jacks are available at different locations where a handset or headset can be connected. The handset or headset contains a microphone, a small speaker and a push-to-talk switch (PTT). The phone jacks and wiring are connected to an audio amplifier so that the volume can be controlled. Switches are available to select the desired system and a ringing system like that of a telephone is used for alerting the other party. On larger aircraft, a PA (passenger address) system is included so that announcements can be made to the passengers by the flight crew or cabin crew. Figure 3-27 shows the interphone system for

*Figure 3-26. An audio control panel performs the switching functions between radios and the microphones and speakers. (Courtesy Terra Corp.)*

a bizjet airplane. External interphone jacks are located in the nosewheel area, avionics equipment bay area and in the aft fuselage near the auxiliary power unit (APU). These external jacks permit communication between the cockpit and maintenance personnel at these locations outside the aircraft.

# D. Communications Radios

There are a number of different radio communications systems available for aircraft use. They differ primarily in the frequencies used and the type of communication involved. The most important use of communications radios is for Air Traffic Control since the controllers need to be in contact with the pilots to give necessary instructions. The general trend since the 1930s has been the use of higher frequencies and the development of specialized communications for other than ATC purposes.

## 1. HF Communications

Up until the 1940s, most aircraft radio communications utilized frequencies in the LF, MF and HF bands because suitable equipment was not available to use higher frequencies. Aircraft HF radios operate on frequencies between 2 and 30 MHz. The only modern aircraft that carry HF comm radios are those that operate long distances over water or in the remote regions of the earth. Air carrier jets and bizjets that routinely fly the Atlantic and Pacific oceans will have HF comm radios for ATC purposes.

The HF comm radios have a maximum reception range of about 1,500 to 2,000 miles compared to a maximum of about 250 miles for VHF comm. The reception range of VHF comm radios is restricted to line-of-sight distances as shown in figure 3-28. The probe and flush mount antennas used for HF comm require a special antenna tuning and coupling device. This is automatically repositioned each time a new frequency is selected in order to tune the antenna for that particular frequency. Smaller aircraft with HF comm will use a long wire antenna that usually extends from a wing tip up to the vertical fin. Up to the 1960s, many aircraft used a long wire trailing antenna which extended out the aft fuselage of the airplane. This antenna could be run in and out to select the proper antenna length. It is not suitable for high speed aircraft, so it is little used today. HF comm radios utilize ground and sky waves to achieve their greater reception range. Aircraft HF transmitters produce an output power of 80–200 watts which is much higher than the output power typically found with VHF transmitters. This is necessary to achieve long distance communication. A disadvantage of HF is that it is more affected by atmospheric interference than

VHF. Sometimes an aircraft in the middle of the ocean will lose communication because of thunderstorms or other disturbances.

## 2. VHF Communication

The use of frequencies in the VHF band for aircraft communication was developed in the 1940s. VHF provides much clearer reception and is much less affected by atmospheric conditions. EM waves in the VHF band are space waves so that the reception range is limited to line-of-sight distances. At 1000 ft., the reception range is about 30–40 miles. The maximum reception range using ground based stations is about 250 miles at altitudes above 35,000 ft. Much less power is required for VHF than for HF comm. Aircraft VHF transmitters have an output power of 5–20 watts. The standard radio communications system in the U.S.A. for ATC purposes is VHF. This is also true for most other countries of the world. The International Civil Aviation Organization (ICAO) has designated VHF as the standard radio communication system for ATC purposes over land.

The range of frequencies used for VHF comm is 118–137 MHz using AM modulation. In the 1950s, an aircraft VHF comm radio could tune only 90 channels or different frequencies. Later the separation between channels was reduced to produce 360 channels. Modern VHF comm radios have 720 or 760 channels available. The spacing between channels is now 25 kHz, so that adjacent usable frequencies would be 120.15, 120.175, 120.20 etc. The latest models of aircraft VHF comm radios use lighted displays that employ LEDs (light emitting diodes), LCDs (liquid crystal displays), or gas discharge tubes. Figure 3-29 shows a complete set of radios that might be found on a typical general aviation airplane. The radios use lighted displays for the frequencies and other information that is needed. The use of lighted displays and crystal controlled tuning has eliminated the complex switching systems employed on earlier tuners. The modern radio displays two different frequencies, the one on the left is the active frequency and the one on the right is the standby frequency that is held in memory. This is a very nice feature which allows the pilot to switch the two numbers in the display by simply pushing a transfer button. The transfer buttons can be seen in figure 3-29 on the VHF comm and NAV radios. Technicians should be familiar with the use of aircraft radios for troubleshooting purposes and also because they might have to taxi an airplane which may require the use of the radio. The antennas used with VHF comm are Marconi ¼ wave monopoles that use

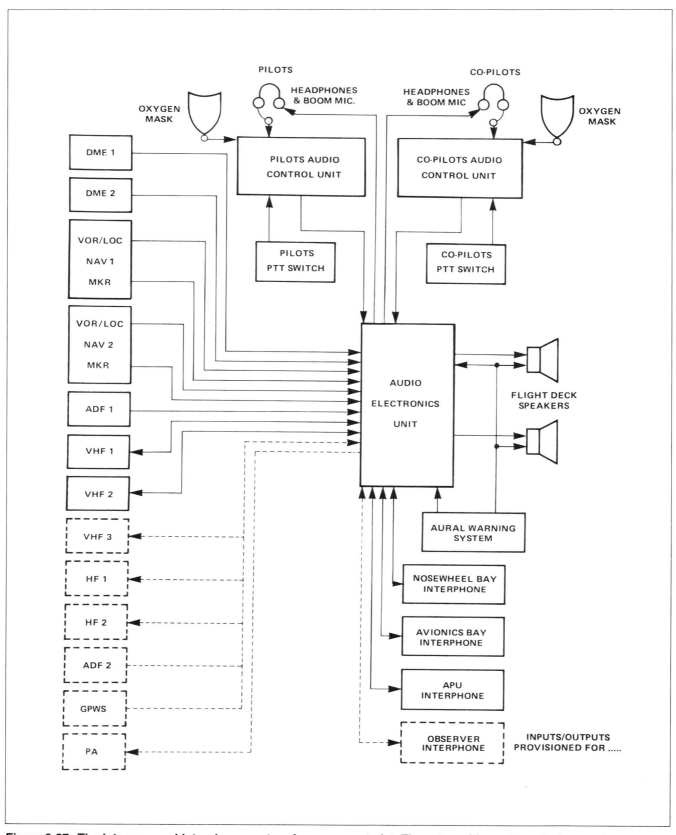

**Figure 3-27. The intercom and interphone system for a corporate jet. The external interphone jacks are shown in the lower right. (Courtesy Canadair Group, Bombardier Inc.)**

118

vertical polarization. There is a separate antenna for each VHF comm radio.

### 3. Radiotelephone

Aircraft often carry a radiotelephone system which is somewhat similar to the portable cellular phone available for cars. It employs radio signals to permit telephone calls to be made from the aircraft in flight. The frequencies used are 450–500 MHz in the UHF band. The antenna used is a Marconi antenna of a slightly different shape and size compared to a VHF comm antenna.

### 4. SATCOMM

A very recent development in aircraft systems is Satellite Communications or SATCOMM. A UHF radio is installed in the aircraft to communicate with commercial satellites in orbit overhead. To date, it is being used primarily for telephone calls from bizjets and air carrier jets. It is beginning to be used for datalinks from an aircraft in flight to the airline computer system. This permits monitoring of the progress of the flight and the status of the aircraft systems. In the future, SATCOMM will be used to replace HF comm for communications and ATC purposes for aircraft over the oceans or remote areas. The equipment currently available is very expensive, usually costing hundreds of thousands of dollars. The antenna used with SATCOMM is a special type that must be installed on the top of the aircraft.

### 5. Selcal

Selcal is an abbreviation of selective calling, a special communications system for air carrier aircraft. Selcal is not a separate radio system, it is a piece of equipment that is connected to the existing comm radios on the aircraft. It is connected to the VHF and HF radios on the aircraft.

The system is used for communications between aircraft in flight and certain airline managers. It is called selective calling because it works somewhat like a telephone system. An example of a SELCAL decoder and the connections to the aircraft's VHF and HF radios is shown in figure 3-30. Each aircraft is assigned a code number which is a part of the SELCAL equipment. When the proper code is received, a tone is heard in the cockpit to tell the crew that someone is calling them. They pick up a handset in the cockpit and talk to the person that has called them. The code consists of four tones that are transmitted to the aircraft in series. Each of the four tones has twelve possible frequencies, so that over 20,000 different codes are available. An example of a SELCAL communication will illustrate the operation of the system. The head dispatcher for the airline is sitting in his office in Chicago and needs to call the flight crew of one of the airline's aircraft to give them a message. According to the schedule, the airplane is somewhere between Boston and Atlanta. The dispatcher picks up his telephone and dials a special access code and the code for that airplane. The signal is sent out over many different ground transmitters and received by hundreds of airplanes in flight. The phone will ring only in the cockpit of the airplane he is calling and he will pass on the message when they answer. The SELCAL system is a great help to the airline when they must reroute a flight or pass along important information to the crew in flight.

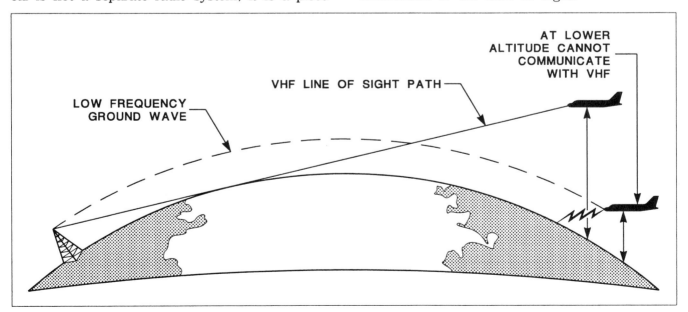

*Figure 3-28. Example of the line-of-sight restriction that applies to VHF and other space wave transmissions.*

## E. Emergency Locator Transmitters (ELTs)

The ELT is a self-contained transmitter that is designed to help locate an airplane after a crash. A typical ELT with its antenna and coaxial cable is shown in figure 3-31. It is required on most small airplanes, but is not required on air carrier jets and bizjets. The ELT is battery powered and is automatically turned on by crash forces. It will transmit a special swept tone for 48 hours on two different emergency frequencies. The two frequencies are 121.5 MHz and 243.0 MHz; 121.5 is the civilian emergency frequency and 243.0 is the military emergency frequency. The transmitter is activated by an acceleration operated switch when a rapid deceleration force is applied along the longitudinal axis of the aircraft. The ELT must be installed as far aft as possible but in front of the tail surfaces since this area has been shown to remain intact in most airplane crashes. The batteries in the ELT must be replaced or recharged at specific intervals as required by the FARs. There are times when an aircraft technician may need to test an ELT so he should be familiar with the procedure. If possible, the ELT should be tested with the antenna disconnected or shielded to prevent the transmission of emergency signals into the air. If this cannot be done, it is still permissible to test the ELT, but only during the first five minutes of any hour and for three audio sweeps maximum. A VHF comm radio is turned on and tuned to 121.5 MHz. The ELT is then switched on manually until the signal is heard on the receiver and then switched off again.

---

### FAR 91.207
### Emergency Locator Transmitters

No person may operate a U.S. registered civil airplane unless it meets the applicable requirements listed below for ELTs.

1. Each emergency locator transmitter must be in operable condition and meet the requirements of TSO-C91 or TSO-C91A and it must be installed as far aft as practicable.

2. Batteries used in the ELT must be replaced or recharged as appropriate:

    a. When the transmitter has been in use for more than one cumulative hour; or

    b. When 50% of the useful life has expired.

**Figure 3-29. A typical set of radios and associated equipment for a small airplane. The VHF com and nav radios show both active and standby frequencies. (Courtesy Terra Corp.)**

3. The expiration date for the replacement or recharge of the battery must be legibly marked on the outside of the transmitter and entered in the aircraft maintenance record.

4. The requirements for ELT do not apply to:

    a. A newly acquired aircraft that must be ferried to a place where the ELT will be installed.

    b. An aircraft with an inoperative ELT that must be ferried to a place for ELT repair.

    c. Turbojet powered aircraft.

    d. Scheduled air carrier flights.

    e. Training flights conducted entirely within 50 nautical miles of the airport of operations.

    f. Design and test flights.

    g. Delivery flights of new aircraft.

    h. Aircraft engaged in aerial application of chemicals for agricultural purposes.

    i. Research and development aircraft.

    j. Exhibition and air racing aircraft.

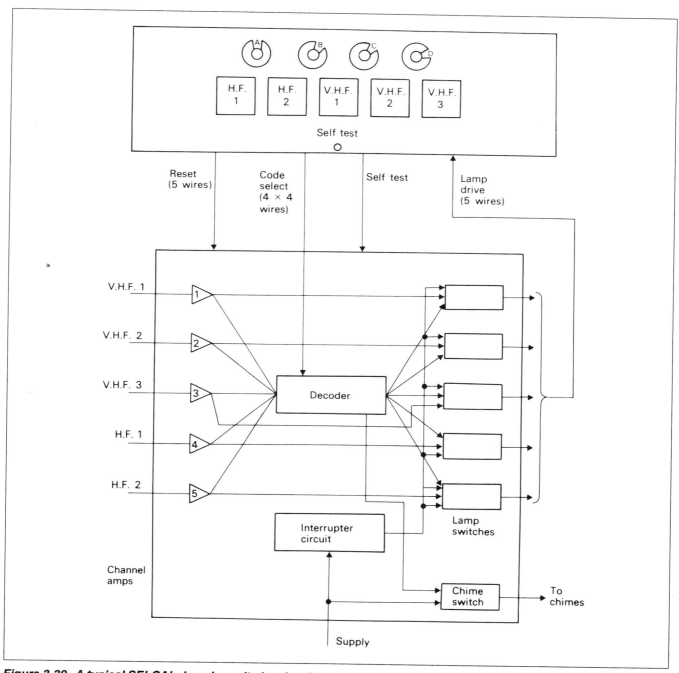

*Figure 3-30. A typical SELCAL decoder unit showing the connections to the VHF and HF com radios.*

k. Aircraft equipped to carry only one person.

l. An aircraft during any period in which the ELT has been temporarily removed for inspection, repair, modification or replacement, subject to the following:

   1. A maintenance record entry must be made that includes the date of removal, the serial number and the reason for removal.

   2. A placard must be placed in view of the pilot which states "ELT not installed".

   3. The aircraft must not be operated more than 90 days after initial ELT removal.

## F. Cockpit Voice Recorders and Flight Data Recorders

The cockpit voice recorder (CVR) and the flight data recorder (FDR) are designed to automatically record information in flight that can be used during an investigation following an accident or serious incident. They are installed on all air carrier jets and some commuter airliners and privately owned aircraft. The recorders are installed in the aft fuselage as shown in figure 3-32 since this area is least likely to be severely damaged in an accident.

The CVR is designed to record sounds in the cockpit and communications on the intercom and radio systems. It has a hot microphone in the cockpit which is always activated to record voices, warning sounds, engine noise etc. The CVR is also connected to the intercom so that conversations between the members of the crew can be recorded. It is also connected to radios so that communications with ATC are recorded. The CVR has a continuous recording system that holds approximately the last 30 minutes of data. It is located in the aft fuselage for better survival and it is waterproof and protected against fire and impact forces.

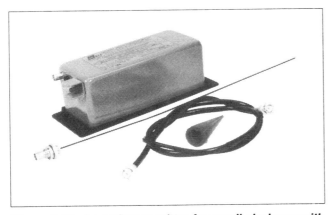

*Figure 3-31. An ELT transmitter for small airplanes with the antenna and coaxial cable.*

The flight data recorder has many more inputs than the cockpit voice recorder. It has a recording time of 8 hours on smaller aircraft and about 24 hours on larger aircraft. The CVR and FDR are located in the same area of the aft fuselage and have similar protection from water, fire etc. Some of the typical types of data that are recorded on the FDR are listed below.

Air carrier jets have been required to carry CVRs and FDRs for some years, but recently new regulations have gone into effect that require these devices on smaller aircraft. Some of these new regulations are summarized here.

### FAR 91.609
**Flight Recorders and Cockpit Voice Recorders**

1. Multi-engine turbine powered airplanes or rotorcraft with 10 passenger seats or more manufactured after October 11, 1991 must have a digital flight data recorder with 8 hours storage.

2. After October 11, 1991, multi-engine turbine powered airplanes and rotorcraft with 6 passenger seats or more and with a required minimum flight crew of 2 pilots must have an approved cockpit voice recorder with minimum storage of 15 minutes.

3. If an accident or incident occurs, the operator must hold the data 90 days or longer if requested.

### FAR 91 Appendix E
**Flight Recorder Specifications**

The flight recorder required for certain aircraft under FAR 91.609 must record the following items:

1. Airspeed.
2. Altitude.
3. Magnetic Heading.
4. Vertical Acceleration.
5. Longitudinal Acceleration.
6. Pitch Attitude.
7. Roll Attitude.
8. Pitch Trim Position.
9. $N_1$, EPR or Prop RPM and Torque.
10. Vertical Speed.
11. Angle of Attack.
12. Autopilot Engagement.
13. TE Flap Position.
14. LE Flap Position.
15. Reverse Thrust.
16. Spoiler/Speedbrake Position.

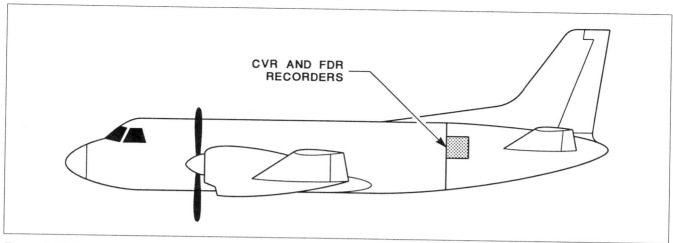

Figure 3-32. Large commuter aircraft and air carrier jets have a Cockpit Voice Recorder and Flight Data Recorder installed in the aft section of the fuselage.

## G. Navigational Systems

There is a much wider variety of navigational systems available to aircraft than communications systems. There is a wide range of capabilities for the various systems and some of them are very specialized. Some of them have been around for 50 years and others are much newer. We will start with a brief description of a NAV system that is now obsolete. A basic understanding of this older system will make clearer the greater capabilities of more modern NAV systems.

### 1. Four-course Radio Range

The four-course radio range was the first radio navigation system developed in the U.S. to guide aircraft in poor weather conditions. Before its invention, the standard navigation system consisted of powerful light beacons that the pilot followed during either day or night flying. The four-course radio range gets its name from the fact that only four pathways or courses were usable with this system. The ground stations transmitted signals in the LF band, so the signals could be very difficult to use when atmospheric conditions caused interference. The antenna arrangement on the ground transmitted four different directional radio beams as shown in figure 3-33. The signals transmitted north and south of the station were modulated with the Morse code letter "N". The signals transmitted east and west were modulated with the letter "A". If the pilot was flying in any one of these sectors and listening to the signals, the Morse code keying for the letter A or N, as appropriate, would be heard. If the aircraft was exactly along a line where the signals merged, a steady hum or tone would be heard in the headphones. The pilot navigated by listening to the sounds and aligning the airplane

along the centerline of one of the four courses. As long as the aircraft was on course, the pilot would hear the steady tone in the headphones. Since the radio signals were affected by atmospheric noise, the pilot often had to fly for hours on end listening to noise and static and trying to pick out the correct signals. The system was not very easy to use and the last one in the U.S. was taken off the air in the 1970s.

### 2. Automatic Direction Finder (ADF)

The ADF system has been in use since the 1930s and even though it is not as accurate or easy to use as the more common VOR system, it is still widely used because it is inexpensive. Many smaller

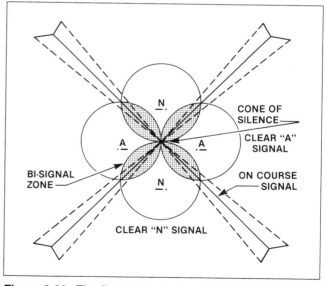

Figure 3-33. The first radio navigation system was the 4 course radio range which operated in the LF band.

airports that have no other radio aids to navigation will have a transmitter that can be used with ADF equipment. The term automatic direction finder applies to the aircraft equipment and the term non-directional beacon (NDB) refers to the associated ground based equipment. For our purposes, we can use ADF and NDB to mean the same thing since the overall system requires both airborne and ground based equipment to operate. The ADF receiver can receive signals transmitted in the range of 190 to 1,800 kHz. The signals are in both the LF and MF bands. The ADF equipment on the aircraft can receive two different types of transmitted signals. The range 190–500 kHz is used by NDB transmitters that are specifically designed for aircraft use. The range of 550–1,800 kHz is the band used by commercial AM broadcast stations. The broadcast stations can be used for navigation, but are not as good as the NDBs because the pilot does not always know exactly where the transmitter site is located. The NDB locations are shown on aeronautical charts so the location of the transmit antenna can be determined more accurately. The signals transmitted from the ground sites are omnidirectional. The ADF equipment determines station direction through the use of a directional antenna. The directional antenna is called a loop antenna. The older versions were actually shaped like a loop as shown in figure 3-34. The strength of the output signal from the antenna depends on the angle between the plane of the loop and the direction of travel of the EM wave. When the EM wave is at right angles to the plane of the loop,

the signal is minimum or a null. When the EM wave and the loop antenna are parallel, the signal strength is at a maximum. As the loop antenna is rotated, there will be a rise and fall in the signal strength received. If the loop is rotated 360°, there will be two peaks and two nulls in the signal strength as shown in figure 3-35. The null is used to determine station direction rather than the peak because there is a greater change in the signal strength when the null is reached than when a peak is reached. With a loop antenna alone there would be two nulls for each 360°, which means the station could be in one of two directions. This ambiguity problem is removed by using a second antenna called the sense antenna. Figure 3-36 shows how the signals from both antennas are combined to determine the direction of the transmit station. Older loop antennas were rotated by electric motors. The newer types of loop antenna do not rotate themselves, they use an electronic system to cause rotation of the signal. In either type, the principle of operation is the same. The simple type of cockpit indicator used with an ADF is called a radio compass indicator or ADF indicator. This type of simple ADF indicator can be seen in figure 3-37. It has a compass rose with degree markings and a pointer which points in the direction of the transmitter site. When the pointer is straight up, it shows that the station is directly in front of the aircraft. If the pilot keeps the pointer at the top of the instrument, it will guide him to the location of the transmitter. On newer types of ADF equipment, the cockpit indicator is called a radio magnetic indicator (RMI).

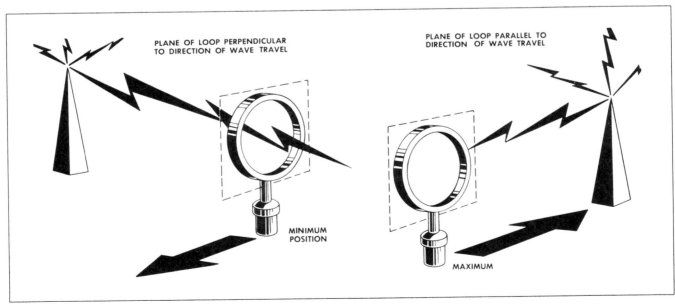

*Figure 3-34. Example of the directional characteristics of a loop antenna.*

The appearance of this RMI is illustrated in figure 3-38. The RMI has two pointers that can be operated by two ADF signals, two VOR signals, or one of each. It also includes a compass card which is

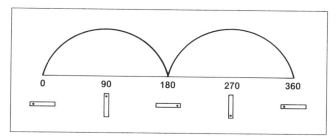

*Figure 3-35. If a loop antenna is rotated 360°, two peaks and two nulls will occur.*

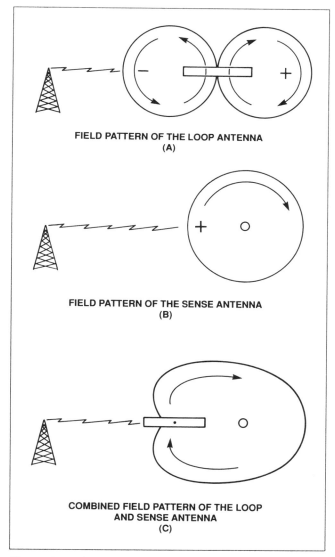

FIELD PATTERN OF THE LOOP ANTENNA
(A)

FIELD PATTERN OF THE SENSE ANTENNA
(B)

COMBINED FIELD PATTERN OF THE LOOP
AND SENSE ANTENNA
(C)

*Figure 3-36. When the signals from the loop and sense antennas are combined, the ambiguity problem is eliminated.*

slaved to a remote DG and flux gate compass as described in chapter 1. The primary use of ADF is for approaches to airports that don't have any better radio aids to navigation available.

## 3. Very High Frequency Omnirange (VOR)

The VOR system is the standard IFR radio navigation system for cross-country flying in the U.S. and most of the rest of the world. The VOR system was developed to overcome some of the problems with the old four course radio range. The major advantages of VOR over the older system are:

1. An infinite number of radials or courses are available, not just four.

2. Since it operates in the VHF band, the VOR is much less affected by thunderstorms and atmospheric conditions.

3. The VOR is much more accurate.

4. The VOR is much easier to use, the pilot follows an indicator needle instead of listening to Morse code signals for navigation.

The first VOR was installed in Indianapolis in 1939 and by the 1950s, coverage was almost complete over the entire U.S. Since the reception range of VOR is limited by the same line-of-sight considerations that apply to VHF comm, about 1,500 VOR ground sites are required for nationwide coverage. The range of frequencies used by VORs is 108–118 MHz. The ground sites transmit two kinds of signals, a reference signal and a rotating signal. The reference signal uses FM and the rotating signal uses AM. The two signals are aligned so that they will be in phase when the receiver is straight north of the ground site. The phase angle

*Figure 3-37. An ADF radio receiver and its indicator instrument.*

125

for east is 90° and for south it is 180°. No matter where the aircraft is in relation to the ground site, the direction can be determined by measuring the phase angle between the two signals. The cockpit indicator for VOR is shown in figure 3-39. This indicator has three different parts: the course deviation indicator (CDI), the omni bearing selector (OBS) and the TO-FROM indicator.

1. OBS — The omni bearing selector is a knob that the pilot rotates to select the desired radial from the station.

2. CDI — The course deviation indicator is the vertical needle or pointer. When it moves to the left of center, the pilot must turn left to get back on the desired radial set with the OBS.

3. TO-FROM Indicator — The to-from indicator is a small window where one of three words is displayed: TO, FROM or OFF. The word TO means that the pilot is flying toward the station. The word FROM means the pilot is flying away from it and the word OFF means that usable signals are not being received or the indication is changing between the TO and FROM conditions.

The procedure for tuning in a station with the VOR is similar to that used for tuning an ADF. The pilot locates the station on an aeronautical chart or other reference and determines the frequency.

The pilot then tunes in the desired frequency and listens for the Morse code identifier. Both VORs and ADFs transmit a two or three letter identifier in Morse code. When the station has been identified, the pilot is ready to use it for navigation by means of the appropriate cockpit indicator instrument.

The latest types of VOR indicators use light bars instead of a needle for the CDI. A VOR indicator that uses light bars can be seen in figure 3-29 on the left side. On aircraft equipped with an HSI or EHSI, the VOR steering commands are displayed on the HSI instead of the more simple VOR indicator. The aircraft VOR equipment must be tested for accuracy if it is used for IFR (this is covered in the FAR section later on).

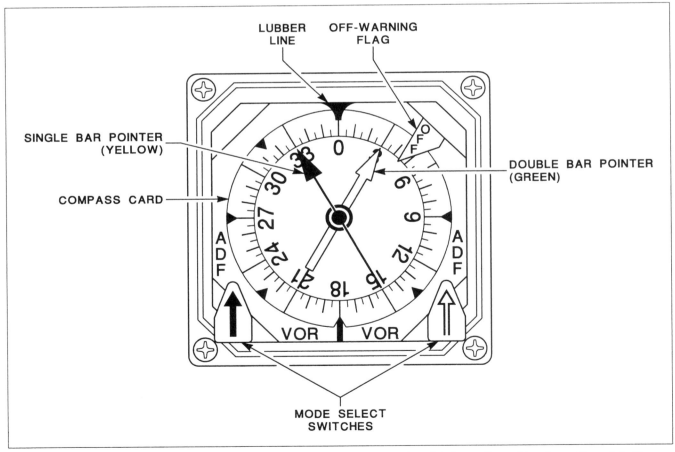

*Figure 3-38. The RMI can display either ADF or VOR radio navigational information. (Courtesy Canadair Group, Bombardier Inc.)*

## 4. Distance Measuring Equipment (DME)

The military services have their own radio navigation system which operates on principles similar to those of VOR. The system is known as TACAN (Tactical Air Navigation) and it uses signals in the UHF band. An additional feature of TACAN that is not a part of the VOR system is the use of distance measuring equipment as an integral part of TACAN. The DME portion of TACAN is used by civilian aircraft to augment the information available from the VOR. The VOR and TACAN transmitters are usually located at the same ground sites and referred to as VORTACs. The frequencies utilized by DME are in the range of 960–1,215 MHz. The basic operation of DME is illustrated in figure 3-40. The airplane DME transmitter sends out a pulse signal in all directions. This is referred to as the interrogation. When a DME ground station receives a valid interrogation from an aircraft, it sends back a reply after a fixed delay of 50 microseconds. The aircraft DME equipment measures the travel time for the signals to be sent and received back, and calculates the distance in nautical miles. The distance information is displayed on an indicator in the cockpit for the pilots. The distance measurement given by DME is a slant range distance so some error will result from the altitude of the aircraft. The amount of difference between slant range distance and horizontal or map distance is normally small and the error can be ignored. If the aircraft is at a high altitude and almost directly over the DME ground site, the error will be at its greatest. For example, if the aircraft is directly over the DME site and 18,000 ft. above it, the DME will indicate 3 nm (1 nm = 6,080 ft.). With the use of microprocessors, a modern DME can give other indications in addition to distance. If the DME distance is known, then groundspeed and time to station can be found through mathematical calculations. The pilot can select which readout is needed; distance in nautical miles, groundspeed in knots or time-to-station in minutes. Due to the fact that most DME ground sites are located in the same place as a VOR, the two radios are tuned at the same time. When the pilot selects the proper frequency for the VOR that is being used, the DME equipment is tuned automatically to the proper DME channel.

## 5. RNAV — Area Navigation

The RNAV equipment in aircraft contains a computer that processes the signals received from VOR and DME ground sites. The main advantage of RNAV is that it permits random direct routes of flight. The use of conventional VOR navigation along airways requires that the aircraft be flown directly from one VOR site to the next. Since the VOR sites seldom line up directly along the desired flight path, the aircraft ends up flying a zigzag course to get from one place to another over long distances. The use of RNAV equipment permits the aircraft to fly directly to the destination without having to fly straight to and from each of the VOR sites. This more direct routing is illustrated in figure 3-41. The RNAV computer processes signals from VOR and DME transmitters and displays steering information to the pilot to guide the aircraft along a direct route of flight.

*Figure 3-39. The VOR indicator contains the CDI needle, the TO-FROM indicator and the OBS knob to select the desired radial.*

Before takeoff the pilot will program the computer with the desired waypoints that establish the desired route of flight. A waypoint is established as a direction and distance from a VOR and DME site. For example, the waypoint OMN 240/25 would indicate a point that is 25 nautical miles southwest of the OMN transmitter site. The pilot programs the RNAV computer by designating a number of waypoints along the desired flight path. During flight, the RNAV computer performs the calculations needed to display guidance commands using a CDI or HSI that will guide the aircraft from one waypoint to the next. Even though the RNAV equipment is designed to permit direct routes, the aircraft must be able to receive usable signals from VORTAC sites. Waypoints cannot be used if they would take the aircraft beyond the line-of-sight reception range. A limitation on the use of RNAV for IFR flight is the ATC system. In congested areas with a lot of air traffic, the direct routes of flight may not be approved by air traffic controllers.

## 6. Transponders

The transponder equipment found on aircraft is designed to make it easier for air traffic controllers to identify specific aircraft so that they can prevent mid-air collisions and provide guidance to the aircraft. The transponder is a device which is related to radar, so we will begin with a short history of the use of radar to identify aircraft. The use of radar to locate aircraft in flight dates back to the 1930s. The principle used is called primary radar or echo location radar. The radar transmitter sends out a brief pulse of EM waves which travel outward at the speed of light and bounce off the metal parts of an airplane. The reflected energy or echo is received back at the radar site where it produces a spot of light on the radar scope. The problem with this primary radar is that all the blips on the radar scope look the same. During World War II, a system was developed to make it easier to distinguish the friendly aircraft from

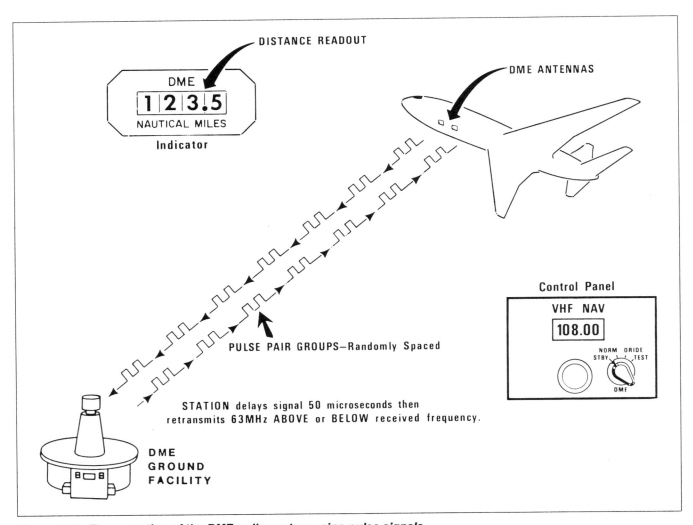

*Figure 3-40. The operation of the DME radio system using pulse signals.*

the enemy aircraft. The system was known as IFF (identification friend or foe) and it is still called that by the military. This type of radar is also called secondary radar. A small radar frequency receiver and transmitter unit is installed in each airplane. When the radar pulse from the ground site strikes the aircraft, the IFF equipment sends a coded signal back to the ground site. The basic operation of the primary and secondary radar systems is shown in figure 3-42. The coded signal received at the radar site from the aircraft permits it to be identified. In the years since World War II, both primary and secondary radar have been adapted for ATC purposes. Transponder is the name of the secondary radar equipment installed on aircraft.

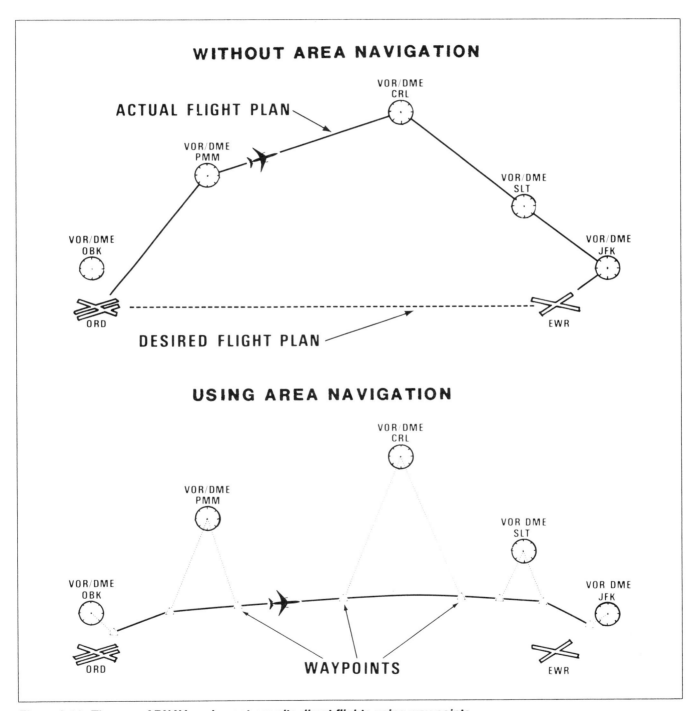

Figure 3-41. *The use of RNAV equipment permits direct flights using way points.*

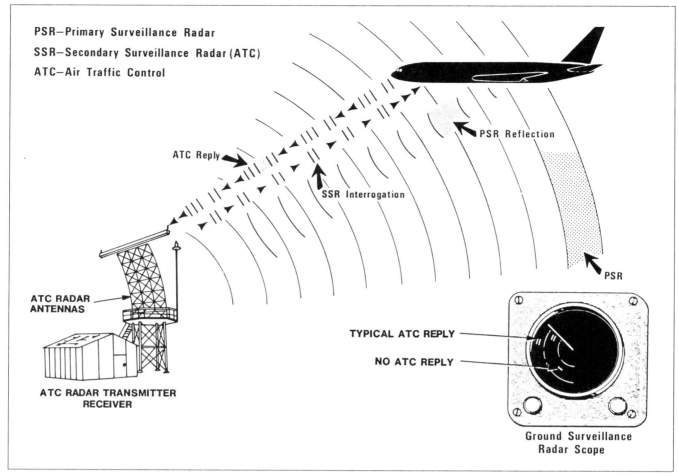

*Figure 3-42. Both primary and secondary radar are used for Air Traffic Control purposes.*

The aircraft transponder system uses only two different frequencies, one to transmit and one to receive. The transponder receives on 1030 MHz and transmits on 1090 MHz (it is a UHF system). The ground radar site sends out a coded interrogation pulse which in effect asks the airborne equipment to answer or reply. When the transponder receives a valid interrogation, it sends back the proper reply signal. The coding used in the transponder signals is digital or binary. Each interrogation and reply signal consists of a number of pulses in a pulse train as illustrated in figure 3-43. For each location in the pulse train, a pulse can either be present or absent. The cockpit controls for the transponder permit the pilot to set one of 4096 different numerical codes. The numbers set into the transponder represent an octal coding so there are no 8s or 9s in the code setting window. The possible code settings range from 0000 to 7777. The computer in the ground radar site can identify the aircraft by the code its transponder is sending out.

Some transponder codes are reserved for special purposes; 0000 is used by the military, 1200 is for VFR aircraft and 7500, 7600 and 7700 are reserved for specific types of aircraft emergency situations.

There are several different operating modes associated with transponder equipment. They are:

1. Mode 3/A — This is the basic transponder mode that can utilize one of 4096 different codes.

2. Mode C — This mode includes the above capabilities but adds a coded message giving

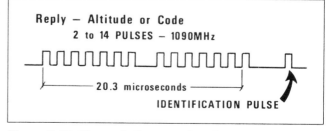

*Figure 3-43. The reply from an aircraft transponder uses binary coded pulses of very short duration.*

the aircraft's pressure altitude using an altitude encoder.

3. Mode S — This is the latest development in transponders and is not yet fully operational, it will have the capability of sending additional messages such as ATC instructions or weather reports that can be viewed on a CRT or printed on paper in the cockpit. Mode S also increases the number of different identification codes for the aircraft to over one million.

### 7. FARs for VOR and Transponder

The FAA regulations which apply to testing and operation of VOR and transponder equipment are summarized here.

---

### FAR 91.171
#### VOR Equipment Check for IFR Operations

(a) No person may operate a civil aircraft under IFR using the VOR system of radio navigation unless the VOR equipment of that aircraft:

1. Is maintained, checked and inspected under an approved procedure; or

2. Has been operationally checked within the preceding 30 days and was found to be within the limits for bearing error set forth below.

(b) The check must use one of the following:

1. An approved FAA or Repair station ground test signal — ±4°.

2. Designated VOR checkpoint on the airport surface — ±4°.

3. Designated airborne checkpoint — ±6°.

4. An airborne check using a VOR radial and prominent ground point that can be seen from the air as established by the person doing the check — ±6°.

5. If two separate VOR receivers are installed, they can be checked against each other — ±4°.

(c) Maintenance record entry

1. Each person performing one of the above checks shall enter the date, place and bearing error in the aircraft log or other record and sign it.

2. If a test signal from a repair station is used, the repair station certificate holder must enter the bearing transmitted and date in the aircraft log or other record.

---

### FAR 91.215
#### ATC Transponder and Altitude Reporting Equipment and Use

(a) TSO requirements

1. All aircraft transponders must meet the appropriate requirements of TSO-C74b, TSO-C74c or TSO-C112.

2. After July 1, 1991, all initial installations of ATC transponders in aircraft must meet the requirements of TSO-C112 (Mode S).

Note: Due to development delays this requirement has been dropped.

(b) Airspace requirements — all aircraft operating in the following airspace must have a 4096 code transponder with Mode C altitude reporting or a Mode S transponder.

1. Terminal Control Areas — TCAs

2. Airport Radar Service Areas — ARSAs

3. In all controlled airspace above 10,000 ft. MSL and over 2,500 AGL.

---

### FAR 91.413
#### ATC Transponder Tests and Inspections

(a) No person may use an ATC transponder that is required by the rules of this Chapter unless it has been tested and inspected within the preceding 24 calendar months and meets the requirement of Part 43 Appendix F.

(b) Following any installation or maintenance which could have introduced errors, the integrated system must be tested in accordance with paragraph (c) of Appendix E, Part 43.

(c) The above tests and inspections must be conducted by:

1. An appropriately rated repair station; or

2. A holder of a continuous airworthiness program as provided in Part 121, 127, or 135; or

3. The manufacturer of the aircraft, if the transponder was installed by that manufacturer.

---

## H. Long Range Navigation Systems

The navigation systems in this section all have usable ranges that exceed those of the VOR, ADF and other systems already covered. Some of these long range navigation systems do not rely on ground based transmitters and some do not use radio signals at all. All of them have been developed since the 1960s so they are relatively more modern than most of the systems previously described. The long range navigation systems use geographical coordinates to establish aircraft position and waypoints along a desired flight path. As shown in figure 3-44, geographical coordinates are based on the grid system of lines of latitude and longitude. Longitude is expressed either east or west of the prime meridian that runs through Greenwich, England. The maximum longitude is 180° which is the International Date Line exactly half way around the earth from the prime meridian. Latitude is measured north and south of the equator with a maximum value of 90° at the poles. Since 1° is equal to approximately 60 nm, for accurate positions each degree is divided into 60 minutes and each minute into 60 seconds. An example of a lat/long position is 29°, 10 minutes, 51 seconds North latitude by 81°, 3 minutes, 22 seconds West longitude. This coordinate position locates the airport at Daytona Beach, Florida.

## 1. Loran C

The first Loran system was developed in the 1940s by the U.S. Navy for use by ships. Modifications were made to produce Loran A, B, C and D. Loran C is the only one that has any large scale use by aircraft. All the early transmitter sites were located along coastlines since it was a system for ships. Starting about 30 years ago, pilots of privately owned airplanes began modifying Loran C units from boats and ships for aircraft use. The system has been improved and newer equipment is now available that make Loran C a very useful radio navigation system. Within the last several years new ground sites have been installed

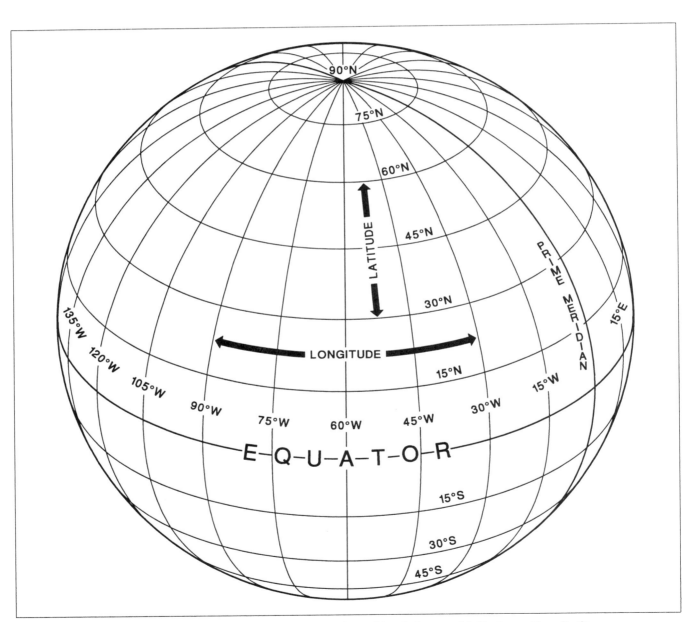

*Figure 3-44. Long range navigation systems define aircraft position in terms of latitude and longitude.*

in the western U.S. to give nationwide coverage. The primary aircraft users of Loran C continue to be general aviation aircraft.

The Loran C system uses ground transmitter sites that all transmit on the same frequency—100 kHz. The EM waves produced are ground waves. The operation of this system involves transmitter chains in which each chain consists of one master station and two or more slave stations. For purposes of explanation, we will consider a chain with two slave stations like that shown in figure 3-45. Each transmitter uses a tower about 1,000 ft. tall and has an output power of approximately 4,000,000 watts.

The transmissions are sequenced so that the master transmits first and then the slaves transmit. The location of the master and slaves are hundreds of miles apart. The signals received by the aircraft will have a time separation that is determined by the aircraft location relative to the transmitter sites. A computer in the Loran C receiver performs the calculations that determine location. The location determination has an accuracy on the order of 400–1,000 ft. in most cases. The Loran C equipment in the aircraft does not have to be tuned since all signals are received on 100 kHz. Each chain can be identified by the time delay between transmission pulses and the information is stored in the computer memory of the aircraft receiver. The reception range is 1,000 miles or more. An advantage of this system is that signals can be received at any altitude, even with the aircraft on the ground. The use of microprocessors has made the modern Loran C unit a very powerful and versatile navigation

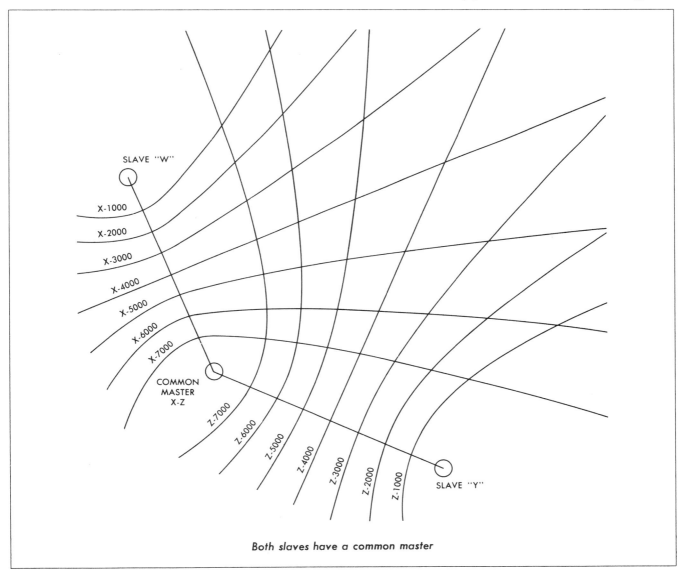

Both slaves have a common master

**Figure 3-45. A Loran C chain consists of one master station and two or more slave stations.**

system. A Loran C receiver contains a large amount of memory which stores the location of every airport and VOR in the U.S. The memory often includes extra information for each airport such as radio frequencies available, runway direction and length, fuel available etc. The memory can also store pilot designated waypoints to enable direct routes to be flown. The output of the Loran C includes a CDI type indicator which can be used to guide the aircraft along the desired route of flight. A Loran C receiver and its digital lighted display can be seen at the bottom of the radio stack in figure 3-29.

## 2. Omega

The Omega radio navigation system was developed by the U.S. Navy for use by ships and aircraft. There are only eight Omega transmitter sites scattered around the earth, but they provide worldwide coverage. The maximum usable reception range is approximately 10,000 miles. The signals are transmitted in the VLF band by powerful ground based transmitters. Each ground station transmits on several different frequencies between 10 and 14 kHz in a repeating pattern. The transmissions from the eight stations are sequenced so that two different stations don't transmit on the same frequency at the same time. The accurate timing required for this is maintained by atomic clocks. When an aircraft Omega receiver is turned on, it automatically selects the strongest signals for navigational use. The processing of signals is performed by computers and the display of position and guidance information

is similar to that used with Loran C. The U.S. Navy also operates a VLF communications system that utilizes seven sites around the world. Many aircraft navigation receivers can pick up both Omega and VLF comm signals. The Omega signals are more accurate for navigation and are used as the primary source, the VLF communications station signals are used as a back-up or secondary means of navigation. The locations for the eight Omega stations and the seven VLF stations are shown in figure 3-46.

## 3. Inertial Navigation System — INS

The inertial navigation system or INS is a long range NAV system that does not rely on the reception of radio waves. The system is totally self-contained within the aircraft. The key to the operation of INS is the very accurate measurement of acceleration forces. The accelerometer sensors measure acceleration in directions parallel to the earth's surface. The INS unit can calculate direction and velocity of the aircraft by measuring acceleration forces, but it cannot determine where the aircraft is when the unit is first turned on. For this reason, the INS must be aligned and calibrated before takeoff. When the INS is first turned on before flight and before the aircraft is moved, the position of the aircraft is entered on a keyboard so the unit can align and calibrate itself. During flight the INS calculates direction and velocity, which when applied to the beginning position gives the present position. During very long flights, the INS will develop a cumulative error. Toward the end

| OMEGA STATIONS | | | | | | VLF COMMUNICATION STATIONS | | | | |
|---|---|---|---|---|---|---|---|---|---|---|
| Letter | No. | Location | Latitude | Longitude | No. | Location | Latitude | Longitude | Frequency (kHz) | Pwr (KW) |
| A | 1 | Aldra, Norway | 66°25′N | 13°08′E | 1 | Maine | 44°39′N | 67°17′W | 17.8 | 1026 |
| B | 2 | Monrovia, Liberia | 6°18′N | 10°40′W | 2 | Japan | 34°58′N | 137°01′E | 17.4 | 48 |
| C | 3 | Haiku, Hawaii, USA | 21°24′N | 157°50′W | 3 | Washington | 48°12′N | 121°55′W | 18.6 | 124 |
| D | 4 | La Moure, North Dakota, USA | 46°22′N | 98°20′W | 4 | Hawaii | 21°26′N | 158°09′W | 23.4 | 588 |
| E | 5 | La Reunion | 20°58′S | 55°17′E | 5 | Maryland | 38°60′N | 76°27′W | 21.4 | 588 |
| F | 6 | Golfo Nuevo, Argentina | 43°03′S | 65°11′W | 6 | Australia | 21°49′S | 114°10′E | 22.3 | 989 |
| G | 7 | Australia | 38°29′S | 146°56′W | 7 | Great Britain | 52°22′N | 01°11′W | 16.0 | 40 |
| H | 8 | Tsushima, Japan | 34°37′N | 129°27′E | | | | | | |

Each station transmits a specific frequency.

Each station transmits three basic frequencies: 10.2 kHz, 11.33 kHz, and 13.6 kHz. To prevent signal interference between stations, transmisisons are timed such that only one station is transmitting a particular frequency at a time.

**Figure 3-46. There are eight Omega transmitter sites that provide world-wide coverage. The seven VLF stations can be used as back-ups.**

of a long flight the error might be 20 miles. To eliminate this cumulative error, modern INS units can be updated using radio signals received from ground stations where they are available. The simple type of INS sensors are small weights which react to acceleration forces by movement about a hinge point as shown in figure 3-47. In order to give accurate readings, the accelerometers must be mounted on a gyro stabilized platform so that they only measure horizontal forces. This stable platform and the control panel for an INS system is shown in figure 3-48(A) and figure 3-48(B). In effect, the accelerometers measure north-south and east-west accelerations in order to determine aircraft position.

The newest type of inertial navigation system does not use conventional spinning gyroscopes and does not need a gyro stabilized platform. A modern Inertial Reference Unit (IRU) for an INS system contains three accelerometers and three ring laser gyros (RLGs). The three accelerometers measure acceleration forces along the aircraft's three axes; vertical, lateral and longitudinal. The RLG is a device with no moving parts that replaces a conventional gyro with a spinning rotor. As shown in figure 3-49, the laser gyro uses a triangular housing and two different laser beams. The mirrors at the corners direct the two laser beams in opposite directions around the triangular course. Sensitive detectors measure the Doppler frequency shift that occurs when the unit is rotated. Three of these RLGs are needed to measure rotation around the three axes of the aircraft. A computer processes the signals from the three accelerometers and the three laser gyro sensors to determine aircraft heading, position and groundspeed.

This modern type of IRU is referred to as a strap-down system because it does not require a gyro stabilized platform like that shown in figure 3-48(A). The corrections that are needed are calculated by the computer. Like any inertial navigation system, the strapdown INS must be given the geographical coordinates for present position during the alignment before takeoff.

Inertial navigation systems can be programmed with complete routes of flight and can be coupled to the aircraft autopilot to provide steering commands.

## 4. Doppler Navigation

The Doppler navigation system does not rely on the reception of radio signals from ground based transmitter sites, but it does use radio waves.

The Doppler system uses radar beams that are projected downward and received back at the aircraft after they have bounced off the surface of the earth. The frequency commonly used is 8.8

GHz. The arrangement of the radar beams is shown in figure 3-50. Notice that two beams are projected forward and two to the rear. When the aircraft is in motion, the frequency of the received signals will be shifted upward or downward compared to the frequency that was transmitted. The change in frequency of a wave when there is relative motion between the source of the wave and the observer is the Doppler effect. Figure 3-51 illustrates the Doppler effect with sound waves where the observer hears a change in pitch or frequency of the sound waves as the ambulance goes by his position. The Doppler effect is the same for both sound waves and radio waves. That is where this system gets its name. If the aircraft is traveling forward over the surface of the earth and not drifting right or left, the frequency of the two forward beams is shifted upward equally and the frequency of the two rearward beams is shifted downward equally. If the aircraft is drifting, there will be a difference in the received frequency between the right side and left side beams. By measuring all four beams, the groundspeed and side drift of the aircraft can be calculated accurately. This information can be used to make a continuous determination of position. Like INS, Doppler NAV systems must be aligned before takeoff and will develop cumulative errors in flight. Doppler can be updated using available ground based radio signals as is done with INS. Doppler navigation units were common in the past, but have now been largely replaced by INS and other newer long range navigation systems.

## 5. Satellite Navigation

The latest development in long range navigation systems is the use of satellites in earth orbit. Two

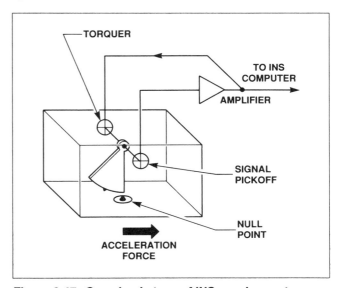

*Figure 3-47. One simple type of INS accelerometer.*

135

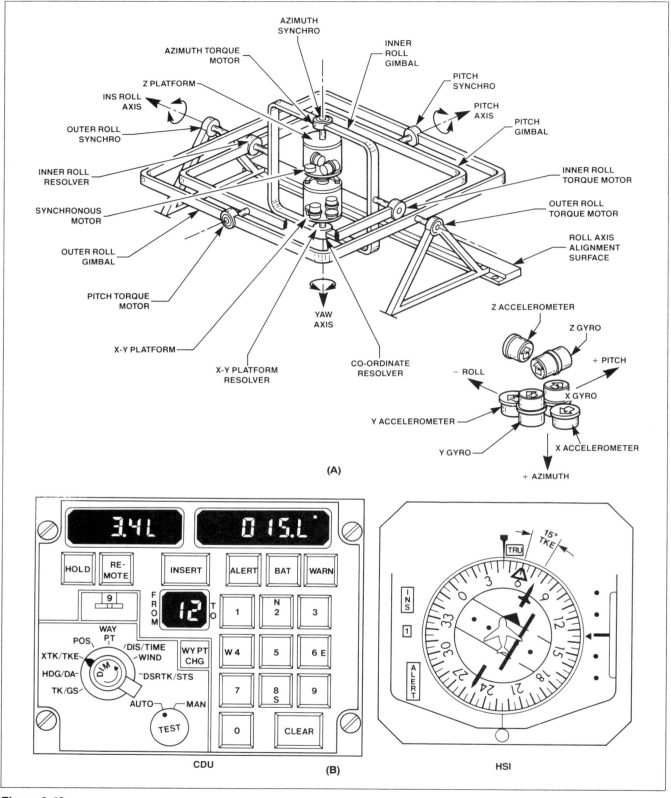

**Figure 3-48.**
(A) *The gyro stabilized platform of INS accelerometers.*
(B) *The keyboard and controls for the INS system and the HSI which can be used to display INS navigational information.*

systems began development in the 1970s, one by the USSR and one by the U.S. The U.S. system is called GPS (global positioning system) and the Russian system is called GLONASS.

Both systems are still incomplete although some satellites are in orbit now and can be used. The two systems are very similar in terms of the frequencies and principles of operation. The GPS system was designed to include 24 satellites, 21 primary and 3 spares. Due to delays caused by the Space Shuttle Challenger disaster and other factors only 18 satellites were in place as of the middle of 1992. The GLONASS system was also designed to use a total of 24 satellites, but only about 15 were in place by the middle of 1992. The satellites of both systems orbit at an altitude of about 10,000 nm with a period of 11 to 12 hours. The position and altitude of the satellites is known with great precision. The aircraft with a satellite navigation system communicates with the satellites using frequencies in the 1.6 GHz range. For accurate navigation, the aircraft must be able to communicate with at least four different satellites as seen in figure 3-52. Currently the coverage in most areas is over 90%. Since the altitude of all the satellites is known, this system can provide altitude as well as position information. The accuracy is on the order of 80 ft. which makes the system potentially more accurate than the other systems so far described. The GPS system was developed and is operated by the Department of Defense. A possible limitation on the use of GPS for IFR is the difficulty in monitoring the accuracy of the satellite signals. Satellite navigation systems can be purchased now, but they are primarily used for VFR navigation or as a secondary system. The use of this system as a sole source for IFR navigation has not yet been approved. It has been predicted that within a few years satellite navigation may become the dominant long range NAV system and may also be used for precision approach guidance to airport runways.

# I. Instrument Landing System (ILS)

An instrument approach procedure is a method used to guide an aircraft to an airport runway for

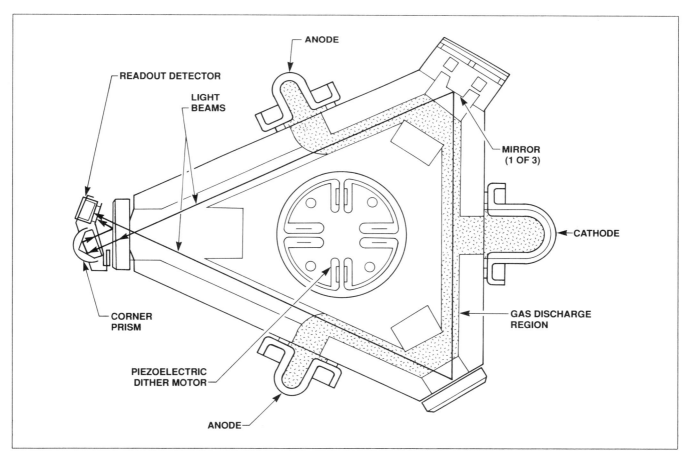

*Figure 3-49. A laser beam IRU (inertial reference unit) which uses laser beams to replace conventional gyros for an INS navigation system.*

landing in bad weather conditions. The procedures must be FAA-approved and are published in special books for pilots to use. There are two basic types of instrument approach procedures: precision approaches and non-precision approaches. The difference is that precision approaches give the pilot vertical or descent guidance while non-precision approaches do not. Signals from VORs and NDBs can be used for non-precision approaches. The standard type of precision approach system used in the U.S. and most of the world for civilian aircraft is the ILS. The military still uses a form of precision approach radar, but that kind of system is no longer operated by the FAA. Instrument approaches have weather minimums which specify the minimum ceiling (cloud height) and visibility needed to successfully complete the approach. The weather minimums for a Category I standard ILS are 200 ft. ceiling and ½ mile visibility. The minimums for a non-precision approach would be about twice as much.

The ground equipment needed for an ILS system has four parts.

1. Localizer — A radio beam for lateral guidance.
2. Glideslope — A radio beam for vertical guidance.
3. Marker Beacons — Radio signals that give distance to the runway data.
4. Runway and approach lights.

The lights will not be discussed further because they require no equipment on board the aircraft.

The first three parts will be described in order. The localizer layout is shown in figure 3-53 with a view from above to show the localizer beam.

The signals transmitted by the localizer are on frequencies between 108 and 112 MHz. A dual beam is transmitted outward from the far end of the runway. The right half of the signal is modulated at 150 Hz and the left half is modulated at 90 Hz. The aircraft receiver measures the relative strength of the 90 and

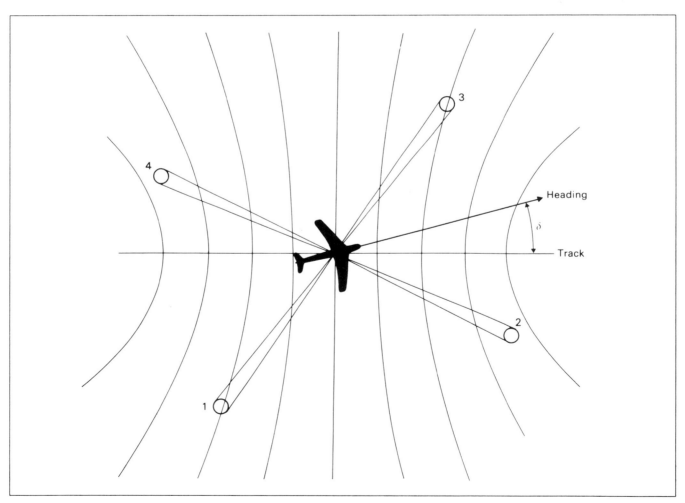

**Figure 3-50. The orientation of the four radio beams projected from the bottom of the aircraft by a Doppler navigation system.**

150 Hz signals that are received. When they are equal, the aircraft is lined up with the centerline of the runway. The cockpit indicator is a vertical needle just like a VOR indicator, in fact it is often the same one. If the needle swings to the left, the pilot must turn left to get back on course.

The glideslope uses a principle like that of the localizer, but it transmits on frequencies of 328 to 336 MHz in the UHF band. A side view of the glideslope and runway is shown in figure 3-54.

The glideslope signal uses 90 Hz modulation above the glidepath and 150 Hz modulation below the glidepath. The center of the glidepath would produce equal parts of 90 and 150 Hz signal in the receiver. The cockpit indicator for glideslope is a horizontal needle as shown in figure 3-55 which shows a simple ILS indicator. A needle deflected upward means the pilot must fly up or decrease his rate of descent. The actual glidepath angle used in an ILS system is about 2½–3°. This angle permits both large and small aircraft to use the ILS. The glideslope and localizer frequencies for an ILS are paired together in set combinations. The glideslope receiver is usually slaved to the localizer receiver so that when a localizer frequency is tuned in, the correct glideslope frequency is automatically set in the glideslope receiver.

The marker beacons are low powered transmitters that transmit a cone shaped pattern straight up into the air. When the aircraft flies directly over the marker beacon site, an indication is given in the cockpit to show the pilot the distance to the approach end of the runway. This is illustrated in figure 3-56 which gives the approximate distances for the outer, middle and inner markers. All marker

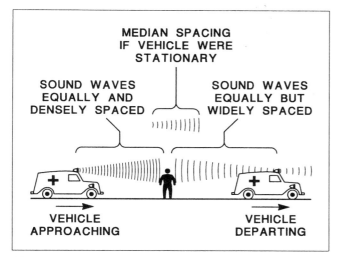

Figure 3-51. Example of the Doppler principle applied to sound waves rather than radio waves.

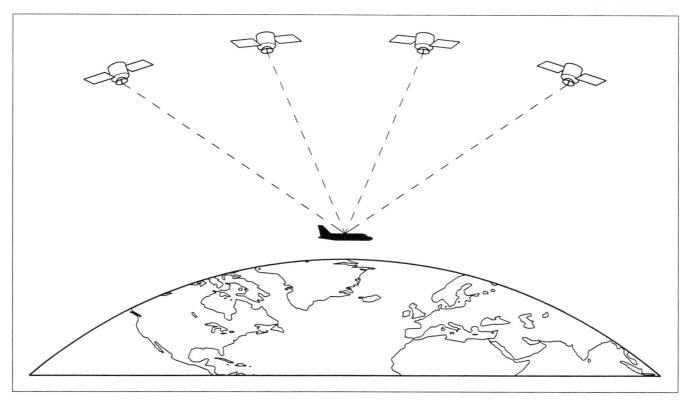

Figure 3-52. When using satellite navigation, the aircraft usually needs to communicate with four satellites for accurate information.

beacons transmit on 75 MHz so different modulations must be used to identify the inner, middle and outer markers. The aircraft receiver does not need to be tuned and in fact is often turned on automatically with the electrical system. The outer marker is modulated with a frequency of 400 Hz and a Morse code sequence of dashes. It also causes a blue light to illuminate in the cockpit so it can be identified by sound or with the blue light or both.

The middle marker is modulated with a frequency of 1300 Hz and a sequence of Morse code dots and dashes.

The amber indicator light comes on over the middle marker. The inner marker is not used with all ILS systems. It uses a modulation of 3000 Hz and a sequence of Morse code dots. The white light comes on over the inner marker. The three marker beacon indicator lights can be seen on the left side of the audio control panel in figure 3-26.

Some ILS systems place an NDB type transmitter at the outer or middle marker locations. These make it easier for the pilot to navigate to the proper location to begin the approach. These are examples of what are called transitional navigational aids. When an NDB transmitter is associated with a marker beacon location, it is called a compass locator. The pilot would tune it in on his ADF receiver and follow the indications as he would for any NDB.

The signals produced by the localizer system are projected in opposite directions so that the localizer is usable from either direction as shown in figure 3-57. The course that is used with the ILS is called the front course and the other is called the back course. The glideslope is projected in one direction

only. If an airport has an ILS for runway 9, the full ILS is only available for landings to the east on runway 9 (090°). The back course of the localizer would be available for landings on runway 27 (the opposite end of the same runway). The back course approach is a localizer only approach which will have higher minimums than the ILS because it does not have the glideslope. The sensing of the indicator needle is backwards on the back course approach. The pilot would have to use opposite corrections on the back course compared to the ILS.

*Figure 3-55. The ILS indicator has two needles: a vertical needle for localizer and a horizontal needle for glideslope.*

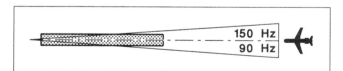

*Figure 3-53. The localizer course is modulated by 150 Hz on the right side and by 90 Hz on the left side of the center line.*

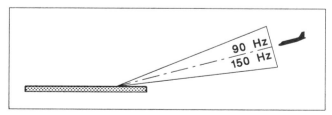

*Figure 3-54. The glideslope signal is modulated by 90 Hz above and 150 Hz below the middle of the glidepath.*

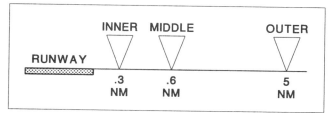

*Figure 3-56. The marker beacon transmitters send signals upward which provide indications in the cockpit of distance to the runway.*

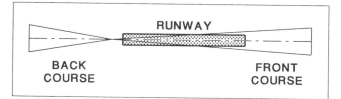

*Figure 3-57. The localizer transmits signals that provide guidance on both the front course and the back course. Only the front course is used for an ILS.*

## J. Microwave Landing System (MLS)

The microwave landing system is a recently developed precision approach system that is in limited use at this time with about eight systems in service in the U.S. The MLS was designed to overcome some of the problems with ILS. A major problem with ILS is that not enough frequencies are available to install the system in all the places it might be needed. ILS is affected by some bending of the beams by obstructions and can only have one glidepath angle that all aircraft must use. The MLS transmitters operate at frequencies between 5.0 and 5.1 GHz. Many new frequencies are available in this range and the signals do not suffer the same kind of interference or bending that affects ILS signals. The principle of operation of the MLS is called a time referenced scanning beam system.

Two beams are used: one that scans side to side and one that scans up and down. The aircraft receiver measures the time difference between reception of the TO and FRO scans for the two beams in order to determine lateral and vertical position. The scanning beams used by the MLS are illustrated in figure 3-58. The cockpit display works in a way similar to the one used with ILS. Because of delays in development, only a few MLS approach systems are in use. One of the first was installed at a small airport in Colorado that is served by a commuter airline. The airline operates STOL (short takeoff and landing) aircraft and the glideslope that is used is steeper than normal. This allows a steep approach which gives greater terrain clearance in mountainous areas. The glidepath angle for MLS is determined by the processing of the signals by the aircraft equipment. It is not determined by the installation of the ground antennas. This means that with MLS a different glidepath angle could be used by aircraft with different flight characteristics. It will probably be many years before MLS has replaced ILS to any great extent, in fact, the FAA just recently ordered new ILS equipment for installation at a number of U.S. airports. The use of MLS requires different receivers and antennas than ILS, but both types of equipment may be found on some aircraft.

## K. Radar Altimeter

The radio altimeter or radar altimeter is a system which measures the aircraft's height above ground level (AGL) with an accuracy of about 5 ft. A conventional altimeter is not that accurate and it measures MSL not AGL altitude. The usable range for a radar altimeter extends up to 2,500 ft., but it is mainly used during instrument approaches in bad weather. The basic Category I ILS minimums are 200 ft. ceiling and ½ mile visibility. There are other categories of ILS with lower minimums. A

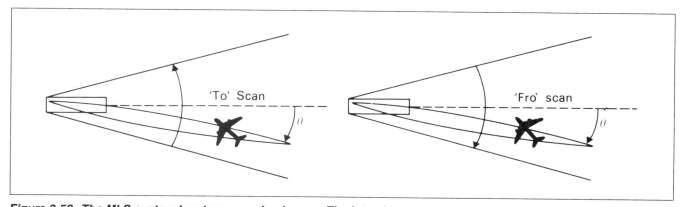

*Figure 3-58. The MLS system has two scanning beams. The lateral beam that scans side to side is shown here.*

Category II ILS has minimums of 100 ft. ceiling and ¼ mile visibility. The minimums for Category III are even lower. When the aircraft is flying below 200 ft. in bad weather, a better method of measuring altitude than a barometric altimeter is needed for safety. This is the main use for a radar altimeter, as a precise way to measure AGL altitude during IFR approaches. The radar altimeter uses antennas that are installed on the belly of the aircraft. The transmitter sends out radio waves at 4.3 GHz which strike the earth and bounce back to the receive antenna. By measuring the travel time for the radio waves, an accurate calculation can be made of AGL altitude. The basic parts of a radio altimeter or radar altimeter system and one type of cockpit indicator are shown in figure 3-59. Another type of cockpit indicator for a radar altimeter that uses a round display is shown in figure 3-60. This instrument has a bug that can be set at 200 ft. or some other altitude to give a warning to the pilot during an instrument approach.

## L. Ground Proximity Warning System (GPWS)

The ground proximity warning system is designed to provide warnings to the flight crew when the aircraft is in danger of striking the ground due to excessive descent rate or rising terrain. This equipment is required on all air carrier jets and it is found on some bizjets and other aircraft as well. The main component in a GPWS system is a computer which monitors numerous inputs and makes calculations to determine if the aircraft is in danger of hitting the ground. Some of the inputs to the computer are barometric altitude, radar altitude, rate of climb or descent, flap position and landing gear position. The GPWS is one of the few

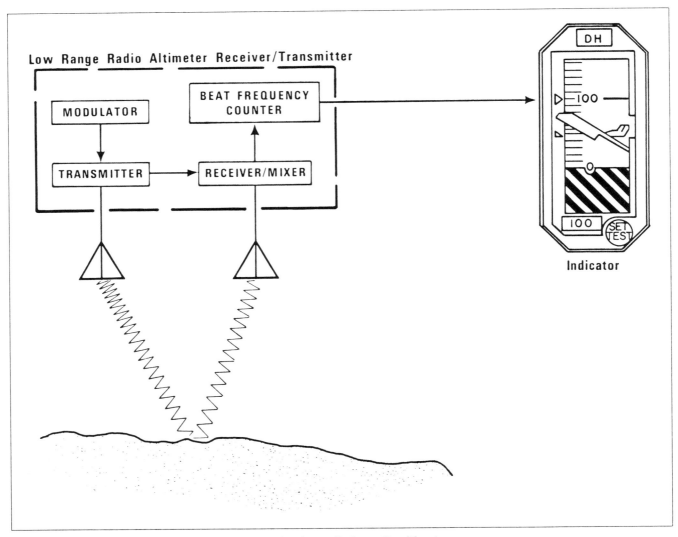

**Figure 3-59. The aircraft radar altimeter system is also called a radio altimeter.**

systems on a civil aircraft that gives a spoken voice command to the flight crew. When it is determined that a warning must be given, a recorded voice on tape is activated which tells the flight crew to "PULL UP, PULL UP" or a similar type of message.

## M. Weather Radar

A radar weather unit is another piece of equipment which is required for all air carrier jets and is common on many other types of aircraft. Aircraft weather radar is a pulse radar that typically operates at 9.375 GHz. The radar antenna is installed on the front of the aircraft where it sends out brief pulses of radar frequency EM waves in order to locate and avoid thunderstorms. There must be something present in a thunderstorm which will reflect the radar pulse. Clouds are invisible to radar, but ice, hail and especially rain will reflect the energy back to the aircraft radar antenna. The strength of the return is affected by the size of the raindrops and the rainfall intensity. Color radars use different colors for different intensity levels. Green, yellow and red are often used with red indicating the highest intensity of rainfall.

Radar signals can also be reflected from the ground and the radar system can be used to locate surface features on the earth below. This mapping feature is especially effective when used to pick up well defined coastlines.

Weather radar is called a pulse radar system because it transmits very brief pulses of energy.

**Figure 3-60. Some radar altimeters use a round indicator instrument.**

This is necessary in order to use the same antenna for transmit and receive and to produce a usable maximum range. The transmitter sends out a pulse that has a duration of about one microsecond. Then the antenna is switched to the receiver for a period of about 2,500 microseconds. The receiver must be connected long enough for the pulse to travel out to the maximum range and back again. The use of pulse radar also makes the system more efficient since the transmit energy is concentrated in brief pulses which permits much higher values of peak power than would otherwise be possible. The major components and their location for a weather radar system on a business jet airplane are shown in figure 3-61.

The major components of a weather radar system and their functions will now be listed:

1. Antenna — The antenna is a parabolic reflector or a newer and more efficient flat plate antenna. It does not rotate 360° like ATC radar, but scans side to side through an arc of approximately 120°.

2. Radar screen or display — This shows the returns picked up on the radar, usually in 3 or 4 different colors.

3. Cavity magnetron — This is a special device used to produce the radar frequency EM waves for the radar system (figure 3-62).

4. Synchronizer — The antenna and the screen must be synchronized in order to show the correct location of the returns.

5. Duplexer — This unit rapidly switches the antenna between the transmitter and receiver.

6. Stabilization System — The antenna unit needs to be gyro stabilized so that pitch and roll attitudes of the aircraft will not cause incorrect display presentations.

7. Waveguide — because of the power and frequency of the EM waves, coaxial cables cannot be used to connect the antenna with the R/T unit. A hollow tube called waveguide is used for this purpose (figure 3-63).

The weather radar has a maximum range from 200–300 miles on a typical installation. The controls allow the pilot to select different ranges and different settings so that the best indications of thunderstorms can be produced depending on the conditions encountered.

A tilt control is included so that the antenna can be tiled up and down to gauge the vertical extent of the storm cell. The radar antenna is protected by a plastic or fiberglass radome which must be carefully maintained to prevent adverse effects on radar performance. The radome often

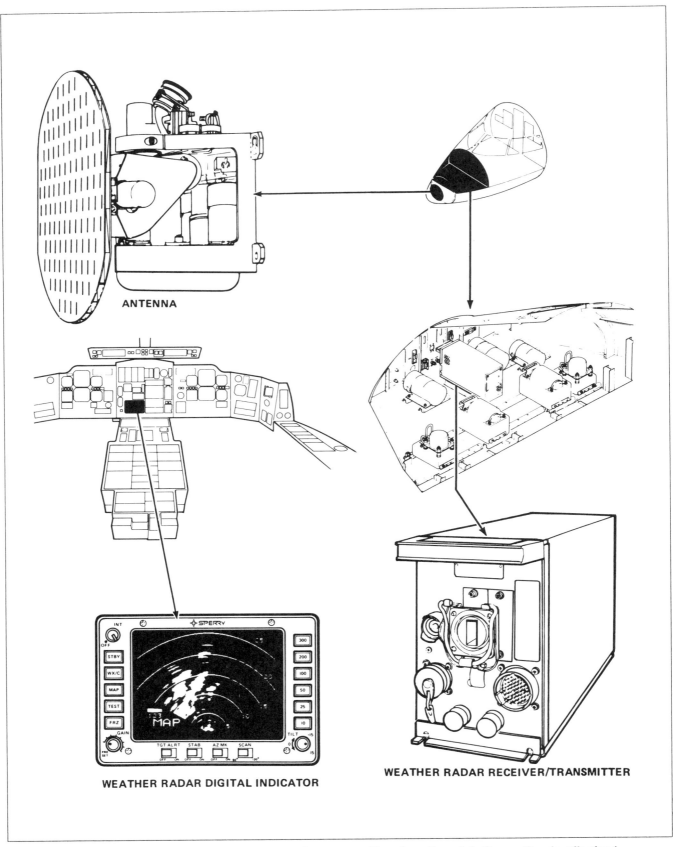

**ANTENNA**

**WEATHER RADAR DIGITAL INDICATOR**

**WEATHER RADAR RECEIVER/TRANSMITTER**

*Figure 3-61. The major components of a weather radar system. (Courtesy Canadair Group, Bombardier Inc.)*

has conducting strips fastened on the outside to conduct static charges and lightning strikes away from the radome. A typical arrangement of lightning diverter strips is shown in figure 3-64. The radome should only be painted with approved types of paint which will not interfere with the radar frequency signals that must pass through the radome.

Personal safety is very important when working on aircraft with radar systems. Some of the components in the receiver/transmitter unit can hold very high voltages and should be worked on only by personnel that are familiar with the necessary safety precautions. The emissions from the radar antenna can be very hazardous to human beings. The radar should never be turned on while on the ground unless special precautions are taken. The manufacturers maintenance instructions usually include some information on the MPEL. The maximum permissible exposure level gives safe distances from aircraft radar antennas. The best procedure is to never walk in front of an aircraft when the radar might be turned on.

## N. Stormscope®

The Stormscope is a weather avoidance system that uses completely different methods to locate thunderstorms than a radar system. The Stormscope is designed to receive the radio frequency EM waves produced by lightning discharges. It uses a directional antenna system similar to that used by the ADF equipment. In fact in some cases it is possible to connect the Stormscope to the aircraft

ADF antennas with special couplers. The direction of the lightning is determined using the directional antenna and the relative intensity of the discharge is measured. The intensity is used as pseudo range on the display. It is not actual range like that obtained from weather radar, but it does give useful information to the pilot. The display instrument in the cockpit is normally a small round LCD display that shows a light dot for each lightning strike that is detected. From the patterns on the display the pilot can determine where the worst areas are located and avoid them. Figure 3-65 shows the appearance of a typical Stormscope display instrument. The purpose of all weather detection systems is avoidance. A very strong thunderstorm cell has the capability of tearing apart even the strongest of aircraft.

Since the Stormscope and the weather radar react to different aspects of thunderstorms, the best weather avoidance system would be to have both installed in the aircraft. Many corporate aircraft in fact do have both systems installed.

## O. TCAS — Airborne Collision Avoidance System

The full meaning of the abbreviation TCAS is traffic alert and collision avoidance system. The prevention

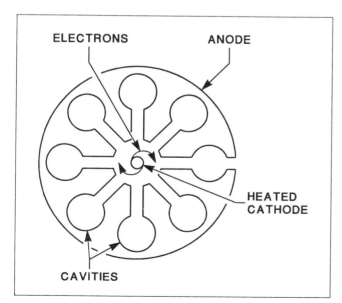

Figure 3-62. A cavity magnetron produces the powerful SHF band EM waves for a weather radar transmitter.

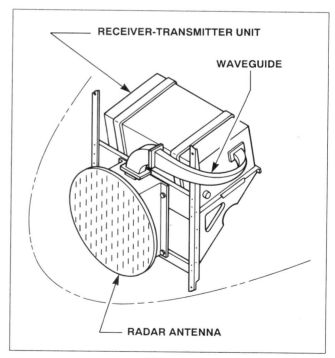

Figure 3-63. Waveguide is used to carry the radar frequency energy between the R/T unit and the antenna in a weather radar system. (Courtesy Piper Aircraft Co.)

of collisions between aircraft is the primary responsibility of the ATC system. This TCAS system was developed because both the FAA and the airlines were interested in having a system which would display collision threats to the pilots. This type of equipment is being installed at the present time in air carrier jets. About half of them have had the equipment installed already. The TCAS equipment uses some of the same equipment and principles as the transponders discussed earlier. The TCAS equipment on the aircraft includes a computer, a display screen in the cockpit and a directional antenna system. The unit sends out interrogations in all directions around the TCAS aircraft. Any transponder equipped aircraft within range will send back a reply and the TCAS calculates direction, range and altitude of the other aircraft. Of course it can only determine altitude if the other aircraft is Mode C equipped. If the other aircraft does not have a transponder, it will not be detected at all. Each aircraft that has been

detected within a certain range will be displayed as a lighted symbol on the display screen. If the other aircraft gets closer and creates a threat, the symbol will change color and shape. If the TCAS equipment determines that a sufficient danger level is present, it will display an avoidance maneuver command to the pilots. The avoidance maneuver will be in the vertical plane only, the present equipment is not able to suggest turns as avoidance maneuvers. The pilot will be told on the display to climb or descend at a certain rate to avoid the threat aircraft. The general appearance of the cockpit indicator for a TCAS is shown in figure 3-66. The aircraft symbols are different shapes and colors with an altitude and climb or descent arrow next to the symbol. The position of the TCAS equipped aircraft is shown by the airplane symbol at the center of the range circle. The installation of TCAS in an aircraft normally uses a Mode S transponder and a special type of directional antenna just for the TCAS equipment.

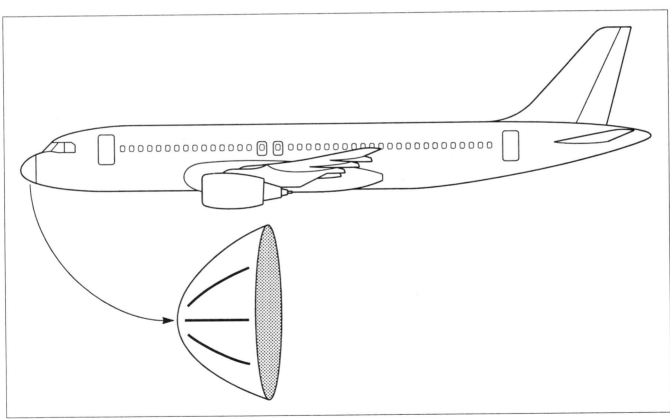

Figure 3-64. Lightning diverter strips are installed on nose radomes to prevent damage due to lightning strikes and static electricity.

146

Figure 3-65. The type of display normally used with a Stormscope.

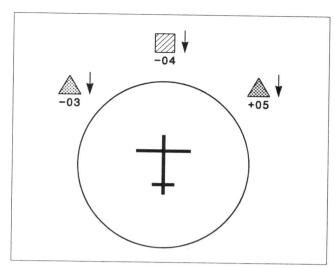

Figure 3-66. Simplified example of a TCAS display. The symbols for threat aircraft use different shapes and colors.

# CHAPTER IV

# Aircraft Antennas and Autopilots

This chapter contains three major topic areas: recommendations for installing and inspecting avionics equipment, additional information concerning aircraft antennas and aircraft autopilot systems.

## A. Installation and Inspection of Avionics

There are a number of factors which make the installation of avionics equipment more critical than the installation of other types of equipment. Radios and avionics are very sensitive to electromagnetic interference which can be created by nearby wiring and other electrically operated devices. The installation and maintenance of good bonding jumper connections is important to ensure proper operation of avionics units. Avionics equipment is easily damaged by excessive heat which requires that provisions be made for adequate air circulation. The most common cause for failures in avionics equipment is probably overheating. Figure 4-1 shows the avionics cooling arrangement for a small airplane. The tubing and plenums in this type of system must be maintained properly to ensure that adequate cooling airflow is available to the equipment. Other types of avionics cooling systems use electric motor driven fans, these must be maintained in good condition to prevent overheating. A thorough knowledge of these and other important considerations is necessary to ensure proper performance from installed avionics equipment in aircraft. The repair of avionics equipment is accomplished by appropriately rated FAA repair stations, but the installation, inspection and routine maintenance on these units is often performed by A&P technicians. Some of the important considerations when installing and inspecting avionics equipment will be discussed next.

### 1. Cleaning of Electronic Equipment

Cleaning of electronic equipment is important in order to remove accumulations of dust, dirt and lint that can block cooling holes and cause overheating. Dirt and lint which collects on open terminal strips and other electrical connections can absorb moisture and cause short circuits. Open terminal strips like those shown in figure 4-2 should be cleaned regularly to prevent the accumulation of dirt and lint that can cause these types of problems.

Electrical connections should be kept clean and free of corrosion and oxidation which can add unwanted resistance. When a mild abrasive is needed to remove corrosion and oxidation on terminal strips and mating surfaces, emery cloth is recommended.

Commutators and slip rings should be cleaned with crocus cloth or very fine sandpaper.

Older electronic equipment made extensive use of rotary selector switches and similar devices with many sets of contacts. Spray cans of a special cleaning solvent are available for cleaning the contacts of these devices. Before using a spray can contact cleaner, you should ensure that it is compatible with any plastic or non-metallic parts of these switches.

### 2. Routing Wires

Wiring of all types should be routed above lines that carry fluids and clamped securely to the aircraft structure. The wires should be routed so as to prevent abrasive damage from control cables, mechanical linkages and other moving parts in the aircraft. Frequent clamps and ties should be used to prevent excessive wire movement due to in-flight vibration and other factors. The proper installation of clamps to prevent excessive wire movement is illustrated in figure 4-3. Where wires terminate at pieces of equipment, enough slack should be left after the last clamp to allow for shock mount motions. If wires are clamped tightly too close to the termination point, normal aircraft motions and vibration will put bending loads on the wire connectors and cause premature failure in the wires.

Another factor to consider when routing wiring for electronic equipment is electromagnetic interference (EMI). Antenna leads and other wiring sensitive to EMI should be routed away from the wires for inverters, power supplies, strobe lights, motors and other components that are known to cause interference. When troubleshooting a noise or interference problem in aircraft radios and sensitive electronic equipment, it is often necessary to reroute wires away from the source of the EMI once it has been located.

### 3. Switches and Circuit Breakers

The radios on aircraft are usually connected to an avionics master switch. This switch is separate from the normal master switch as shown in figure 4-4. This is a useful feature which makes it easier for the pilot to ensure that all the radios are turned off when starting and stopping the engine. The radios should be turned off when the engine is started and stopped in order to prevent damage caused by surge currents and spikes of high voltage that can occur during engine starts and engine shut down. When installing switches in aircraft circuits, the rating of the switch must be adequate to handle both the type and amount of current and voltage for the circuit. Figure 4-5 shows a typical

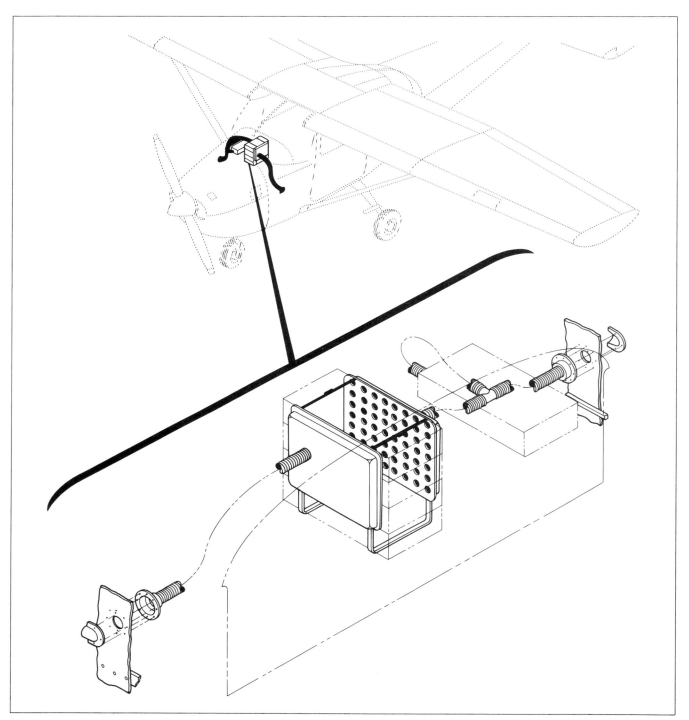

**Figure 4-1. Avionics cooling installation for a small airplane that uses vents on the sides of the fuselage to move air across the radios.**

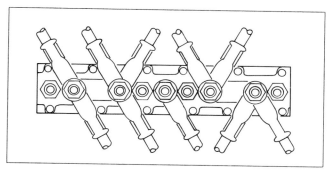

Figure 4-2. *Open terminal strips should be kept clean and free of corrosion. Check for metal objects that could fall across the terminals and cause shorts.*

aircraft toggle switch. Whether the circuit is AC or DC makes a significant difference in the proper selection of switches.

For example, there is a common aircraft quality switch that is rated for 10 amps at 125–250 volts AC. The same switch is rated at 0.3 amps when it is used in a DC circuit up to 125 volts DC. If this switch was installed in a 10 amp DC circuit the points would quickly burn and fail. The reason for this difference in ratings is that the current in an AC circuit drops to zero twice each cycle, this greatly reduces the problem of arcing as the points in the switch are opening. The proper rating of a switch in terms of both current flow and AC

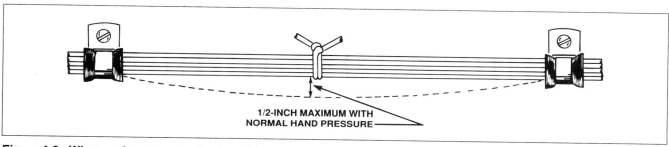

1/2-INCH MAXIMUM WITH
NORMAL HAND PRESSURE

Figure 4-3. *Wires and antenna leads should be supported with proper clamps and ties.*

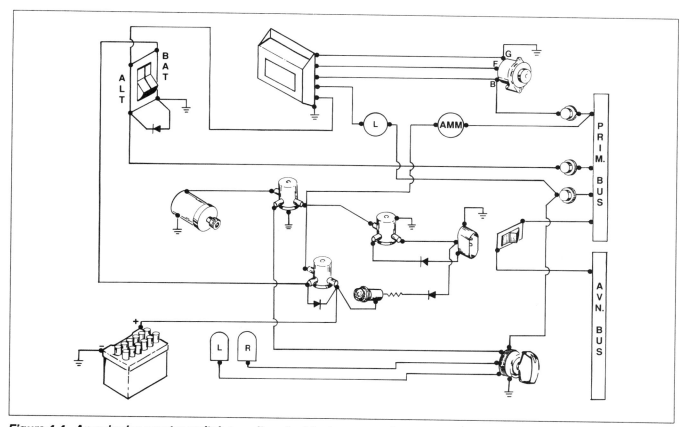

Figure 4-4. *An avionics master switch supplies electrical power to the avionics bus. It should be off when starting and stopping the engine.*

versus DC rating is very important to ensure adequate performance and service life. The condition of switches can be checked during an inspection by operating the switch and checking the "feel" during operation. Many switches have over-center mechanisms and other devices that produce a distinct feel to the switch. When the switch is getting worn and ready to fail, it often starts to feel sloppy in operation.

Circuit breakers for aircraft circuits should be the "trip free" type. This means that the circuit breaker cannot be overridden by holding it in the engaged position. It will open the circuit regardless of the position of the control toggle or push button. Various types of circuit breakers are available as shown in figure 4-6 and the correct selection of circuit breaker ratings for the particular circuit is important to prevent dangerous overloads in the aircraft's circuits. During inspections, the proper operation of the circuit breaker should be

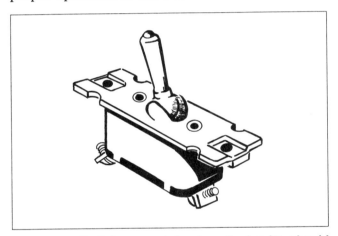

Figure 4-5. Switches used in aircraft circuits should have the appropriate AC or DC rating to prevent premature failures.

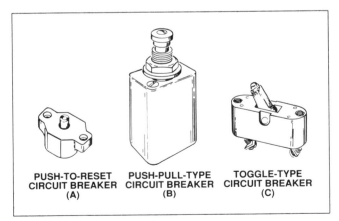

PUSH-TO-RESET CIRCUIT BREAKER (A)    PUSH-PULL-TYPE CIRCUIT BREAKER (B)    TOGGLE-TYPE CIRCUIT BREAKER (C)

Figure 4-6. Circuit breakers should be the trip-free type and inspected regularly for proper operation.

determined. Most types can be manually opened to interrupt current flow. Even a small general aviation airplane may have a large number of switches and circuit breakers as shown in figure 4-7. These should be inspected for proper operation and for any abnormal "feel" which could indicate an impending failure.

## 4. Bonding and Shielding

Radio reception can be completely blocked or severely interfered with by improper bonding and shielding in the aircraft. The source of the noise interference that affects aircraft radios is both inside and outside the aircraft. Outside interference comes from precipitation static and thunderstorms. Inside interference can be produced by current flow in other circuits and EMI emitters like ignition systems. The proper installation and maintenance of bonding jumpers is a key factor in preventing radio interference. Both braided wire bonding jumpers and thin metal straps are used for bonding connections. An installation of a braided bonding jumper on a shock mount is shown in figure 4-8. All parts of the aircraft that could create noise problems should be bonded. Electrical equipment that is shock mounted should have adequate bonding jumpers to carry the ground path current without producing excessive voltage drop.

When the bonding jumpers carry ground path currents, always use more than one. If there is only one and it breaks, the radio or other piece of equipment will be inoperative. When attaching bonding jumpers all dirt, grease, paint and coatings such as anodizing should be removed to ensure good electrical contact. A heavy bonding jumper for installation on airframe parts is shown in figure 4-9. The general rule is that the maximum resistance for a bonding jumper connection should be .003 ohms. The FAA in AC 65.15 does state that if a bonding jumper is only used for static electricity purposes and does not carry ground path currents, 0.01 ohms maximum is acceptable. Bonding jumpers accomplish a number of different functions on aircraft, some of these are listed below.

1. Supply the ground path for current flow for electrical equipment, especially shock mounted equipment.

2. Reduce radio interference.

3. Decrease possibility of lightning damage (at control surface hinges, for example).

4. Allow static charges to equalize between different parts of the airframe. This can reduce the fire hazard caused by arcing near fuel tank vents, etc.

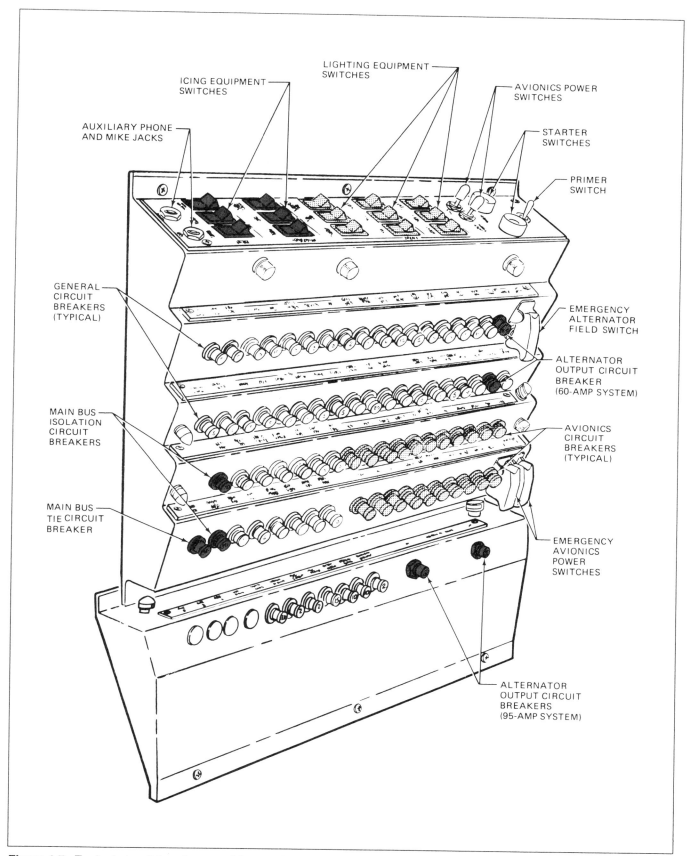

**Figure 4-7. Typical circuit breaker panel for a twin-engine airplane. (Courtesy Cessna Aircraft Co.)**

153

A number of factors should be kept in mind when installing and inspecting bonding jumpers. Some recommendations concerning bonding jumpers are:

1. Bonding jumpers should be as short as possible (however, allow for any necessary motion as with a control surface).

2. Do not solder bonding jumpers. It makes them brittle and they break.

3. Do not paint bonding jumpers. This also makes them brittle.

4. Ensure good contact by removing dirt, grease, paint and other coatings.

5. Use compatible hardware to prevent corrosion.

6. Use compatible bonding jumpers (aluminum alloy for aluminum alloy structures and copper or brass jumpers for parts made of steel, stainless steel, brass or bronze).

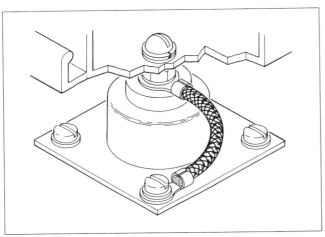

Figure 4-8. Bonding jumpers on shock mounts must allow freedom of movement on the shock mounts and should be inspected regularly to detect breakage or corrosion.

Figure 4-9. Heavy duty bonding straps are often required for bonding of major airframe components.

Shielding is an important part of noise suppression for aircraft radios. Shielding can be applied at the source of the noise or at the component or circuit that is sensitive to EMI. Shielding consists of a metal outer cover for a wire or component. Electromagnetic fields that could cause interference are captured in the metal cover and sent to ground. The ignition system of an aircraft engine can produce serious interference and so all parts of the ignition system need to be shielded.

On a reciprocating engine, for example, the magneto, ignition wires, spark plugs and "P" lead need to be shielded as illustrated in figure 4-10. The magneto and spark plugs are shielded by being made with a metal housing or outer cover. The ignition wires use an outer wire braid shielding. The primary or "P" lead is the wire that connects the magneto to the cockpit ignition switch. It should be a shielded wire to prevent noise. If all parts of the ignition system have been shielded and ignition noise is still present, it may be necessary to install a filter capacitor on the magneto. This is a condenser or capacitor of the correct size which will help to filter out noise at the source. Other aircraft components may require filters also, such as certain motors and power supplies.

Under certain circumstances noise and interference can be caused by the shielding on electrical wiring. The use of shielded wires can sometimes result in a phenomenon known as ground-loop interference. This ground-loop problem is illustrated in figure 4-11.

Circuit A in figure 4-11 uses a shielded wire with the shielding grounded at both ends. Circuit B is a single-wire circuit with ground connections at both ends. There is nothing to prevent the ground path currents for circuit B from flowing along the wire shielding of circuit A. Depending on the types of electrical signals involved, groundloops can cause interference between different circuits in the aircraft. The way to prevent groundloop problems is to leave one end of the shielding "floating" or ungrounded. If one of the grounds for the shielding in circuit A was disconnected, currents for circuit B could not use the shielding as a current path. Special precautions are recommended in AC 43.13-2A for the installation of inverters to prevent these kinds of problems. The recommended procedures to prevent inverter interference are:

1. Install inverters in separate areas, away from sensitive electronic circuits.

2. Separate the input and output wires of the inverter.

3. Properly bond the inverter case to the airframe.

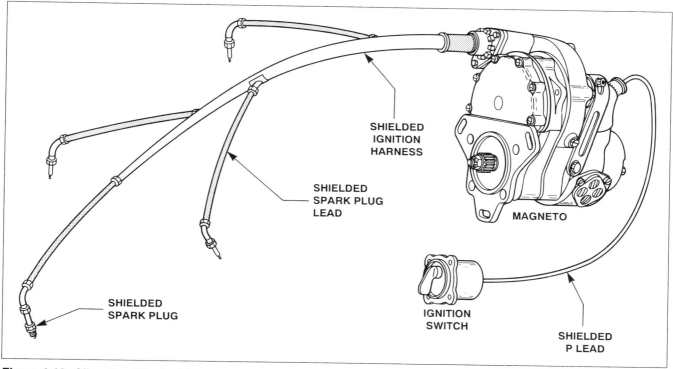

*Figure 4-10. All parts of the ignition system should be shielded to prevent radio noise.*

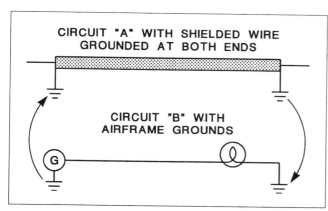

*Figure 4-11. Example of how "ground loop" interference can occur.*

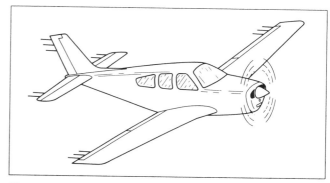

*Figure 4-12. Static wicks are installed on the trailing edges of the flight control surfaces to help remove static charges in flight in order to prevent noise in the radios.*

4. Use shielded wires for inverter output wires and ground the shielding at the inverter end only.

A number of items of aircraft equipment can create special interference problems, examples include inverters, motors, strobe lights, rotating beacon lights etc. Sometimes trial and error is necessary to eliminate noise and interference problems. The use of shielded wires and physical separation are basic techniques that can be used to prevent or eliminate noise and interference between different aircraft systems and equipment.

## 5. Static Dischargers

A common cause of noise in aircraft radios and related equipment is P-static interference. Precipitation or P-static noise is caused by static electricity that builds up on an aircraft in flight. The static electricity is produced by friction and can build up to 80,000 volts or more under certain conditions. Friction between the metal skin of the aircraft and particles in the atmosphere is a common cause of P-static. Flying through rain, snow, ice or even dust particles can result in a static charge on the airframe. The exhaust stream of a turbine engine can cause static electricity due to friction between particles in the exhaust and the metal tailpipe. P-static is a greater problem for high speed aircraft because higher speeds produce more friction and higher charges. High speed aircraft usually require more static dischargers to reduce the static charge on the aircraft. Static dischargers are small devices fastened to the extremities of the aircraft that are designed to discharge the aircraft to the atmosphere. They are commonly installed on all classes of aircraft that operate IFR and require all weather radio reception. Static dischargers are fastened to the trailing edges of the primary flight control surfaces: ailerons, elevators and rudders. A recommended installation of static dischargers for a small airplane is shown in figure 4-12. High speed aircraft may have additional static dischargers on the outboard tips of the wing and horizontal stabilizer. The static dischargers reduce the threshold for discharge to the atmosphere so that the voltage on the aircraft is reduced. The locations of the static dischargers for a business jet are shown in figure 4-13.

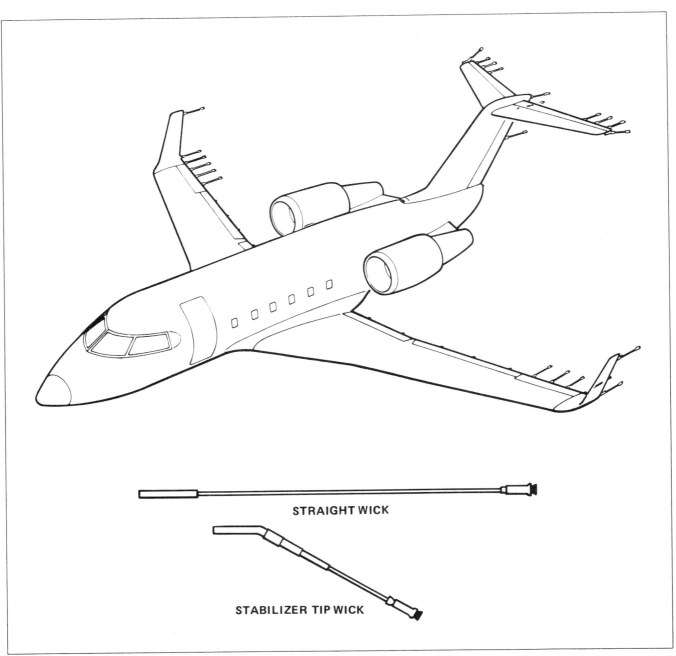

STRAIGHT WICK

STABILIZER TIP WICK

Figure 4-13. The installation of static dischargers for a corporate jet airplane. (Courtesy Canadair Group, Bombardier Inc.)

Corona is a term associated with P-static charges on aircraft. Corona refers to the glow that is sometimes visible on the extremities of the aircraft when static electricity is discharging to the atmosphere. St. Elmo's Fire is an older term that means the same thing. The installation of static dischargers will eliminate or reduce corona by controlling the discharges to the atmosphere.

There are three basic types of static dischargers used on aircraft: static wicks, wire braid dischargers and null field dischargers. The static wick is also called a flexible static discharger and is found on low speed aircraft. It consists of a plastic tube or outer covering with a fabric braid inside. The inner braid can be cotton, nylon, or some other material. The inner braid extends beyond the plastic covering where it is fanned out to produce the discharge points. The FAA recommends that one inch of the inner braid should extend beyond the outer cover.

When they become worn, they can be retrimmed to this dimension until they become too short and must be replaced. The inner braid of a static discharger is designed to have some built-in resistance to control the discharge current and further reduce noise. The wire braid static dischargers are also called the semi-flexible type. This type is simply a piece of wire braid made of stainless steel wires as shown in figure 4-15. The wire braid does not have any built-in resistance, so this kind is not as effective as the other two kinds of static dischargers. Jet airplanes normally use the null field discharger which is more rugged than the others for high speed aircraft use. The null field discharger consists of a rigid shaft made of fiberglass or composite materials with very sharp metal points at the aft end. The metal points are sometimes made of tungsten for longer life. Static wicks and null field dischargers are illustrated in figure 4-14. As shown in figure 4-14, the metal points of the null field dischargers are at right angles to the direction of flight. This feature helps to further reduce noise compared to the other kinds of static dischargers.

Static dischargers should be maintained properly to ensure that they will perform their intended function. The attachment to the aircraft must be tight and with good electrical contact. Any corrosion or looseness at the attachment point can create noise in the radios. Damaged or badly worn static dischargers should be replaced with new ones of the approved type. The noise produced by P-static affects the frequency bands of HF and below more than the higher frequency bands. If the pilot complains

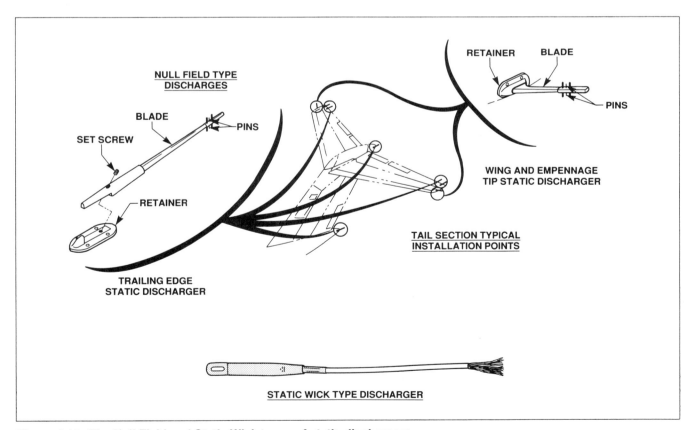

**Figure 4-14. The Null Field and Static Wick types of static dischargers.**

157

of noise on a radio system that operates at HF or below, the static dischargers should be inspected to determine if the noise is P-static related.

## 6. Installation Methods

The installation of electronic equipment and radio equipment follows some of the same basic practices that are used for other equipment, but special procedures may be required to prevent interference or other problems that especially affect these types of aircraft systems. The specific instructions of the manufacturer should always be followed when available. Some general recommendations from AC 43.13-1A and -2A will be described here along with some precautions that should be observed for all types of installations.

### a. General Precautions

If a standard location and mounting rack is available from the aircraft manufacturer, it should be used to install items of equipment. A standard type of shock mounted installation for electronic equipment is shown in figure 4-16. If this is not available, the installer will have to determine the best location and means of mounting for the equipment. Some of the factors that should be considered when making this type of determination are:

1. Sufficient air circulation to prevent overheating. This might require a certain free air space in some cases and the installation of a cooling fan in other cases.

2. Adequate clearance from high temperatures and flammable materials (next to a combustion heater would not be good place to install a radio).

3. Protection from water, fumes, hydraulic fluid, etc.

4. Protection from damage by baggage or seat deflection.

5. Sufficient clearance to prevent rubbing or striking aircraft structures, control cables, movable parts, etc.

6. Preventing interference and noise. Separate sensitive electronic equipment from inverters, power supplies, strobe lights, motors, etc.

7. If shock mounts will be used, ensure that the equipment does not exceed the weight carrying capability of the shock mounts and install adequate bonding jumpers or straps.

### b. Static Loads

Whenever it is necessary for the installer to fabricate a mounting for aircraft equipment, the strength of the mounting should be verified with a load test. An example of a fabricated mounting for aircraft equipment is illustrated in figure 4-17. The equipment installed in aircraft must be able to withstand the acceleration forces or "G" loads that are experienced in flight. In a steep turn, for example, the additional "G" load is felt by the equipment in the aircraft as well as by the wings and other structures.

A simple example of how a static load test might be performed will be explained here. The load factors for the test can be obtained from AC 43.13-2A which has a table similar to figure 4-18.

We will use the example of a radio that weighs 5 lbs. and will be installed in the baggage compartment behind the rear seats of a Normal category airplane. The mounting that is fabricated to hold

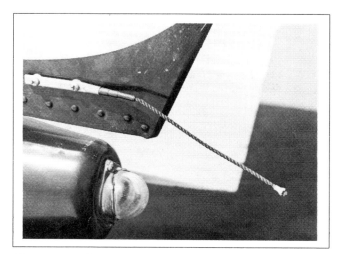

*Figure 4-15. The semi-flexible wire braid static dischargers do not have any built-in resistance.*

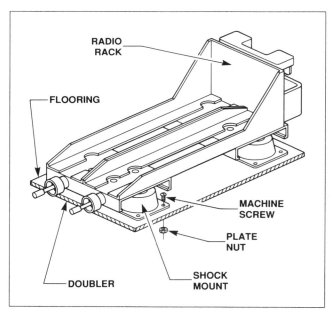

*Figure 4-16. A standard mounting rack for avionics equipment that includes shock mounts.*

the radio would be tested by applying loads equal to the weight of the equipment multiplied by the appropriate load factor. The sideward test load would be 7.5 lbs., upward load 15 lbs., forward load 45 lbs. and the downward load 33 lbs. If a location was chosen that was in the nose section of the aircraft and forward of all occupants, a forward test load of 2.0 Gs or 10 lbs. would have been sufficient. The mountings for aircraft equipment must be able to withstand the appropriate level of acceleration forces or load factors that might be experienced in flight. Standard industry practices for rivets, bolts, screws, etc. would be followed to ensure that adequate levels of strength are provided in the fasteners and in mounting brackets and similar parts. The

FAA in AC 43.13-2A recommends the use of machine screws and anchor nuts for the removable fasteners to hold aircraft radios in place. Where possible, existing plate nuts should be used or new ones installed. If that is not practical, then machine screws and self-locking nuts can be used.

When radios or other equipment are installed in an instrument panel and the item will extend some distance behind the instrument panel, a brace or support should be installed to the side or back of the equipment to minimize the load on the instrument panel itself. An example of a rear brace for an item of equipment installed in an instrument panel is shown in figure 4-19.

## B. Antenna Installations

The antennas found in aircraft radio installations are critical to the proper operation of the radio system. Antennas must be carefully installed and maintained in order to provide the efficiency that is needed for good radio reception and transmission. There are many factors that can affect the efficiency of aircraft antennas. An A&P technician should be familiar with the basic factors that affect the proper operation of an antenna. The inspection and maintenance of aircraft antennas is part of an A&P technicians responsibility in most cases because the antennas are fastened to the skin or other structure of the aircraft. Some of the key concepts that affect antenna operation will be covered in this section.

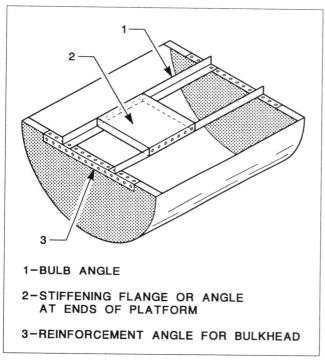

1—BULB ANGLE

2—STIFFENING FLANGE OR ANGLE AT ENDS OF PLATFORM

3—REINFORCEMENT ANGLE FOR BULKHEAD

**Figure 4-17. A fabricated mounting unit for avionics equipment.**

| CERTIFICATION CATEGORY OF AIRCRAFT | | | |
|---|---|---|---|
| DIRECTION OF FORCE APPLIED | NORMAL/ UTILITY | ACROBATIC | ROTORCRAFT |
| SIDEWARD | 1.5 Gs | 1.5 Gs | 2.0 Gs |
| UPWARD | 3.0 Gs | 4.5 Gs | 1.5 Gs |
| FORWARD* | 9.0 Gs | 9.0 Gs | 4.0 Gs |
| DOWNWARD | 6.6 Gs | 9.0 Gs | 4.0 Gs |

*When equipment mounting is located externally to one side, or forward of occupants, a forward load factor of 2.0 g is sufficient.

**Figure 4-18. Static test load factors that could be used for testing equipment mountings and attachments.**

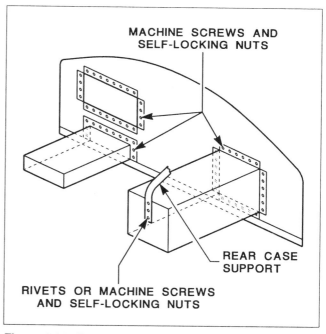

MACHINE SCREWS AND SELF-LOCKING NUTS

REAR CASE SUPPORT

RIVETS OR MACHINE SCREWS AND SELF-LOCKING NUTS

**Figure 4-19. Example of the installation of a rear brace or support for radio equipment installed in an instrument panel.**

## 1. Standing Wave Ratio

The standing wave ratio is a measure of the efficiency of an antenna installation. The standing wave ratio (SWR) is also referred to as voltage standing wave ratio (VSWR). In order to demonstrate the principle of VSWR, we will consider what would happen if just one sine wave was sent down a transmission line from a radio transmitter. Figure 4-20(A) shows this sine wave traveling from left to right. If the transmission line had an infinite length, the sine wave signal would eventually be reduced to zero by line resistance. In an actual installation, the transmission line is of a limited length and terminates at the antenna. The purpose of the antenna is to transform the sine wave signal into radio waves, but this can never be accomplished with 100 percent efficiency. The result of this less than perfect efficiency is that some of the energy is reflected back toward the transmitter from the antenna end of the transmission line. This is illustrated by figure 4-20(B) which shows some energy being reflected back toward the transmitter and moving from right to left. The output of the transmitter is not just one sine wave at a time, but a continuous series of sine waves. The reflected waves will combine with the transmitter output waves to produce standing waves on the transmission line as indicated by figure 4-20(C). A calculation based on the relationship between forward power and reflected

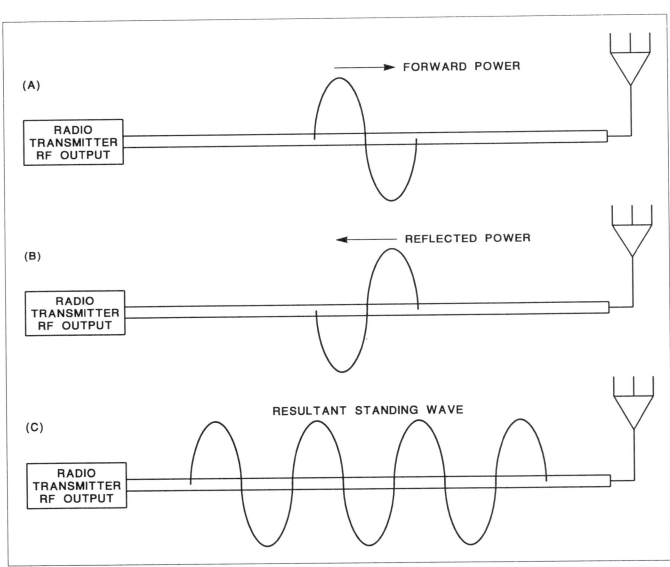

**Figure 4-20. Illustration of the principle involved in the standing wave ratio for an antenna installation.**
*(A) Forward power.*
*(B) Reflected power.*
*(C) Resultant Standing Wave.*

160

power gives the voltage standing wave ratio, which is a measure of efficiency. With a perfect antenna installation, there would be zero reflected power and the VSWR would be 1:1 or simply 1. In an actual aircraft antenna system, the lowest VSWR is the most efficient. Typical values for VSWR of aircraft antennas are in the range of 1.1 to 5.0 for the various types of antennas. Manufacturer's catalogs usually list the VSWR for antennas so that the relative efficiency of different types can be compared when selecting an antenna. The listing of VSWR in the specifications for an aircraft antenna can be seen in figure 4-21.

The example given here was for the VSWR of a transmit antenna, but the manufacturer's data also lists the VSWR for receive only antennas. If the transmission line or coaxial cable that connects the antenna is in good condition and properly suited to the installation, the VSWR is affected by the antenna itself. However, if there is a fault in the coaxial cable the VSWR will go up significantly, which reduces efficiency. Special types of wattmeters and VSWR meters can be used to measure the VSWR of an aircraft antenna installation for troubleshooting purposes.

## 2. Coaxial Cables and Connectors

Coaxial cables are required for the antenna connections on most aircraft radios because of the RF frequencies that are used. A coaxial cable is shown in figure 4-22. The proper installation and maintenance of coaxial cables is very important since large losses can occur if a fault is present. Coaxial cables should be rejected if they have become dented or if kinks are found. Any distortion or crushing which causes the cable to be oval in shape or flattened are also cause for rejection. If abrasion or rubbing has exposed or damaged the wire braid, the cable should be replaced. Coaxial cable should be supported by clamps about every 2 ft. to help prevent damage. A good rule of thumb for coaxial cable bend radius is to use a minimum bend radius of 10 times the cable diameter. This will help to reduce the possibility of kinks from sharp bends. Special types of end connectors are used with coaxial cable and they come in a number of different styles. Some can be removed and reused and other types are crimped or swaged on and cannot be reused. When installing and removing coaxial cable connections, care should be used to prevent damage to the connectors. If corrosion is found on connectors, it is usually better to replace them rather than try to clean them. Even small amounts of corrosion or corrosion pits can cause a signal loss. Figure 4-23 shows a reusable coaxial cable connector. When installing this type, the wire braid should be carefully spread out over the braid clamp and breakage of the wires should be avoided. The connector should be assembled carefully to provide tight connections with good electrical contact and to avoid distorting the coaxial cable or the connector itself. If it is necessary to solder a connector pin onto the center conductor, only an approved electrical solder should be used—never use acid core solder or acid flux on electrical connectors. An acceptable solder is 60/40 rosin core solder. Great care must be used in soldering to prevent excessive heat damage to the coaxial cable insulation materials.

Some antenna cables are matched to the radio and antenna and should not be shortened or spliced.

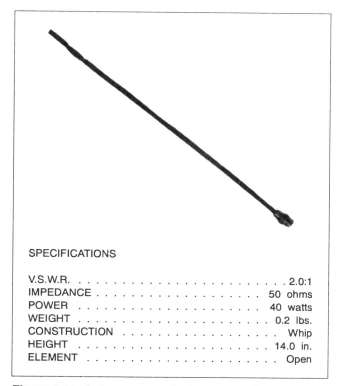

SPECIFICATIONS

V.S.W.R. . . . . . . . . . . . . . . . . . . . . . . . . . 2.0:1
IMPEDANCE . . . . . . . . . . . . . . . . . . . 50 ohms
POWER . . . . . . . . . . . . . . . . . . . . . 40 watts
WEIGHT . . . . . . . . . . . . . . . . . . . . . 0.2 lbs.
CONSTRUCTION . . . . . . . . . . . . . . . . . . Whip
HEIGHT . . . . . . . . . . . . . . . . . . . . . 14.0 in.
ELEMENT . . . . . . . . . . . . . . . . . . . . . Open

*Figure 4-21. Antenna manufacturers catalogs usually list the V.S.W.R. for each antenna. (Courtesy of Dayton-Granger, Inc.)*

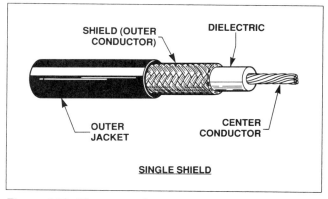

*Figure 4-22. The parts of a coaxial cable for antennas.*

This is true for some ADF antenna leads, for example. On other installations the antenna coax should be kept as short as possible and routed as directly as possible to reduce line loss.

The specific antenna or radio manufacturers installation instructions should be followed carefully in this area since there are many different procedures that may apply depending on the specific installation.

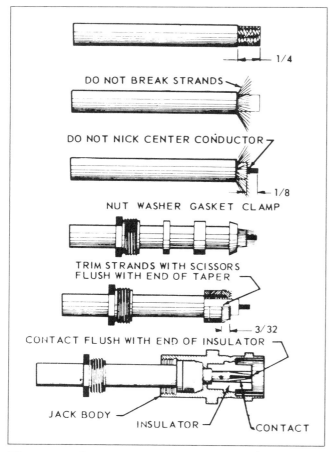

Figure 4-23. Installation procedure for a reusable coaxial cable connector.

## 3. Wire Antennas

A wire antenna is a length of wire that is supported by masts and attachments above or below the aircraft fuselage. They are found most often on smaller aircraft and older aircraft. Jet airplanes seldom use wire antennas because of the vibration and increased chance of damage at high speeds. The type of wire used is most often a copper coated steel wire that is a solid single strand. Wire with an outer covering of insulating material is superior to non-insulated wire in reducing noise caused by P-static.

A type of wire antenna that is seldom used today is the trailing wire antenna. The trailing wire antenna was a roll of wire on a drum in the aft fuselage which could be extended out the back of the aircraft in flight. It was very common in the 1930s and 1940s for HF communications radios. The advantage was that 200 ft. or more of wire could be extended out the back of the airplane for better radio performance. The disadvantages were the added complexity and weight of the mechanism to extend and retract the antenna. It is not suitable for high speed aircraft and is rarely used on modern aircraft.

The wire type marker beacon antenna is shown in figure 4-24. This type may still be found on small airplanes. It is about 4 ft. long and fastened to standoff and support masts on the bottom of the aircraft. The minimum fuselage separation should be 6 inches.

A long wire antenna for HF communications is still commonly used on general aviation aircraft that have HF equipment. Figure 4-25 shows a typical installation with the wire running from a wing tip to the vertical fin and then down to a feed-through on the top of the fuselage. The long wire antenna includes a tensioning device to maintain the proper tension on the wire and insulators at the appropriate points. A long wire antenna normally employs a weak point at the aft end so it cannot wrap around the aircraft if it breaks due to excessive tension.

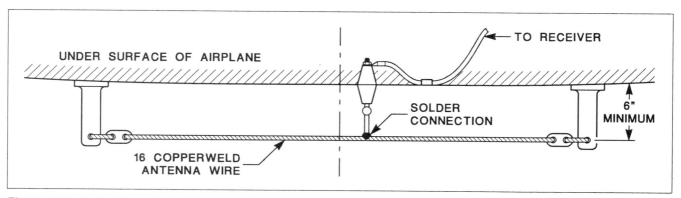

Figure 4-24. A wire-type marker beacon antenna.

The most common use of wire antennas on modern aircraft is as an ADF sense antenna. These will be described in the next section.

## 4. ADF Antennas

All aircraft ADF receivers require two antennas, the loop antenna and the sense antenna. The loop antenna is the directional antenna and the sense antenna is needed to eliminate the ambiguity caused by the two nulls in the reception pattern. Air carrier jets have an ADF antenna that combines the loop and sense antennas in one housing that is a low profile or flush mount and it is installed on the top or bottom of the fuselage. The ADF antennas on general aviation aircraft come in a greater variety and are most often separate loop and sense antennas.

The loop antenna that is rotated by an electric motor is still used, but is being replaced by the type that rotates the signal rather than the antenna itself. A motor driven loop antenna for installation inside a housing is shown in figure 4-26. The newer non-rotating types are usually contained in a teardrop shaped streamlined housing that installs on the top or bottom of the aircraft as shown in figure 4-27. The sense antennas used with the dual antenna

installations are either the wire type or whip type. The whip type sense antenna is a metal rod about 4 ft. long and installed on the top or bottom. It is still found on some helicopters were there isn't enough room for a long wire sense antenna, this is shown in figure 4-28. The long wire sense antenna is about 15–20 ft. long and most often installed using the vertical fin as the aft anchor point to gain more fuselage clearance. The recommended minimum clearance from the fuselage is 12". A top installation for a sense wire is shown in figure 4-29. The sense wire can be installed on the bottom as shown in figure 4-30 if adequate ground and fuselage clearance can be obtained. Like the long wire HF antenna, the ADF sense wire will use masts, tension units and weak links as part of the installation.

In order to give accurate navigational information, ADF antennas must be installed and calibrated correctly. The loop antenna normally needs to be installed close to the electrical center of the sense antenna to give accurate indications of station passage. This relationship is illustrated in figure 4-31.

Both the loop and sense antennas can be installed on the top or the bottom, but they must have the

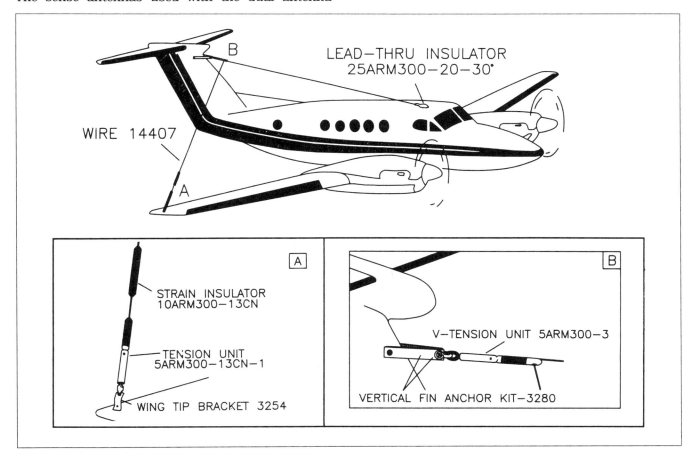

*Figure 4-25. A long wire HF comm antenna installation. (Courtesy Dayton-Granger Inc)*

correct relationship to each other for accurate readings to be obtained. Since the ADF antenna system is highly directional, it must be calibrated to give the correct indications of ground station direction.

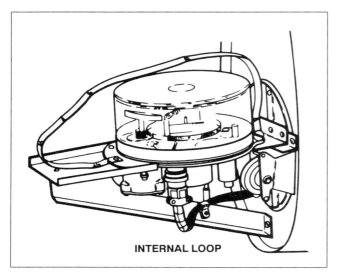

**Figure 4-26. A motor-driven ADF loop antenna for internal installations.**

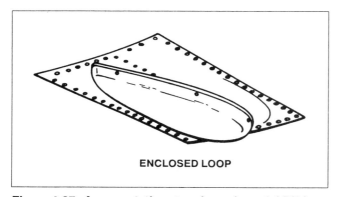

**Figure 4-27. A non-rotating, teardrop-shaped ADF loop antenna.**

This is called the check for quadrantal error or the calibration check. Whenever an antenna is installed or any change is made which could affect the accuracy of the ADF, a check for quadrantal error should be performed. The checks can be made on the ground, but should always be confirmed with a flight check. To perform the ground check a nearby NDB of known location is tuned in and the bearing is checked and adjusted at least every 45° as the aircraft is turned on the ground. The flight check involves locating geographical points on the ground with known bearings from the NDB and flying the aircraft over those locations to confirm the accuracy of the ADF bearing information. This flight check should be performed at low altitude to reduce errors in established the aircraft position accurately.

## 5. Groundplane Considerations

When a ¼ wave, Marconi-type antenna is installed on an aircraft, an adequate groundplane or counterpoise is required for proper operation. The aircraft systems that use ¼ wave antennas are VHF communications, ATC transponder, DME and UHF radiotelephone. When these antennas are installed on metal skinned aircraft, the metal skin supplies the groundplane. If the antenna is installed too close to fiberglass areas or windshields, the groundplane area is reduced and may result in poor performance. A basic rule of thumb that is sometimes used is that the groundplane should extend in all directions outward from the base of the antenna a distance equal to the height of the antenna. A shorter antenna does not need as much groundplane as a longer antenna. The groundplane cannot be too big, but it can be too small which has an adverse effect on signal pattern and strength. For DME and transponders, which use similar frequencies, the groundplane should extend 8–12″ in all directions

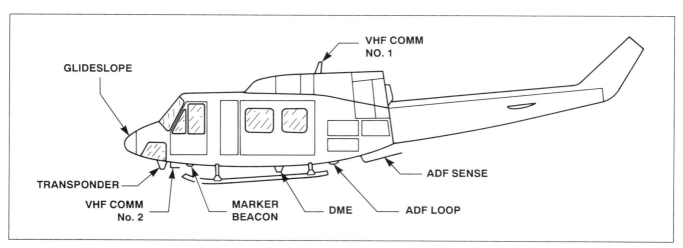

**Figure 4-28. Helicopter antenna installations are difficult because of limited skin area and limited ground clearance.**

from the antenna base. For VHF communications antennas a groundplane that extends 24″ in all directions is desirable. These sizes would give a groundplane that is a little larger than if the length of the antenna was used as the dimension. It is not always possible to supply a large enough groundplane when installing antennas on aircraft with limited metal skin area such as small helicopters, but the groundplane area should always be considered and provided for to the extent possible.

If it is necessary to install these types of antennas on aircraft with non-metal skin, a groundplane must be provided by the installer. This usually means installing metal foil strips or wire mesh fastened on the inside of the aircraft covering. The same rules would apply as to desirable lengths. An example of the use of a foil strip groundplane is seen in figure 4-32.

When installing ¼ wave antennas, it is recommended that all grease, dirt and paint be removed from the skin area under the base of the antenna. Some avionics experts recommend that a gasket not be used so that the base of the antenna contacts the skin of the aircraft. Whether or not a gasket is used, the skin should be cleaned and stripped and a sealant applied around the base of the antenna after installation.

The installation of antennas to the skin of aircraft requires that some additional reinforcement be given

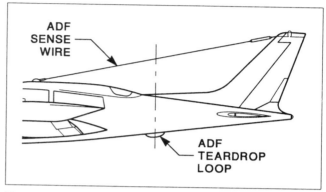

Figure 4-31. The ADF loop antenna should normally be installed near the electrical center of the sense wire antenna.

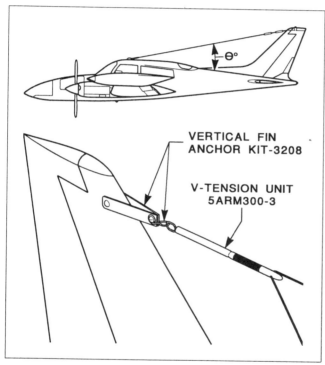

Figure 4-29. Top-mounted ADF sense wire antenna. (Courtesy Dayton-Granger Inc.)

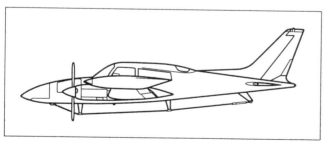

Figure 4-30. Bottom-mounted ADF sense wire antenna. (Courtesy Dayton-Granger Inc.)

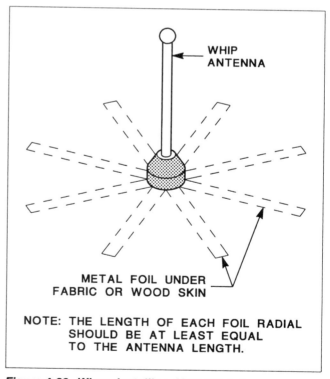

NOTE: THE LENGTH OF EACH FOIL RADIAL SHOULD BE AT LEAST EQUAL TO THE ANTENNA LENGTH.

Figure 4-32. When installing Marconi antennas on an aircraft with non-metal skin, a groundplane must be provided.

to preserve the strength of the aircraft structure. The use of a doubler as shown in figure 4-33 will reinforce the aircraft structure and provide the additional support needed for antenna drag loads.

## 6. Reducing Antenna Interference

A very important factor in the proper performance of aircraft antennas is the prevention of interference between one system and another. Interference can also occur between a radio system antenna and other components of the aircraft. A basic consideration is that antennas for systems that operate on similar frequencies must be separated by a certain minimum distance to prevent interference. The possible interactions that can adversely affect aircraft radio systems are many and varied. The more common problems that can occur will be described here, but sometimes a particular interference problem may require trial

and error to eliminate the cause of the antenna interaction.

The important factors that affect mutual interference are frequency and wavelength, polarization and type of modulation. The operating frequencies for the various radio systems are listed in the frequency chart in chapter 3. The polarization of radio waves is based on the orientation of the electric field relative to the earth's surface. The field orientations for vertical and horizontal polarization can be seen in figures 4-34 and 4-35. The antenna installed on the aircraft needs to have the proper polarization relative to the ground based antenna for optimum performance—particularly at frequencies above HF. Figure 4-36 gives the polarization for the various types of aircraft radio systems.

From the information in figure 4-36, it can be seen that all the systems use vertical polarization except for VOR and the three parts of the ILS instrument approach system.

### a. VHF Communications Antennas

Aircraft that are equipped for IFR operations commonly have 2 or 3 separate VHF comm radios which utilize separate antennas. The VHF comm antennas should be separated from each other by at least 5 ft. This is easily accomplished on an air carrier jet which has a lot of fuselage skin area available, but may be difficult on small aircraft which have much less available skin area. Figure 4-37 shows the antenna locations for a Boeing 767 with good separation between similar systems. The VHF comm antennas use vertical polarization and require a suitable groundplane. When two antennas are installed on small aircraft, the best coverage is usually obtained with one antenna on the top and the other on the bottom of the fuselage. This desired top and bottom separation is shown in figure 4-38 on a twin-engine airplane. The ELT antenna can cause serious interference with VHF comm and should be separated by at least 5 ft. from any VHF comm antenna. Radio

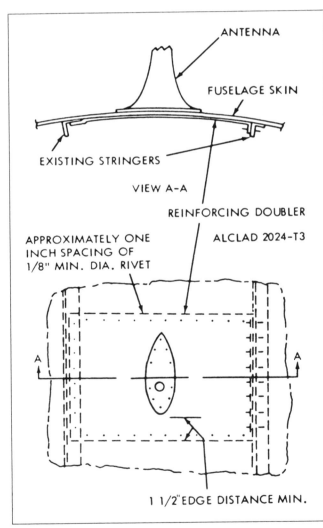

Figure 4-33. A reinforcing doubler should be installed inside the skin at the base of the antenna.

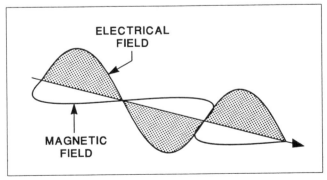

Figure 4-34. When an EM wave has vertical polarization, the electric field is in the vertical plane.

interference can be caused by parts of the aircraft as well as by other antennas. The vertical fin of an aircraft can cause significant signal blockage to any VHF comm antenna that is installed too close. A top mounted VHF comm antenna that is installed closer than 5 ft. to the vertical fin will result in blockage and poor radio reception and transmission to the rear of the aircraft. The VHF comm antenna is a ¼ wave Marconi antenna which must have an adequate groundplane or counterpoise for proper operation. A common mistake is the installation of a VHF comm too far forward on the upper fuselage. If it is less than 24″ from the top of the windshield, the signal pattern can be distorted by the lack of groundplane in the forward direction.

### b. DME and Transponder Antennas

These two antennas are treated as equals because they use similar frequencies, polarization and modulation. The antennas used for these two systems are ¼ wave Marconi antennas with vertical polarization and they both transmit and receive. Since the wavelength is shorter at higher frequencies, the minimum separation distance is less than that for VHF comm antennas. The DME and transponder antennas should be separated from each other by at least 2 ft. and an adequate groundplane must be provided around the base of the antenna. These antennas are normally installed on the bottom of the aircraft to prevent signal blockage by the fuselage. A top mounted antenna may be used on a narrow portion of the aircraft that will not cause significant blockage. The top of the tail boom on a helicopter can be an acceptable location.

### c. VOR and Localizer

VOR antennas are most often installed on the vertical fin of the aircraft. This gives good reception

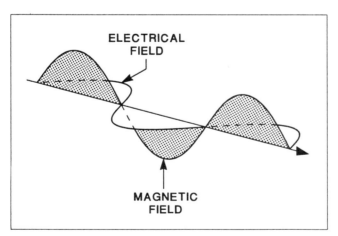

**Figure 4-35. When an EM wave has horizontal polarization, the electric field is in the horizontal plane.**

characteristics from all directions on most aircraft. On small aircraft, the VOR antenna is sometimes mounted on the top of the fuselage. If the VOR antenna is mounted too far forward, a propeller modulation problem can occur. When signals are being received from the front of the aircraft, the radio wave is chopped by the propeller blades. At certain RPMs, this can cause serious propeller modulation interference. The cure for this involves changing propeller RPM or relocating the antenna. Small aircraft often use the same antenna for both VOR and localizer reception. This is practical because the two systems operate on similar frequencies. When the localizer is being used for an instrument approach, the signals are always received from the front of the aircraft. On a large aircraft, it is not possible to use the tail mounted VOR antenna for localizer reception because of fuselage blockage. These aircraft will use a separate localizer antenna or antennas that are mounted in the nose section inside the radome for the weather radar.

The location of the VOR and localizer antennas usually provides sufficient separation that interference from other antennas is not a problem. If a VHF comm or other antenna is mounted closer than 5 ft. from the VOR, it can cause some interference depending on the type of VHF comm antenna used.

### d. Glideslope Antennas

Like the localizer, the signals from the ground transmitters for the glideslope are always received from the front of the aircraft. Some small aircraft use the VOR antenna to receive glideslope signals as well as localizer signals. The glideslope operates on frequencies that are the third harmonic of VOR frequencies. This means that the glideslope frequencies are three times the frequencies for VOR. A special antenna coupler is used so that the VOR antenna can supply two separate VOR and localizer receivers and also supply signals for the glideslope receiver.

| RADIO SYSTEM | RECEIVE, TRANSMIT OR BOTH | POLARIZATION |
|---|---|---|
| LORAN C | RECEIVE | VERTICAL |
| ADF | RECEIVE | VERTICAL |
| VHF COM | BOTH | VERTICAL |
| DME & TRANSPONDER | BOTH | VERTICAL |
| ELT | TRANSMIT | VERTICAL |
| VOR & LOCALIZER | RECEIVE | HORIZONTAL |
| MARKER BEACONS | RECEIVE | HORIZONTAL |
| GLIDESLOPE | RECEIVE | HORIZONTAL |

**Figure 4-36. The polarization for various types of aircraft radio systems.**

The same fuselage blockage problems occur on large aircraft for both localizer and glideslope reception. The glideslope antenna or antennas for air carrier jets are installed inside the radome on the nose of the aircraft. Aircraft that do not have a nose radome can utilize a separate glideslope antenna that is mounted on the forward fuselage on either the top or bottom. Blockage of signals by the fuselage or other parts of the aircraft is the primary consideration in locating localizer and glideslope antennas. Interference from other antennas is not as great a problem with these systems as it is for some other radio systems.

### e. Loran C and Omega

Loran C and Omega system antennas are receive only antennas and they operate at frequencies that are widely separated from those of most other aircraft radios. The major sources of interference for these radio systems are P-static noise and noise from aircraft electrical systems. The Loran C and Omega antennas can be mounted on the top or the bottom of the aircraft. The best location for these types of antennas is based on preventing interference from aircraft motors, generators, power supplies and similar systems. The proper installation and maintenance of bonding jumpers and static dischargers is critical to ensure good performance from these lower frequency radio systems.

### f. ADF Antennas

The primary consideration in locating ADF antennas is to obtain the proper relationship between the loop and sense antenna to ensure accurate indications of station direction. The ADF antennas can be installed with both loop and sense antennas on the top of the fuselage, both on the bottom or one on the top and one on the bottom.

The most common installation on small aircraft is with a wire sense antenna on the top and the loop antenna on the bottom of the aircraft. In any

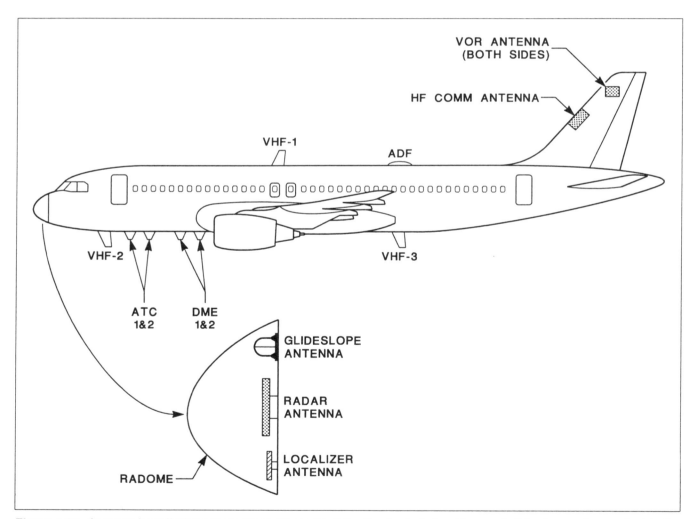

**Figure 4-37. Antenna installations on modern air carrier jets often include localizer and glideslope antennas inside the radome and flush mount VOR and HF comm antennas in the vertical fin.**

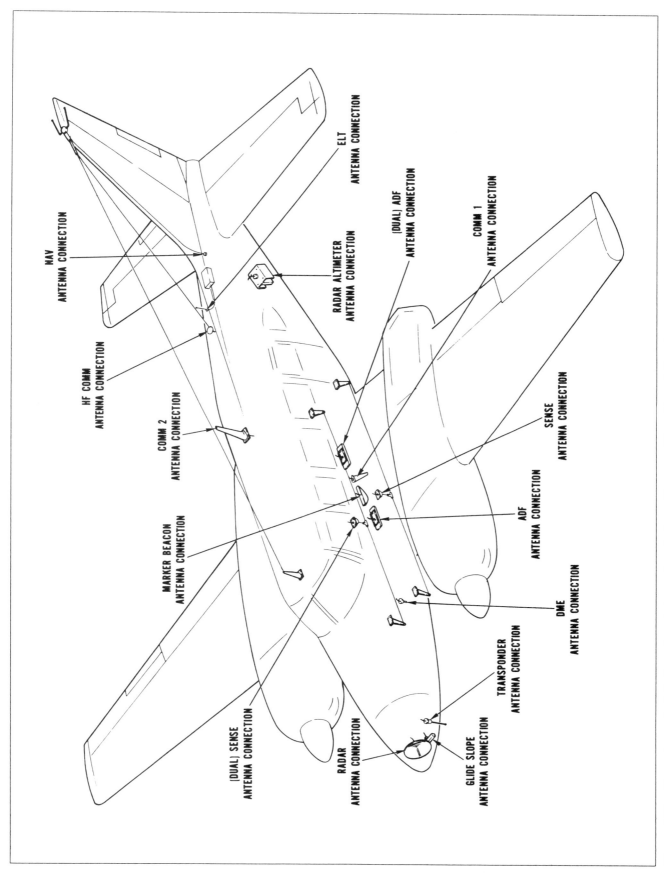

Figure 4-38. The antenna installations for a twin-engine airplane. (Courtesy Piper Aircraft Corp.)

169

case, the loop antenna must be located in the electrical center of the sense antenna for accurate readings. The ADF antenna system is a directional antenna system and interference from parts of the aircraft can sometimes cause bearing errors. This is one reason that a check of quadrantal error should always be performed when ADF antennas are installed or relocated. Proper bonding jumper and static discharger installations are important to prevent P-static noise in ADF receivers. ADF antennas should be located to minimize interference from aircraft generators and alternators. Filter capacitors can be used to reduce interference from alternators and similar devices.

## 7. Types of Antennas

Many different types of antennas are used in aircraft radio systems. Aviation technicians should be familiar with the common types of antennas so that they can properly identify, inspect and maintain them. Some of the common types of aircraft antennas and their basic characteristics will be described in this section. Aircraft antennas usually have a speed rating and should only be installed on aircraft that operate at and below their rated speed.

### a. VOR Antennas

There are two basic types of VOR antennas found on aircraft: the half-wave dipole and the balanced loop types. The half-wave dipole antenna is a "V" shaped antenna that has a figure eight-shaped reception pattern. This kind of antenna is shown in figure 4-39. The antenna has two metal rods in the shape of the letter "V" or a fiberglass covered element made of thin sheet metal. It is installed on the aircraft on the vertical fin or on top of the fuselage with the open end of the "V" pointed either forward or aft. The figure 8 reception pattern works well for normal VOR airway flying because the station is either in front of or behind the aircraft. It does not work well for RNAV when the VOR station may be off the side of the aircraft. The dipole VOR antenna requires a special impedance matching device called a "balun". The balun is located at the antenna end of the coaxial cable for more efficient transfer of energy from the antenna to the coax and receiver. A balun is illustrated in figure 4-40. The balanced loop VOR antenna has a circular reception pattern and is therefore the better type of antenna for RNAV. There are three types of balanced loop antenna: the open loop towel bar, the blade and the internal mount. The towel bar and blade types are shown in figure 4-41. These antennas come in two halves that are mounted on opposite sides of the vertical fin on airplanes. On helicopters or in special cases they are mounted on each side of the aft fuselage or

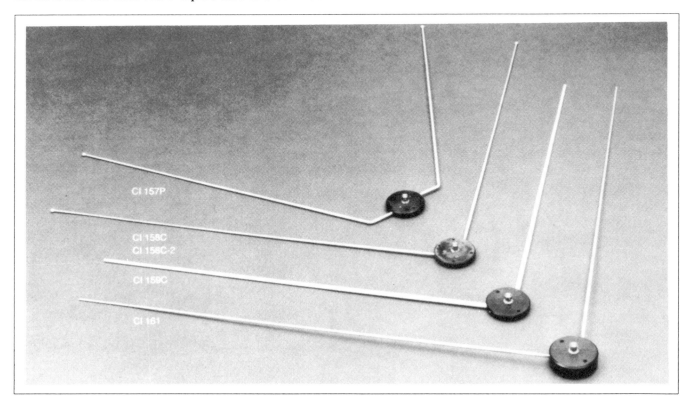

*Figure 4-39. Hertz dipole "V" type antennas for VOR reception. (Courtesy Comant Industries Inc.)*

tail boom. The blade-type, balanced loop VOR antenna has a higher speed rating than the towel bar or V-type and is used on bizjets and similar aircraft. Air carrier jets use a VOR antenna that is mounted inside the vertical fin with non-metallic flush covers on each side. This kind of antenna is shown in figure 4-37.

### b. Localizer

Small airplanes usually do not have a separate localizer antenna, the VOR antenna is used to receive localizer signals. On air carrier jets and similar aircraft, the large fuselage can cause blockage of the localizer signals so a separate localizer antenna is installed. A type of separate localizer antenna is seen in figure 4-42. This antenna is installed inside the radome on the nose section of the aircraft.

### c. Glideslope

The signals from glideslope transmitters can be received on a VOR antenna because they operate at a frequency that is approximately the third harmonic of the VOR frequency. Single-engine airplanes commonly use a signal splitter or coupler to supply the glideslope receiver from the VOR antenna. Other general aviation airplanes often use a V-shaped glideslope antenna like that shown in figure 4-43 to receive glideslope signals. This antenna looks a lot like a V-shaped VOR antenna but it is only about ⅓ the size because of the shorter wavelength of glideslope signals. When a separate glideslope antenna is installed on the aircraft, it needs to be located on the front of the aircraft to prevent blockage. The loop type glideslope antenna in figure 4-44 can be

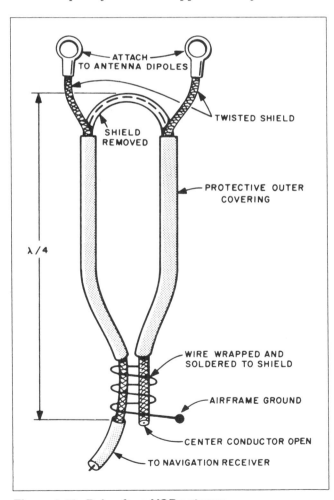

*Figure 4-40. Balun for a VOR antenna.*

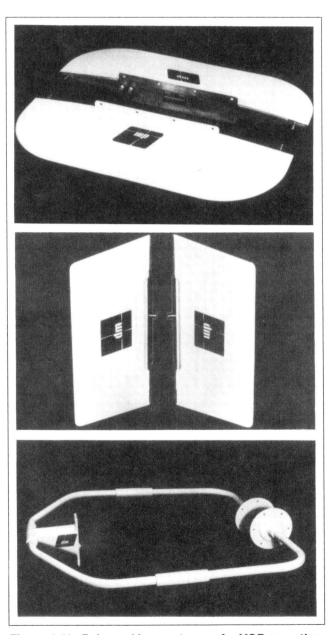

*Figure 4-41. Balanced loop antennas for VOR reception.*
*(Courtesy Dorne & Margolin Inc.)*

installed either externally or internally on the forward part of an aircraft. The dipole glideslope antenna in figure 4-45 is designed to be installed inside a radome as it is not a streamlined design.

### d. Marker Beacon

The older style wire-type marker beacon antenna has been previously described under the heading of wire antennas. All marker beacon antennas need to be installed on the bottom of the aircraft because the signals are received when the aircraft is directly over the transmitter site. Another type of marker beacon antenna found on smaller aircraft is the sled type. This is a bent metal rod which is about 3-½ to 4 ft. long and uses a sliding clip for the lead-in connection. When the antenna is installed on the aircraft, the clip can be loosened and moved to tune the antenna. A newer type of marker beacon antenna is the boat type antenna that is illustrated in figure 4-46. This antenna is smaller and more streamlined than the wire or sled type antennas.

Air carrier jets most often use a flush mounted marker beacon antenna that is installed in the belly of the airplane.

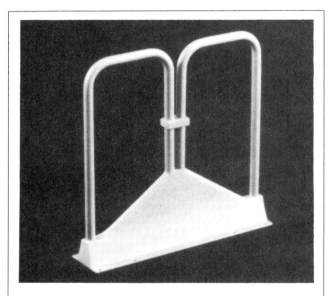

**DESCRIPTION**
**S65-147-2:** Constructed with high-strength aluminum tubing and extrusion, with fiberglass base housing.

*Figure 4-42. A localizer antenna for installation inside a radome. (Courtesy Sensor Systems)*

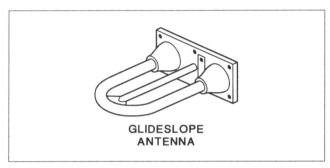

GLIDESLOPE
ANTENNA

*Figure 4-44. A loop-type glideslope antenna for internal or external mounting.*

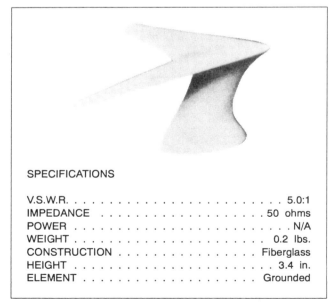

SPECIFICATIONS

```
V.S.W.R. . . . . . . . . . . . . . . . . . . . . . . . . 5.0:1
IMPEDANCE . . . . . . . . . . . . . . . . . 50 ohms
POWER . . . . . . . . . . . . . . . . . . . . . . . . . N/A
WEIGHT . . . . . . . . . . . . . . . . . . . . . 0.2 lbs.
CONSTRUCTION . . . . . . . . . . . . . . Fiberglass
HEIGHT . . . . . . . . . . . . . . . . . . . . . 3.4 in.
ELEMENT . . . . . . . . . . . . . . . . . . . Grounded
```

*Figure 4-43. A "V"-type glideslope antenna. (Courtesy Dayton-Granger Inc.)*

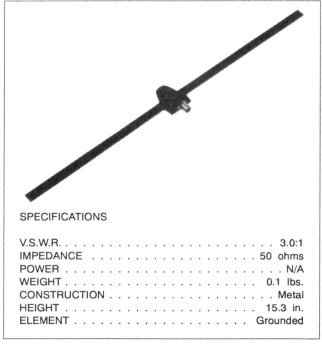

SPECIFICATIONS

```
V.S.W.R. . . . . . . . . . . . . . . . . . . . . . . . . 3.0:1
IMPEDANCE . . . . . . . . . . . . . . . . . 50 ohms
POWER . . . . . . . . . . . . . . . . . . . . . . . . . N/A
WEIGHT . . . . . . . . . . . . . . . . . . . . . 0.1 lbs.
CONSTRUCTION . . . . . . . . . . . . . . . . Metal
HEIGHT . . . . . . . . . . . . . . . . . . . . . 15.3 in.
ELEMENT . . . . . . . . . . . . . . . . . . . Grounded
```

*Figure 4-45. A glideslope antenna for internal installation. (Courtesy Dayton-Granger Inc.)*

### e. HF Communication

The trailing wire and long wire HF antennas found on older aircraft and slow speed aircraft have already been covered. Older air carrier jets used a probe-type HF antenna similar to the vertical fin mounted antenna shown in figure 4-47. This antenna includes a special coupler/tuner that retunes the antenna each time the frequency is changed on the HF radio. This kind of antenna can be mounted on the vertical fin as shown or on a wing tip. The later model air carrier jets use a flush mounted HF comm antenna that is installed inside the vertical fin as seen in figure 4-37. This antenna also requires a special tuning device that is installed at the antenna connection point.

### f. VHF Communication

The VHF comm radios on aircraft use a separate antenna for each radio. These antennas are ¼ wave, monopole antennas that can be mounted on the top or bottom of the aircraft. Lower speed aircraft use the thin whip type antennas while higher speed aircraft employ blade type antennas that create less drag. The antenna may either be straight or bent, the bent antennas having the advantages of less drag and less height for belly mountings. A variety of VHF comm antennas is shown in figure 4-48 of both whip and blade types. Some blade-type VHF comm antennas have a stainless steel leading edge to prevent damage, this feature can be seen on the antenna in figure 4-49.

### g. DME/Transponder

The same type of antenna can be used for either DME or transponder systems on aircraft. This is practical because they operate at similar frequencies and have similar characteristics. These antennas are almost always installed on the bottom of the aircraft, but they can be located on the top of a narrow tail boom or other location that does not cause serious blockage. The two common types are the spike and blade antennas as illustrated in figure

4-50. The spike is a short metal rod with a ball on the end. This type is cheaper and easier to install, but it is more easily damaged and creates more vibration and drag. The blade type is the most common type on modern aircraft. This antenna can be distinguished from the VHF comm blade because it is much smaller, about 2–4″ long. These antennas are all ¼ wave monopoles with vertical polarization so an adequate groundplane must be provided during installation.

### h. ELT Antennas

Figure 4-51 shows the common type of ELT antenna, it is a thin metal rod that is located close to the ELT itself. The antenna is a Marconi ¼ wave antenna that requires a groundplane. It should normally be installed as close as possible to the ELT because of the low output power of ELT transmitters. A blade type of ELT antenna is also available for higher speed aircraft.

### i. Satellite Navigation

The signals from GPS and GLONASS satellites are received from above the aircraft so the antenna needs to be installed on the upper surfaces of the aircraft. A typical GPS antenna is shown in figure 4-52. This small, round antenna creates very low drag and yet has a VSWR of 2:1 which provides good signal reception for the GPS/GLONASS navigation system.

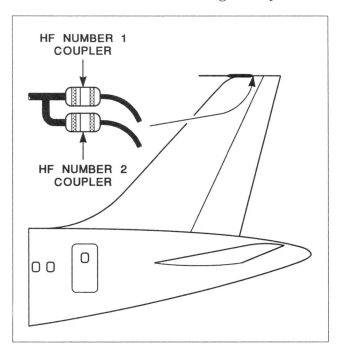

*Figure 4-47. Some jet transports have an HF probe-type antenna installed in the vertical fin. Two antenna coupling and tuning devices are also installed in the fin to retune the antenna when different frequencies are selected.*

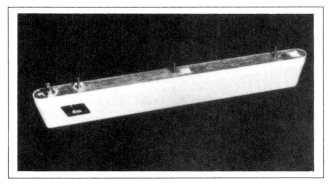

*Figure 4-46. A boat-type marker beacon antenna. (Courtesy Dorne & Margolin Inc.)*

## j. Satellite Communications

The SATCOM antenna, like the SATNAV antenna, must be installed on the top of the aircraft to prevent signal blockage. A variety of different designs are produced for this kind of antenna. The antenna in figure 4-53 is just one of the kinds of antennas being produced for satellite communications systems for aircraft.

## k. Loran C

An ADF antenna can be used to receive Loran C navigational signals by utilizing a special antenna coupler. Specific antennas for Loran C are now being produced and they often bear a resemblance to VHF comm antennas as indicated in figure 4-54. These antennas can be installed on either the top or the bottom of the aircraft and still provide good reception because of the frequencies involved. These antennas often include a special anti-static coating to reduce P-static noise in the radio.

## l. Omega

Aircraft antennas designed to receive Omega/VLF signals are available in two basic types: the "E" field and "H" field types. The antenna shown in figure 4-55 is the "E" field kind. These antennas can be installed on either upper or lower surfaces of the aircraft. The most important consideration when choosing a location is to reduce noise interference from aircraft systems. A "skin noise map" is often required which consists of measuring the VLF noise on various parts of the aircraft to find the best antenna location. The lowest noise is usually found on the aft underbelly of most aircraft.

## m. MLS

The MLS receive antenna seen in figure 4-56 is a low profile, vertically polarized antenna designed to receive the MLS signals that operate on frequencies of 5.03 to 5.09 GHz. This kind of antenna should be located on the nose section of the aircraft for

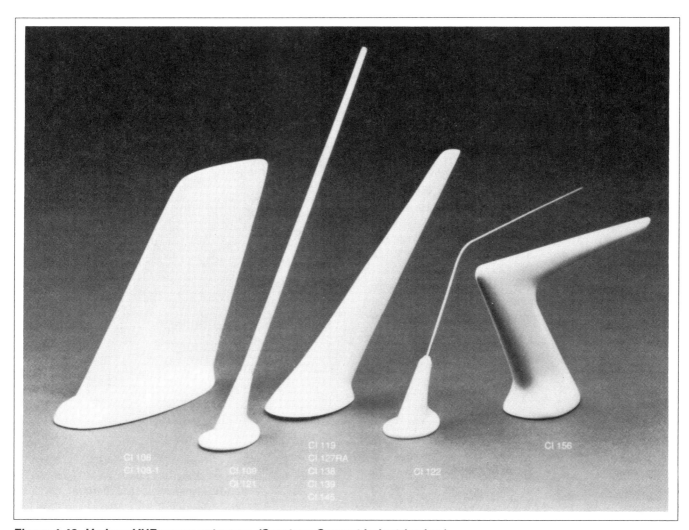

*Figure 4-48. Various VHF comm antennas. (Courtesy Comant Industries Inc.)*

best reception and minimum blockage. Some MLS systems require two antennas to be installed on the aircraft for proper signal reception.

### n. TCAS

The Traffic Alert and Collision Avoidance system found on air carrier jets requires a special type of directional antenna like that seen in figure 4-57. This TCAS I antenna is normally located on the

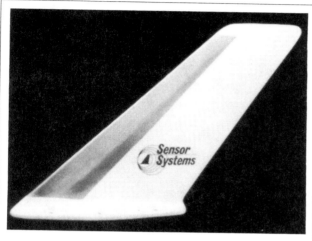

**DESCRIPTION**
**S65-8282:** This broadband fixed tuned antenna operates in the frequency range of 116-156 MHz.

*Figure 4-49. A blade-type VHF comm antenna with a stainless steel guard on the leading edge. (Courtesy Sensor Systems)*

top of the fuselage and has three connector ports for connection to the aircraft's TCAS I equipment.

### o. Radiotelephone

Radiotelephone antennas come in a wide variety of shapes and sizes. These UHF antennas are normally installed on the bottom of the aircraft since they operate in conjunction with ground based line-of-sight radio waves. A number of different kinds of radiotelephone antennas are shown in figure 4-58. A major consideration when installing this type of antenna is preventing noise that can be caused by loose joints and poorly bonded surfaces on the aircraft.

## C. Autopilots and Flight Directors

The FAA classifies autopilots as aircraft instruments so A&P technicians cannot repair or alter autopilots. There are many tasks related to autopilots that might be performed by aircraft technicians such as installation, inspection, troubleshooting etc. An autopilot is an expensive and complicated device. It often has various components located in many different areas of the aircraft and many interconnections. The autopilot is connected to the flight control system of the aircraft and autopilot malfunctions can be very serious indeed.

An autopilot system must always be approved by the FAA for the specific make and model of aircraft in which it will be installed. A type of autopilot may be approved for a number of different

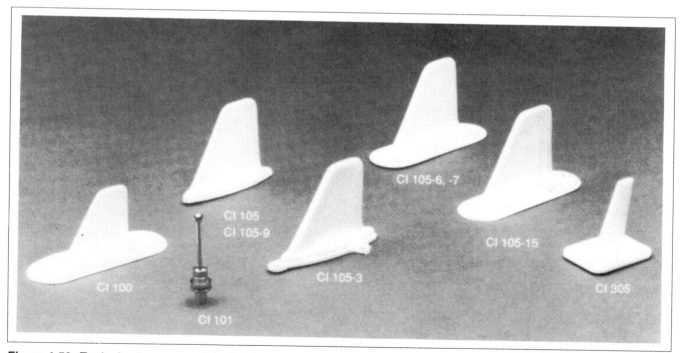

*Figure 4-50. Typical antennas used for DME and transponder. (Courtesy Comant Industries Inc.)*

aircraft, but different torque settings and adjustments may have to be made for each application. The maintenance instructions that apply to the specific autopilot installation should always be followed as there are many differences in adjustments and testing for the various aircraft installations. The basic principles of operation for aircraft autopilots will be described here along with some specific examples of aircraft autopilot installations.

## 1. Types of Autopilots

Autopilot systems are categorized according to the number of aircraft axes of rotation they control and according to their complexity. The autopilot utilizes the same control surfaces that the human pilot does. The three control axes of an airplane are shown in figure 4-59. The rudder controls aircraft rotation about or around the vertical or yaw axis. The elevators control rotation about the lateral or pitch axis. The ailerons control aircraft rotation about the longitudinal or roll axis. Autopilots can be described as single-axis, two-axis or three-axis types. The single-axis autopilot usually operates the ailerons only and is often referred to as a wing leveler. The two-axis autopilot controls

the ailerons and elevator to provide additional control of the aircraft. A three-axis autopilot operates all three types of control surfaces: ailerons, elevator and rudder. There is a very large difference in the capabilities of a three-axis autopilot found on a small general aviation airplane and the three-axis autopilot found on air carrier jets and similar

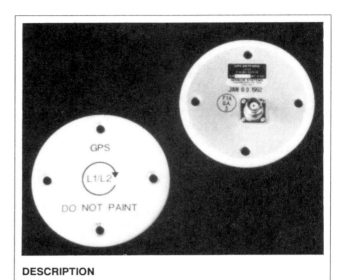

**DESCRIPTION**
**S67-1575-14:** Dual band L1/L2 GPS Antenna provides coverage at 1227.6 MHz and 1575.42 MHz with a VSWR of 2.0:1.

*Figure 4-52. GPS antenna for satellite nav. (Courtesy Sensor Systems)*

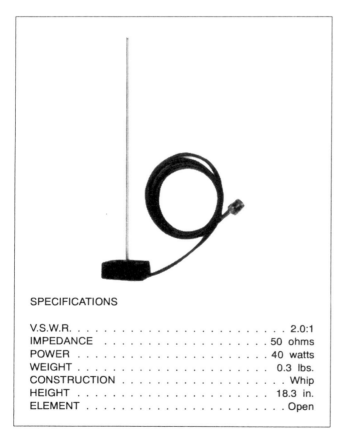

SPECIFICATIONS

V.S.W.R. . . . . . . . . . . . . . . . . . . . . . . . . 2.0:1
IMPEDANCE . . . . . . . . . . . . . . . . . . 50 ohms
POWER . . . . . . . . . . . . . . . . . . . . . . 40 watts
WEIGHT . . . . . . . . . . . . . . . . . . . . . 0.3 lbs.
CONSTRUCTION . . . . . . . . . . . . . . . . . . Whip
HEIGHT . . . . . . . . . . . . . . . . . . . . . 18.3 in.
ELEMENT . . . . . . . . . . . . . . . . . . . . . Open

*Figure 4-51. A whip-type ELT antenna. (Courtesy Dayton-Granger Inc.)*

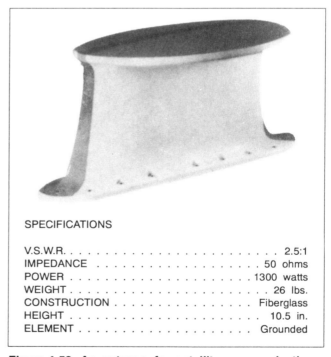

SPECIFICATIONS

V.S.W.R. . . . . . . . . . . . . . . . . . . . . . . . . 2.5:1
IMPEDANCE . . . . . . . . . . . . . . . . . . 50 ohms
POWER . . . . . . . . . . . . . . . . . . . . 1300 watts
WEIGHT . . . . . . . . . . . . . . . . . . . . . 26 lbs.
CONSTRUCTION . . . . . . . . . . . . . . . Fiberglass
HEIGHT . . . . . . . . . . . . . . . . . . . . . 10.5 in.
ELEMENT . . . . . . . . . . . . . . . . . . . . Grounded

*Figure 4-53. An antenna for satellite communications. (Courtesy Dayton-Granger Inc.)*

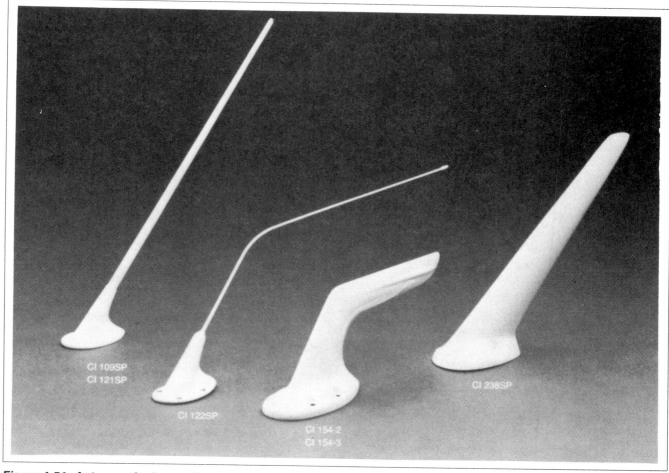

*Figure 4-54. Antennas for Loran C nav receivers. (Courtesy Comant Industries Inc.)*

aircraft. For this reason two other categories of autopilot will be added to the three already mentioned. Two common abbreviations for these advanced autopilots will be used to distinguish them from the other types.

The term "Automatic Flight Control System" (AFCS) generally represents the state-of-the-art that was reached a few years ago. The autopilot in the Lockheed L-1011 is an example of an AFCS.

This is a three axis autopilot that can control the aircraft during climbs, descents, cruise flight and during instrument approaches. It also has an auto-throttle system which will automatically control engine power or thrust. Some AFCS autopilots have auto-land capability where the autopilot can actually land the airplane on the runway. These types of autopilots require many back-up systems and high levels of redundancy. The AFCS includes a flight director function which will be explained later.

The latest types of autopilots are referred to as Flight Management Systems (FMS). These include

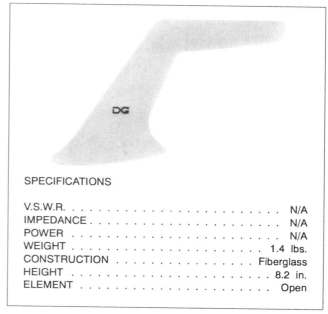

SPECIFICATIONS

```
V.S.W.R. . . . . . . . . . . . . . . . . . . . . . . . . N/A
IMPEDANCE . . . . . . . . . . . . . . . . . . . . . N/A
POWER . . . . . . . . . . . . . . . . . . . . . . . . . N/A
WEIGHT . . . . . . . . . . . . . . . . . . . . . . . 1.4 lbs.
CONSTRUCTION . . . . . . . . . . . . . . Fiberglass
HEIGHT . . . . . . . . . . . . . . . . . . . . . . . 8.2 in.
ELEMENT . . . . . . . . . . . . . . . . . . . . . . . Open
```

*Figure 4-55. An "E" field Omega antenna. (Courtesy Dayton-Granger Inc.)*

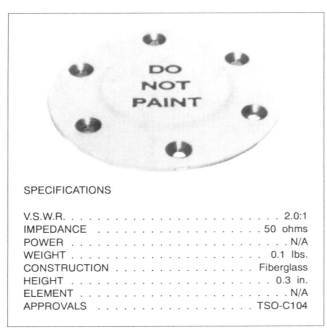

SPECIFICATIONS

```
V.S.W.R. . . . . . . . . . . . . . . . . . . . 2.0:1
IMPEDANCE  . . . . . . . . . . . . . . . . 50  ohms
POWER . . . . . . . . . . . . . . . . . . . . . N/A
WEIGHT . . . . . . . . . . . . . . . . . . . . 0.1  lbs.
CONSTRUCTION . . . . . . . . . . . . . Fiberglass
HEIGHT  . . . . . . . . . . . . . . . . . . . 0.3  in.
ELEMENT . . . . . . . . . . . . . . . . . . . N/A
APPROVALS  . . . . . . . . . . . . . . . TSO-C104
```

*Figure 4-56. An antenna for MLS reception. (Courtesy Dayton-Granger Inc.)*

additional computers called Flight Management Computers that permit an entire flight from just after takeoff to landing to be programmed in the computers and automatically controlled. The Flight

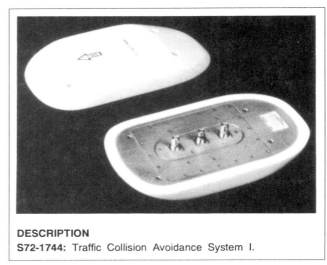

DESCRIPTION
**S72-1744:** Traffic Collision Avoidance System I.

*Figure 4-57. A TCAS I antenna. (Courtesy Sensor Systems)*

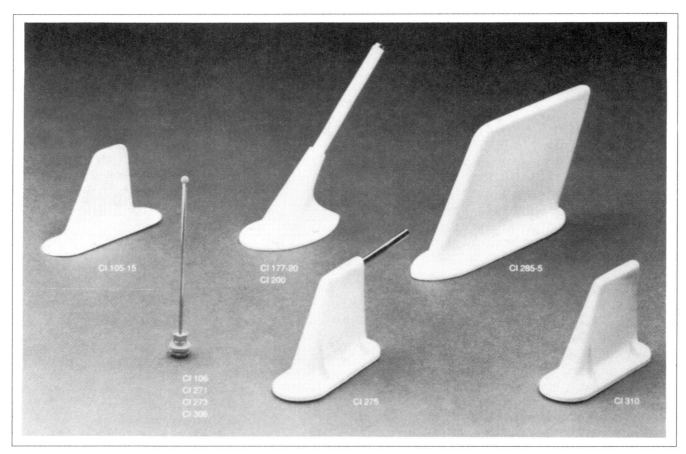

*Figure 4-58. A variety of radiotelephone antennas. (Courtesy Comant Industries Inc.)*

Management Computer can be thought of as a master computer which controls the autopilot and auto-throttle computers. The computers can store in their memory many different routes and flight profiles and they can be used to provide a maximum economy in fuel consumption or other desired controlling factor. The standard Boeing 767 autopilot systems will be used later as an example of the capabilities of an FMS installation.

## 2. Basic Autopilot Operation

The FAA states in AC 65-15A that the purpose of an automatic pilot system is primarily to reduce the work, strain and fatigue of controlling the aircraft during long flights. The capabilities of a modern autopilot go way beyond simply controlling the aircraft during cruise operations. A sophisticated autopilot system can land the airplane in weather conditions that are so bad that the human pilot could not legally land the airplane. We would have to say that the statement is true for simple autopilot systems, but is obsolete or outdated in describing a sophisticated modern autopilot. In this section, the basic parts and operation of simple autopilots will be described. Figure 4-60 shows the basic parts of the rudder control channel of an autopilot. The aileron and elevator channels would work in a similar fashion. The basic parts and their functions are:

1. Sensors or Gyros — These detect a change in aircraft attitude using gyros or similar sensing devices.

2. Amplifier or Computer — This component processes the signals from the sensors and sends signals to the servos to correct the attitude.

3. Servos — The servos receive the signals from the computer and supply the physical force necessary to move the flight control surface.

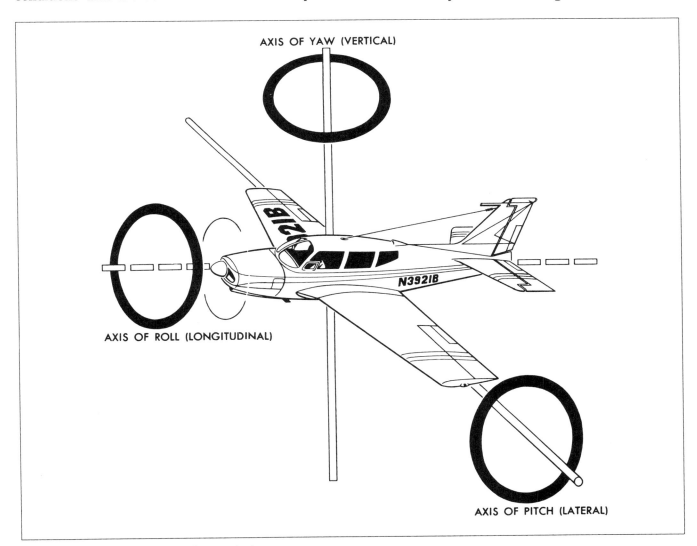

*Figure 4-59. The control axes for an airplane.*

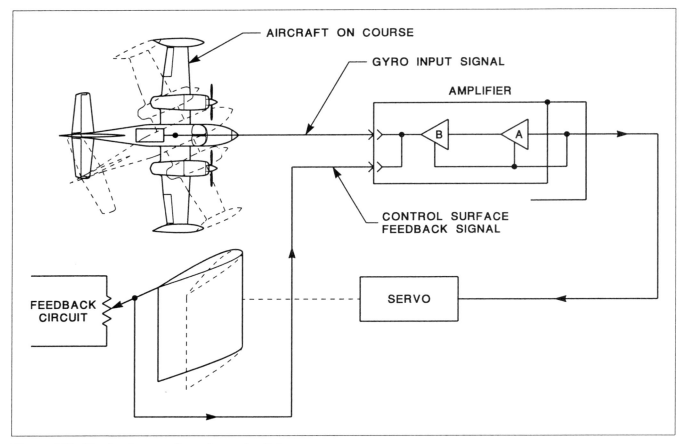

*Figure 4-60. The basic operation of an autopilot.*

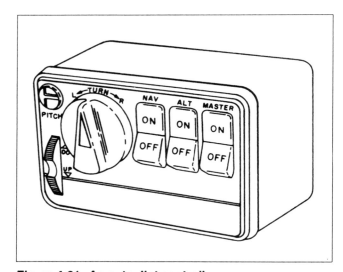

*Figure 4-61. An autopilot controller.*

4. Feedback — All but the simplest autopilots have a feedback system that sends signals back to the computer that indicate the motion of the flight control surface. Without feedback the control of the aircraft would not be smooth and precise.

5. Controller — Figure 4-61 shows a typical controller. This unit is located in the cockpit and contains the actuating switches and the pitch and turn knobs. The pilot can move the pitch knob or turn knob to supply manual commands to the autopilot that change the pitch attitude or command a turn.

The operation of any autopilot follows these basic principles although different types of sensors, servos, etc. may be used. On a modern autopilot the computers are digital computers and there are often three different computers for each of the three control axes.

### 3. Sensors

The gyroscopic sensors used with autopilots are similar to the gyro instruments described in chapter 1. The pitch, roll and yaw of the aircraft are detected by gyro sensors that send signals to the computer. The output signals of the sensors are most often electrical signals. A common method of producing the output signals is a special type of variable transformer called an EI pick-off which detects the motion between the gyro rotor and its gimbals. The latest types of autopilots use a sensor that employs laser beams instead of a spinning gyro rotor. Figure 4-62 shows one of these laser sensors that are called

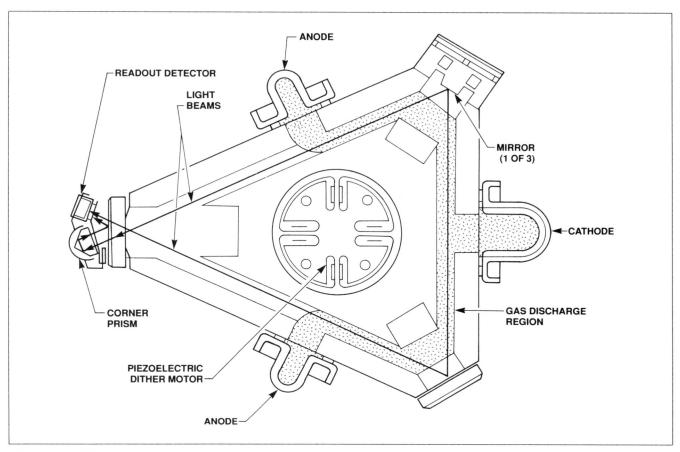

*Figure 4-62. Ring laser gyro sensor for an autopilot.*

ring laser gyros or RLGs. The RLG has two laser beams that travel in opposite directions around a triangular course. Sensitive detectors measure the Doppler shift or frequency change whenever the unit is rotated. One of these is needed for each axis that must be measured for the autopilot. These RLGs are much more expensive than an actual gyro, but they eliminate the moving parts that cause a conventional gyro to gradually wear out.

### 4. Servos

The servos supply the force needed to move the flight control surfaces of the aircraft. There are four basic kinds which will be described here. Some simple autopilots found on small airplanes use vacuum sources like those used to operate gyro instruments. The vacuum is directed to pneumatic servos that are connected mechanically to the normal flight control system. As seen in figure 4-63, the pneumatic servo is an air tight housing which contains a movable diaphragm. When vacuum is applied to the servo, the diaphragm is displaced which pulls on the bridle cable that is connected to the main control cable by a bridle clamp. Two of these servos would be needed for each control axis.

Servos that utilize electric motors are shown in Figures 4-64 and 4-65.

The servo shown in figure 4-64 uses a reversible DC motor and reduction gearing to supply the force to move the control surface in both directions. The servo in figure 4-65 has an electric motor that runs continuously and uses magnetic clutches to engage the mechanism and apply torque to the capstan and control cable. This type has the advantage that the inertia forces in starting and stopping the motor are eliminated. It can be engaged and disengaged more rapidly and precisely.

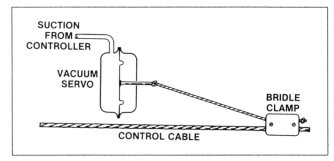

*Figure 4-63. Pneumatic servo for a small aircraft autopilot.*

Air carrier jets and some of the larger bizjets use hydraulically powered flight controls. The normal flight control system employs mechanical linkages that control hydraulic units called Power Control Actuators or PCAs. The autopilot servos on these types of aircraft are electro-hydraulic servo valves that utilize electrical signals from the autopilot computers to direct hydraulic fluid under pressure to a hydraulic actuator. The actuator portion of the electro-hydraulic servo valve supplies mechanical force to the normal linkage of the flight control system. Figure 4-66 shows the electro-hydraulic servo valve for a typical large aircraft autopilot system. Figure 4-67 shows an autopilot servo for elevator control in the tail section of an air carrier jet. The mechanical force produced by the autopilot servo is transmitted by a push-pull tube to the normal flight control linkage that activates the PCAs. The level of redundancy in this system is typical for this class of aircraft.

## 5. Small Aircraft Autopilots

A single-axis autopilot for a single engine airplane is shown in figure 4-68. This simple autopilot uses pneumatic servos to actuate the ailerons. The source of power is a dry air vacuum pump which is engine driven. The sensor is a gyro turn coordinator which controls the pneumatic power applied to the servos. Some of the torque settings and rigging instructions for the autopilot can be seen in this drawing. This is the type of autopilot which is often called a wing leveler since it controls only the aileron control surfaces.

A three axis autopilot with electric motor servos is illustrated in figure 4-69. The sensors used with this system include gyro sensors and an altitude sensor. The altitude sensor shows that this autopilot would have an altitude hold capability.

Radio signals from the aircraft's navigation radios can be used by the autopilot to steer the aircraft along a desired VOR or localizer course. The pitch, roll and yaw servos receive electrical signals from the computer that activate the electric motors to move the control surfaces. A pitch trim servo is included so that the autopilot can apply nose up or nose down pitch trim as required. The aircraft can operate with a wide range of CG positions and the autopilot, like the human pilot, uses pitch trim to reduce the elevator control force to an acceptable level. The autopilot controller has switches to engage the heading, radio NAV and altitude operating modes. It also contains an on/off switch, a pitch control indicator and the knobs for manual control of autopilot pitch and turns. It should be noted that these autopilot components are located in various parts of the aircraft and some of the minor components such as bridle cables are not shown. This autopilot system has the ability to guide the aircraft on an ILS approach using both localizer and glideslope signals. This feature is called an approach coupler and is required for certain types of instrument approaches as will be covered later in the section on FARs.

## 6. Flight Management System (FMS)

The Boeing 767 will be used as an example of a flight management system or FMS. This system has the capability of automatically controlling the airplane from just after takeoff (above 400 ft. AGL)

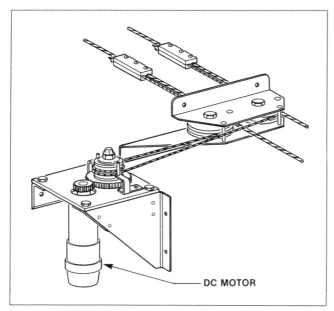

*Figure 4-64. Autopilot servo with reversible DC motor, reduction gears and bridle cables.*

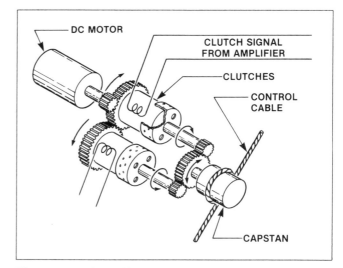

*Figure 4-65. Autopilot servo with a motor that runs continuously and is engaged by magnetic clutches.*

through roll out on the runway after landing at the destination airport. The human pilot must take over to turn off the runway and taxi to the gate. This does not mean that all flights will use all these capabilities, but the autopilot and flight director will be used for some portion of each flight under normal circumstances.

### a. Flight Management Computers

The Flight Management Computers (FMCs) provide a number of advanced features and functions which were not found on earlier autopilot systems. Some of the functions of the Flight Management Computer are:

1. Flight Planning — The entire flight can be programmed into the computer using a cockpit keyboard.
2. Performance Management — The system can provide optimum profiles for climb, cruise, descent and holding patterns. A minimum cost flight can be flown automatically by using optimum climb settings, cruise settings etc.

3. Navigation Calculations — The FMC can calculate great circle routes, climb and descent profiles etc.
4. Auto Tune of VOR and DME — The FMC can automatically tune the radios to the correct station frequencies.
5. Autothrottle Speed Commands — These are displayed on the EADI as FAST/SLOW indications.

The FMC is in effect a master computer which integrates the functions of the laser sensors, Flight Control Computers, Thrust Management Computers, Air Data Computers, navigation sensors and EICAS computers. The autopilot sensors are called Inertial Reference Units (IRUs) and they are the same in basic operation as the Ring Laser Gyros (RLGs) previously described.

### b. Flight Control Computers

The flight control computers are the autopilot computers and there are three of them. A block diagram of the connections to the three Flight Control Computers is shown in figure 4-70. The three computers

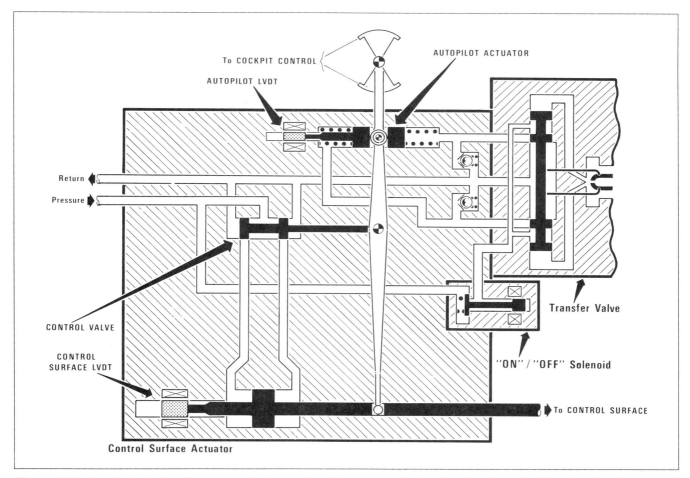

**Figure 4-66.** *An electrohydraulic servo valve is employed in an autopilot system for aircraft with hydraulically powered flight controls. Linear variable differential transformers (LVDTs) provide feedback signals of the movement of the mechanical parts of the system.*

are independent so that a failure in one will not affect the other two. The computers are modern digital computers that are more compact and faster than earlier types of computers.

### c. Thrust Management Computer (TMC)

The purpose of the TMC is to automatically set the proper thrust level for the engines. A diagram of the autothrottle system is shown in figure 4-71. The output servo moves the throttle linkage to set the level of engine power calculated by the TMC. The system includes sensors on the engines which monitor the important engine operating parameters. The monitoring of engine parameters

is used to prevent exceeding any engine operating limitation for RPM, EPR, EGT, etc. The autothrottle system can be used to maintain a given climb rate, indicated airspeed, Mach number or descent rate. Since the 767 has autoland capabilities, the autothrottle system will automatically close the throttles just prior to landing so that a smooth touchdown can be made. The TMC system also provides a minimum speed protection which will maintain a safe margin above stall speed for the particular flight configuration. The autopilot system and the autothrottle system can be engaged separately or together using the controls on the flight control panel.

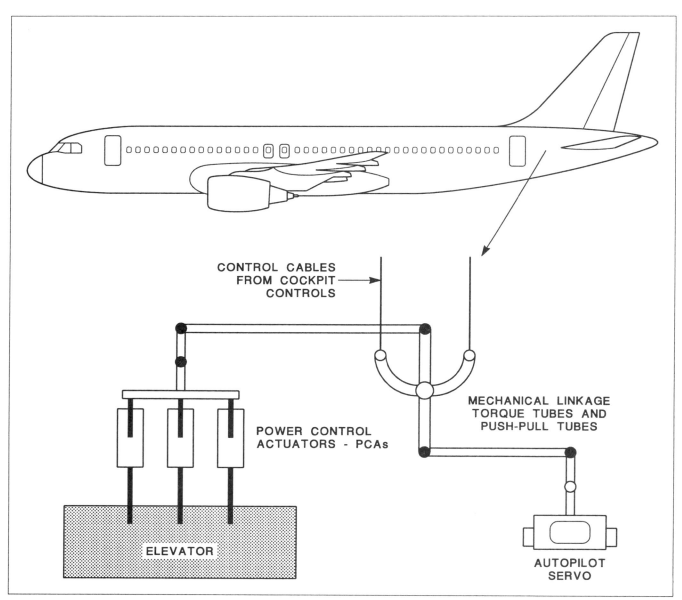

**Figure 4-67.** *The autopilot servos on a large jet airplane provide mechanical force to move the normal control linkage and activate the hydraulic PCAs that move the flight control surfaces.*

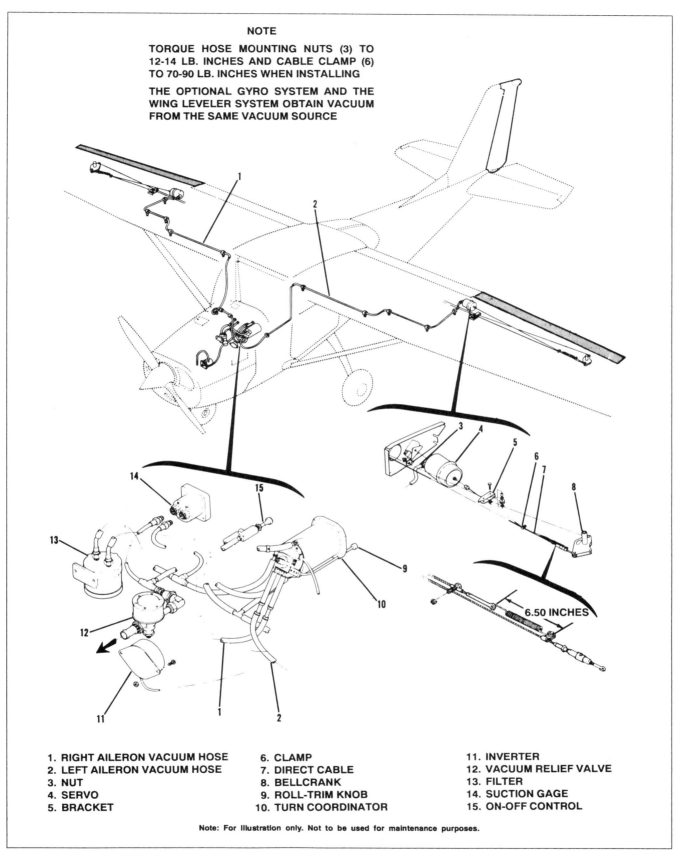

NOTE

TORQUE HOSE MOUNTING NUTS (3) TO
12-14 LB. INCHES AND CABLE CLAMP (6)
TO 70-90 LB. INCHES WHEN INSTALLING

THE OPTIONAL GYRO SYSTEM AND THE
WING LEVELER SYSTEM OBTAIN VACUUM
FROM THE SAME VACUUM SOURCE

6.50 INCHES

1. RIGHT AILERON VACUUM HOSE
2. LEFT AILERON VACUUM HOSE
3. NUT
4. SERVO
5. BRACKET

6. CLAMP
7. DIRECT CABLE
8. BELLCRANK
9. ROLL-TRIM KNOB
10. TURN COORDINATOR

11. INVERTER
12. VACUUM RELIEF VALVE
13. FILTER
14. SUCTION GAGE
15. ON-OFF CONTROL

Note: For illustration only. Not to be used for maintenance purposes.

**Figure 4-68. A single-axis autopilot with pneumatic servos. (Courtesy Cessna Aircraft Corp.)**

## d. Flight Control Panel

The flight control panel contains the switches to activate the various functions of the autopilot and to adjust the settings for the desired vertical speed, IAS, Mach number, etc. The indicator lights for the different modes of operation are also included in the flight control panel. This panel is located in the glareshield above the center instrument panel and it is illustrated in figure 4-72.

## e. Control Wheel Steering (CWS)

Control wheel steering is an operating mode for the autopilot in addition to the command operating

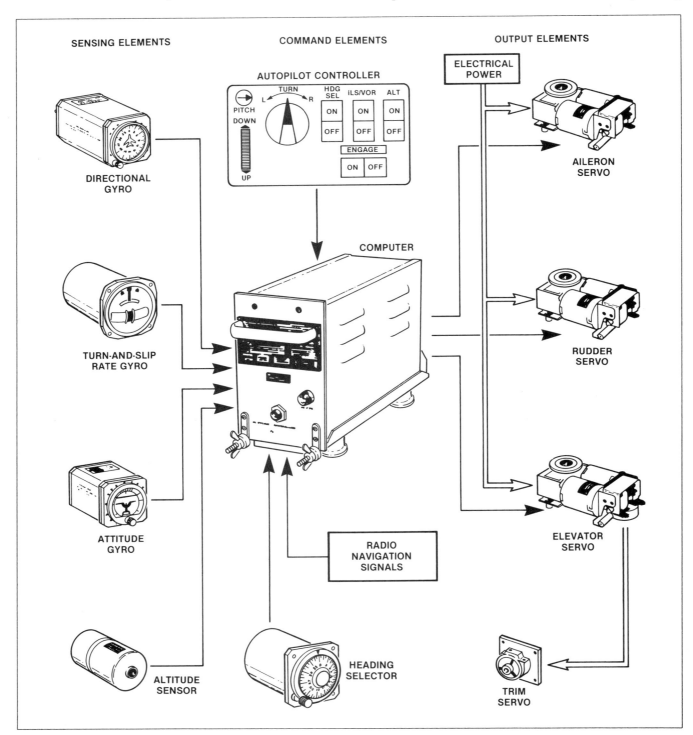

**Figure 4-69.  Diagram of a 3-axis autopilot that can be coupled to radio navigation receivers.**

mode. The command mode is the normal autopilot mode where the pilot does not touch the controls because the autopilot is flying the airplane. In the CWS mode, the controls are moved by the pilot as in normal flight and the force that is applied to the controls is measured and used as an input signal to the autopilot computers. In effect, the human pilot is flying the airplane, but the autopilot is helping to move the control surfaces. Figure 4-73 shows the connections between the force transducer and the flight control computer. The operation of a typical force transducer is illustrated by figure 4-74. The three electrical windings and the armature

above them make up a special type of variable transformer. The AC input signal is applied to the center winding and the outer windings produce the output signal. The housing of the force transducer is flexible so that its length will change based on the force applied to it. When the housing changes in length, it causes relative motion between the armature and the coils. This motion alters the magnetic coupling and therefore produces a change in the output signal.

### f. Flight Director

A flight director is a system that uses some of the basic components of an autopilot, but not all

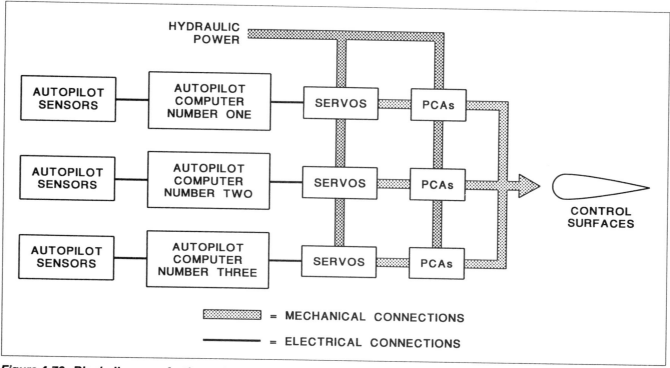

Figure 4-70. Block diagram of a three-channel autopilot for a large aircraft with hydraulically powered flight controls.

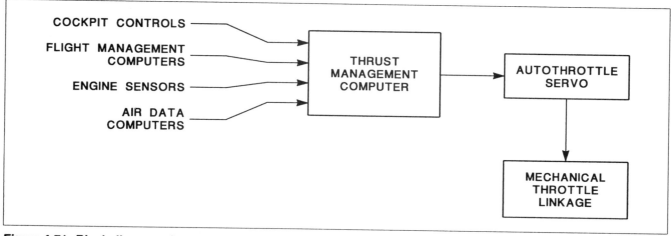

Figure 4-71. Block diagram of an autothrottle system with a thrust management computer.

of them. A flight director uses sensors and computers, but it does not have servos. The flight director computer uses the signals from sensors to calculate a correction which is then displayed as a command for the pilot to follow. The commands from the flight director are displayed to the pilot on the EADI by the command bars. The operation of the command bars on the EADI is shown in figure 4-75. On the left, the command bar symbol is above the airplane symbol. The indication is that the pilot needs to raise the nose to satisfy this flight director command. On the right, the nose of the airplane has been raised so that the airplane symbol aligns with the command bar. During flight director operations the pilot maintains manual control of the aircraft, but follows the steering commands indicated by the command bars. One of the primary uses for the flight director is during an instrument approach. By using the flight director the pilot can more accurately fly the airplane on an ILS approach because the computer is making rapid calculations to predict the optimum heading and attitude for the approach. Corrections for wind drift are automatic, all the pilot has to do is follow the flight director commands.

Another condition when the flight director is helpful is in setting the proper takeoff pitch attitude.

### g. Additional Features

Some of the additional features of the Boeing 767 Autopilot and Flight Director System that are typical for this class of aircraft will be described briefly.

The Stability Augmentation System (SAS) involves certain functions of the yaw control system. One of the purposes of the SAS is to eliminate a potential problem known as Dutch Roll. Many large swept

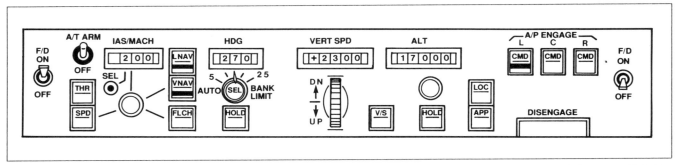

Figure 4-72. *The autopilot control panel for a sophisticated autopilot includes switches to control the autopilot, the flight director and the autothrottle systems.*

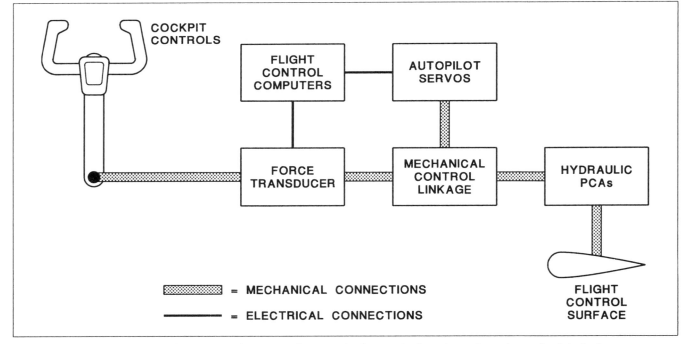

Figure 4-73. *Location of the force transducers and servos in the control system of an air carrier jet airplane.*

188

wing airplanes display a peculiar type of instability at high altitudes under certain flight conditions. This can result in a continuous pitching and rolling motion known as Dutch Roll. The SAS will automatically make rapid and precise rudder movements to reduce Dutch Roll motions of the airplane. The system is also referred to as the yaw damper and it can be engaged separately from the rest of the autopilot.

The runway alignment feature of the Boeing 767 is a part of the autoland system. It will automatically align the longitudinal axis of the airplane with the runway prior to touchdown. This feature is important during crosswind landings because it is designed to prevent the airplane from landing at a crab angle to the runway. This is illustrated in figure 4-76. The runway alignment feature is limited to control surface deflections of 25° for the rudder and 2° for ailerons. A very strong crosswind at 90° to the runway could not be completely counteracted. This same feature will also provide

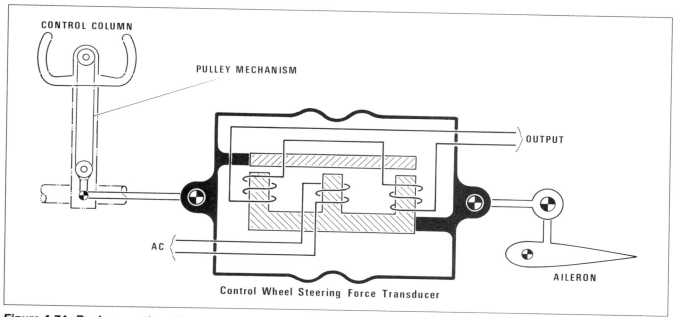

**Figure 4-74. Basic operation of one type of force transducer.**

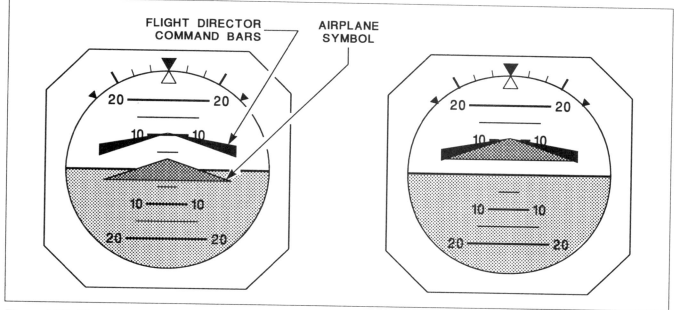

**Figure 4-75. The command bars in an ADI are positioned by signals from the flight director computer. The pilot follows the commands by aligning the airplane symbol with the command bars.**

corrections if an engine fails during the landing approach. It would supply the control corrections to counteract the asymmetrical thrust situation.

## 7. FARs for Autopilots

Some of the Federal Aviation Regulations that apply to autopilots and related systems will be given here. Most of the references are to FAR Part 23 and FAR Part 91 which apply mainly to small airplanes. The requirements for transport category aircraft autopilots include some of these same requirements, but with many additional requirements that won't be discussed here.

### FAR 23.1329
#### Automatic Pilot System

A. An automatic pilot system must be designed so that:
   1. It can be quickly and positively disengaged or
   2. One pilot can overpower the autopilot to control the airplane.
B. Unless there is automatic synchronization, a means must be provided to indicate to the pilot the alignment of the actuating device in relation to the control system it operates.
C. The controls must be readily accessible to the pilot and operate in the same plane and sense as the cockpit controls.
D. The autopilot must not produce hazardous loads on the airplane or produce hazardous deviations in the flight path in the event of malfunctions.
E. Each system must be designed so that a single malfunction will not produce a hardover signal in more than one control axis.
F. There must be protection against adverse interaction of integrated components resulting from a malfunction.
G. If the automatic pilot system can be coupled to navigation equipment, a means must be provided to indicate the current mode of operation. Selector switch position is not acceptable as a means of indication.

### FAR 23.1335
#### Flight Director Systems

A means must be provided to indicate the current mode of operation. Selector switch position is not acceptable as a means of indication.

### FAR 91 Appendix A
#### Category II Operations: Required Instruments and Equipment

Refer to figure 4-77 for an example of the weather minimums associated with Category II and Category III ILS approaches.

2A9  An automatic pilot approach coupler or a flight director system is required for Category II ILS operations.

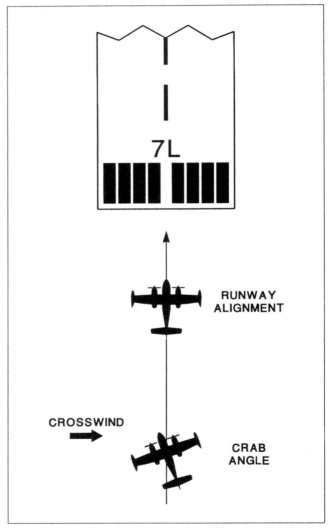

*Figure 4-76. The stability augmentation system (SAS) in an aircraft with autoland capability has a special operating mode called runway alignment. At approximately 500 ft. the runway alignment feature will eliminate the crab angle caused by a crosswind so that the aircraft will be pointed down the runway at touchdown.*

2B1 For Category III ILS operations additional equipment requirements are a radio altimeter and autothrottle system.

## FAR 135.105
### Autopilot in Place of Second Pilot

The certificate holder may use an autopilot in place of a second pilot if:

A. The autopilot and its operation are approved.

B. The Administrator issues an approval amendment.

C. The autopilot is a 3-axis type.

D. The certificate holder shows that operations can be conducted safely.

E. Exceptions: A second pilot must be used:

    1. For IFR operations.

    2. For Category II approaches.

    3. If required by the aircraft manufacturer.

## 8. Autopilot Maintenance

The information in this section is not meant to relate to any particular aircraft autopilot system. The procedures are general and could be applied to most autopilots as appropriate. Maintenance of autopilots consists of visual inspections, replacement of components, cleaning, lubrication, troubleshooting and operational checkouts of the system.

An operational check of the autopilot should be performed whenever an autopilot is installed, when components are replaced and whenever a malfunction is suspected. Many things can be operationally checked on the ground, but some situations may require a test flight with an airborne checkout of the autopilot. Some general procedures for a ground checkout of an autopilot are as follows.

With the autopilot disengaged, manipulate the flight controls to see if they function smoothly and without excessive drag or interference from autopilot components. The alignment of the autopilot to the aircraft should be checked. This normally involves checking such things as cable tension, torque settings, dimensional adjustments etc.

Before engaging the autopilot for an operational check, allow the gyros to come up to speed. This normally requires from 2–4 minutes. After engaging the autopilot, the following checks should be made.

1. Rotate the turn knob on the controller to the left. The rudder pedals and control column should move in the proper directions to indicate a left turn. The motion should be smooth and without excessive binding, jerking or hesitation.

2. Rotate the turn knob to the right and watch for the proper operation and motion of the controls.

3. Rotate the pitch knob up and down and watch for the correct motion of the control column aft and forward.

4. If the autopilot has automatic pitch trim, check the proper motion of the trim control as the control column moves fore and aft. When the control column moves back, the system should apply nose up trim and vice versa.

5. With the autopilot engaged, try to overpower it by grasping the controls and applying force. It should be possible to overpower the autopilot if it is adjusted properly.

6. Check all of the controls and switches for proper actuation and correct indications.

7. It may be desirable to taxi the aircraft in order to check out some of the operating modes. If you engage the heading hold mode and make a taxi turn to the right, the controls should show motion commanding a turn to the left.

8. Check the autopilot disconnect switches to ensure that the autopilot disconnects rapidly and positively. There may be several ways to disconnect the autopilot; check them all.

9. If the aircraft has a flight director, check for proper indications by the command bars in the ADI or EADI. Check the autopilot mode indicators in the ADI or EADI if so equipped.

If the aircraft has both an autopilot and flight director, they can be checked against each other as an aid in troubleshooting. The autopilot and flight director share some components while others are only used by the autopilot. This can be used to help locate the source of the problem when malfunctions are suspected. A ground checkout can often help to locate the source of a problem by comparing the indications of the flight director and autopilot. If the flight director is commanding an incorrect control movement and the autopilot is

| ILS APPROACH CATEGORY | RUNWAY VISUAL RANGE (RVR) | DECISION HEIGHT (ALTITUDE) |
|---|---|---|
| Category I | 2400 feet | 200 feet |
| Category II | 1200 feet | 100 feet |
| Category IIIA | 700 feet | None |
| Category IIIB | 150 feet | None |
| Category IIIC | None | None |

*Figure 4-77. The airport weather minimums for the various ILS approach categories.*

moving the controls in the same incorrect direction, then the fault is most likely a component they share such as the sensors or computer. If the flight director shows a correct command for nose up pitch, but the autopilot does not move the controls to agree with this command then the problem is likely not in the sensors or computer.

Some complaints about autopilot malfunctions are the result of faults in components other than the autopilot itself. If a pilot reports that the autopilot will not track a VOR radial, the problem could be a wiring fault in the wires that carry radio signals to the autopilot rather than a problem with the autopilot itself. Conditions such as rigging problems or binding of the main control cables in the aircraft itself can adversely affect the operation of the autopilot. Because the interactions and interconnections associated with autopilots can be very complex, a good system schematic and a thorough knowledge of the autopilot are necessary for efficient troubleshooting and maintenance of autopilot systems.

# APPENDIX A — Glossary

**Accelerometer** — A device or instrument which measures acceleration forces. The unit of measure is most often "Gs" based on the acceleration of gravity.

**Aircraft** — A machine that operates in the air. Examples include airplanes, gliders, balloons, airships and rotorcraft.

**Airplane** — An engine-driven, fixed-wing aircraft that is heavier than air and supported in flight by wings.

**Altitude engine** — A reciprocating aircraft engine that employs a supercharger to maintain sea level power at higher altitudes.

**Annunciator** — The indicating lights that are used to alert crew members to operating conditions that they need to be aware of. As in warning, caution and status indicator lights.

**Appliance** — Any instrument, mechanism, equipment, part, apparatus, appurtenance or accessory, including communications equipment, that is used in operating or controlling an aircraft in flight and is not part of an airframe, engine or propeller.

**Artificial horizon** — An aircraft instrument used to indicate pitch and roll attitudes. A gyro instrument used for IFR and also known as a gyro horizon, attitude gyro, bank and pitch indicator etc.

**Autosyn** — A synchro system that transmits positional information electrically from one place to another. The Autosyn type uses AC power and electromagnet rotors in both the sending and receiving units.

**Avionics** — Aircraft electronic equipment. Most often refers to aircraft radios and similar components.

**Balun** — A special type of impedance matching device used with V-shaped aircraft VOR antennas.

**Bellows** — A mechanical device for measuring pressure. It is a thin metal container with accordion shaped folds on the sides. Often separated into two chambers for use as a differential pressure measuring sensor.

**Bonding jumper** — A metal conductor used to electrically connect two parts of an aircraft. Most often a wire braid or thin metal strap.

**Bourdon tube** — A curved, hollow metal tube used as a pressure measuring sensor. Used for relatively higher pressures than a bellows or diaphragm.

**Calibrated airspeed** — Indicated airspeed that has been corrected for airspeed system errors and errors caused by the location and alignment of the pitot and static ports or sensors.

**Category II operation** — An ILS instrument approach using the specified procedures and meeting the requirements for operations in weather conditions below those required for a Category I approach.

**Category III operation** — An ILS instrument approach using the additional procedures and requirements for operations in weather conditions below those required for a Category II approach.

**Class B Airspace** — This is the same as a TCA (termimal control area), the airspace around a major airport where special equipment and flight restrictions apply.

**Class C Airspace** — this is the same as an ARSA (airport radar service area), the airspace around a busy airport where special equipment and flight restrictions apply.

**Coaxial cable** — A special conductor having a center conductor, a layer of dielectric insulation and an outer conductor. Designed to carry radio frequency electrical signals as in an antenna lead.

**Compass dip** — The tilting of the float in a magnetic compass due to the curvature of the earth. Compass dip becomes greater as the distance from the equator increases. Magnetic compass acceleration error and north turning error are a result of compass dip.

**Compensator** — A device to adjust or compensate for some error in an aircraft instrument or radio system. The compensator magnets in an aircraft compass installation.

**Critical engine** — The engine whose failure would most adversely affect the peformance or handling qualities of an aircraft.

**Dashpot** — A small acceleration operated air pump used in an aircraft IVSI to decrease the lag in the indication.

**Deviation** — An error in a magnetic compass caused by magnetic fields in the aircraft. This error is minimized and recorded in a procedure called swinging the compass.

**Diaphragm** — A small lens shaped metal container that is used as a sensor to measure pressures. Used in altimeters and airspeed indicators because of its sensitivity.

**Doppler effect** — The apparent change in frequency of a sound wave or radio wave when there is relative motion between the observer and the source of the waves. Used in the Doppler navigation system by bouncing radar waves off the surface of the earth. The Doppler principle is also used on the latest types of weather radar systems on aircraft.

**Drip stick** — A fuel quantity measuring system that uses a tube or stick that is extended below the wing of the airplane. It is a mechanical measuring system that requires no outside power.

**Encoding altimeter** — An altimeter or sensor that supplies electrical outputs related to aircraft altitude. The output is supplied to the aircraft transponder which transmits the data to a ground station. Also referred to as Mode C.

**Erector mechanism** — A device or mechanism in an artificial horizon that maintains the vertical spin axis of the gyro to ensure accurate readings.

**Flight level** — A level of constant atmospheric pressure related to a reference level of 29.92 in. Hg. Flight levels are indicated in hundreds of feet as in FL310, FL330, FL350 etc. Aircraft must use flight levels rather than MSL altitudes at and above 18,000 ft.

**Flux valve** — The sensor for a flux gate compass system. The flux valve produces an electrical output from the earth's magnetic field to operate remote compass systems and other devices.

**Gyroscope** — A small wheel or rotor that is spun at high speed to operate aircraft intruments. Also used to stabilize certain components such as radar antennas and INS accelerometers.

**Heading indicator** — A gyro instrument that indicates the magnetic heading of the aircraft. Also called the DG, gyro compass, heading gyro etc.

**IFR conditions** — Weather conditions below the minimum for VFR flight.

**Inclinometer** — An aircraft instrument that indicates slips and skids. Also called the slip-skid indicator. Usually a small curved glass tube with a ball in it.

**Indicated airspeed** — The speed of an aircraft as shown on its pitot-static airspeed indicator calibrated to reflect standard atmospheric adiabatic compressible flow at sea level and uncorrected for airspeed system errors.

**Instrument** — A device using an internal mechanism to show visually or aurally the altitude, attitude, or operation of an aircraft or aircraft part. It includes electronic devices for automatically controlling an aircraft in flight (autopilots).

**Knots** — A velocity in units of nautical miles per hour. To convert from knots to MPH, multiply by 1.151.

**Kollsman window** — The small window on the face of an altimeter that indicates the barometric pressure for which the altimeter has been set with the setting knob. Unit of measure is inches of mercury or millibars.

**Large aircraft** — Aircraft of more than 12,500 lbs. maximum certificated takeoff weight.

**Logic gate** — A semi-conductor device that produces an output from one or more inputs. It uses digital signals and is a basic component in many aircraft electronic systems.

**Loran C** — A radio navigation system that uses signals transmitted from ground stations on a frequency of 100 KHz. Most often used by general aviation aircraft.

**Lubber line** — The line on a magnetic compass that is used to take readings. The numbers on the compass card are read against the lubber line.

**Mach number** — The ratio of true airspeed to the speed of sound for the specified flight condition and altitude.

**Magnesyn** — A synchro system used on aircraft. The Magnesyn system uses AC power and permanent magnet rotors in the sending and receiving units.

**Manifold pressure** — The absolute pressure measured at the appropriate point in the induction system of a reciprocating aircraft engine and expressed in inches of Mercury.

**Octal** — A binary code system used with integrated circuits and logic gates. The octal code uses three bit bytes.

**Omega** — A radio navigation system that employs ground stations that transmit on frequencies from 10-14 KHz. It provides world wide coverage. VLF ground sites are also used by aircraft Omega systems.

**Piezoelectric** — A device that employs a crystal sensor that produces electrical output signals when it is squeezed or vibrated. An example is the piezoelectric sensor for an engine vibration indicator.

**Polarization** — The orientation of the electric field portion of an electro-magnetic radio wave. Vertical polarization would mean that the electric field is vertical relative to the earth's surface.

**Precession** — The displacement of a gyro rotor by an outside force. The gyro will precess as if the force was applied 90° ahead in the direction of rotation from the actual point of application of the disturbing force.

**Pressure Altitude** — The altitude shown on an aircraft altimeter when 29.92 is set into the barometric pressure setting window. This represents the altitude in a Standard Atmosphere.

**Proximity sensor** — A sensor or transducer used to replace microswitches in an aircraft position indicating system. It is an electronic device with no moving parts and is considered to be more reliable than microswitches.

**Quadrantal error** — The error in indication for an aircraft ADF system. A check of quadrantal error should be made whenever an antenna is installed or other maintenance is performed which could affect the accuracy of the ADF system.

**Radar** — Radio detection and ranging. Used in aviation for ATC purposes, weather avoidance systems, navigation and precision altitude measurement.

**Ratiometer** — An electrical circuit used to operate an aircraft instrument. It is called a ratiometer because the pointer is positoned by the ratio of the field strength of two electromagnetic fields.

**Rigidity** — The characteristic of a gyro rotor that causes it to try to maintain its spin axis fixed in space.

**Sea level engine** — A reciprocating aircraft engine having a rated takeoff power that is producible only at sea level. An unsupercharged engine.

**Selsyn** — A synchro system used on aircraft. The Selsyn uses DC power with a variable resistor in the sending unit and a permanent magnet rotor and three section coil in the receiving unit.

**Slip-skid indicator** — The same as inclinometer. See above.

**Small aircraft** — Aircraft of 12,500 lbs. or less maximum certificated takeoff weight.

**Thermocouple** — A device which uses two different metals to produce a DC output at the cold junction when the hot junction is heated. Commonly used for CHT, EGT and other relatively high temperature measurements in an aircraft.

**Torquemeter** — An instrument system that measures torque delivered to a shaft, usually by the aircraft engine. Common on large recip engines, turboprop engines and turboshaft engines.

**True Airspeed** — True airspeed is calibrated airspeed that has been corrected for altitude and temperature effects. An airspeed indicator is designed to be accurate for the standard pressure and temperature at sea level. At higher altitudes, indicated or calibrated airspeed is less than true airspeed.

**Variation** — The apparent error in the indication of a magnetic compass caused by the fact that the north geographic pole and the north magnetic pole of the earth are not in the same location.

**Venturi** — A tube with curved inner walls that produces a reduction in pressure in accordance with Bernoulli's Principle. Used in aircraft to produce suction to operate gyros and as a jet pump.

**Waveguide** — A hollow tube used as a conductor for radar frequency EM waves. Usually rectangular in cross-section and found in aircraft weather radar systems.

**Wheatstone bridge** — A bridge circuit with three fixed resistors and a variable resistor. It is used to operate a meter movement that rotates a pointer in an aircraft instrument for temperature measurements.

# APPENDIX B — Abbreviations

**ADC** — *Air data computer*: A computer which processes inputs from pitot tubes, static ports and TAT probes and provides outputs to the typical pitot-static instruments as well as other aircraft systems.

**ADF** — *Automatic direction finder*: A radio navigation system using signals in the LF and MF bands.

**ADI** — *Attitude director indicator*: An instrument that combines pitch and roll data with the command bars of a flight director.

**AF** — *Audio frequency*: 20,000 Hz and below.

**AFCS** — *Automatic flight control system*: Usually refers to more advanced autopilots that include features such as auto-throttle and stored flight plan routes.

**AFM** — *Aircraft flight manual*: An FAA-approved manual that lists operating requirements. Useful to mechanics as well as to pilots.

**AGL** — *Altitude above ground level*.

**AM** — *Amplitude modulated*: This refers to a radio wave that has been modulated in such a way that the amplitude of the signal varies up and down to match the modulating signal.

**AOA** — *Angle-of-attack*: The angle between the chord line of an airfoil and the relative wind. Also AOA instrument presentation.

**ARINC** — *Aeronautical Radio Incorporated*: This is an organization made up of airlines and manufacturers which establishes standards for aircraft equipment. For example, ARINC 429 for digital data.

**ARSA** — *Airport radar service area*: An area of airspace around an airport with radar air traffic control (ATC) in which special restrictions are placed on aircraft flight operations.

**ATC** — *Air traffic control*.

**BCD** — *Binary coded decimal*: A binary code system that uses four bit bytes.

**BIT** — Each individual binary digit or number in a digital word or message.

**BYTE** — A group of binary bits which are treated together as in a binary word with 32 bits. In this example, one byte = 32 bits.

**CADC** — *Central air data computer*: Same as ADC.

**CAS** — *Calibrated airspeed*.

**CAT II** — Category II ILS instrument approaches.

**CAT III** — Category III ILS instrument approaches.

**CFM** — *Cubic feet per minute*: A measure of flow rate used with air-operated gyros.

**CHT** — *Cylinder head temperature*: An instrument found on many aircraft with air-cooled reciprocating engines, usually a thermocouple system.

**CIT** — *Compressor inlet temperature*: Also called $Tt_2$, it refers to the temperature of the air entering the inlet of a turbine engine.

**CPU** — *Central processing unit*: One of the major components of a computer, the CPU contains the ALU, control and memory functions.

**CRT** — *Cathode ray tube*: This is the display for electronic aircraft instruments. It looks like a TV screen, but is specially designed to be readable in the bright conditions of the cockpit.

**CVR** — *Cockpit voice recorder*: Records cockpit sounds and conversations from radio and intercom systems.

**DG** — *Directional gyro*: An instrument which gives information concerning aircraft rotation about the vertical axis. Usually referenced to magnetic headings.

**DME** — *Distance measuring equipment*: A two-way radio system for determining aircraft distance in nautical miles from a ground site.

**EADI** — *Electronic attitude director indicator instrument*: A display which combines pitch and roll data along with indications from the flight director in the form of command bar movements. Other data such as radio navigation displays are also included. A CRT instrument.

**EGT** — *Exhaust gas temperature*: An instrument which displays the temperature of the engine exhaust gasses. Found on both reciprocating and turbine engines.

**EHSI** — *Electronic horizontal situation indicator*: A display which combines gyro stabilized magnetic heading information along with radio navigational information using a deviation bar indicator. A CRT instrument.

EICAS — *Engine indication and crew alerting system*: An electronic instrument system that provides indications for powerplant and aircraft system instruments, and provides alert, caution and status messages for the crew. EICAS typically uses two CRTs.

ELT — *Emergency locator transmitter*: A small self-contained radio transmitter for crash location purposes found on most small aircraft.

EM WAVES — *Electro-magnetic waves*: Most often used to mean radio waves.

EPR — *Engine pressure ratio*: An instrument which indicates the power being produced by certain turbojet and turbofan engines. EPR is the ratio of total outlet pressure divided by total inlet pressure.

FCC — *Federal Communications Commission*: This government agency establishes rules for many types of electronic equipment including the radio equipment on aircraft.

FDR — *Flight data recorder*: A system which records many different operating parameters such as altitude, airspeed, engine power, G loadings, flap settings, etc. Used for accident investigation.

FM — *Frequency modulation*: A radio carrier wave uses FM when the carrier wave frequency is varied up and down by the modulating signal.

FMS — *Flight management system*: A sophisticated autopilot system that includes advanced features for managing virtually the entire flight. Uses an FMC (flight management computer).

FPM — *Feet per minute*: The standard unit of measurement for aircraft rate of climb indicators and similar devices.

GPH — *Gallons per hour*: A standard unit of measurement for fuel flow or fuel consumption for aircraft. Usually used for reciprocating engines.

GPS — *Global positioning system*: A satellite navigation system being developed for the military, but available for use by civilian aircraft.

GPWS — *Ground proximity warning system*: Designed to give a warning to the flight crew to avoid ground impact due to excessive rates of descent, rising terrain, etc.

HSI — *Horizontal situation indicator*: An integrated aircraft instrument which displays magnetic heading, radio navigation steering information and sometimes additional information. It replaces the simpler DG instrument.

IAS — *Indicated airspeed*.

IC — *Integrated circuit*: A semi-conductor device that incorporates a number of logic gates in one compact unit.

ICAO — *International Civil Aviation Organization*.

IFR — *Instrument flight rules*: Aircraft must operate IFR if weather conditions are below the minimums for visual reference flying.

ILS — *Instrument landing system*: A precision approach using radio guidance signals to guide an aircraft to a landing runway.

INS — *Inertial navigation system*: A navigational system that uses very accurate measurements of acceleration to calculate aircraft position, course and speed.

IRU — *Inertial reference unit*: Most often refers to the laser device which is the sensor for INS and other aircraft systems.

ITT — *Inter-turbine temperature*: This refers to a gas temperature measurement on a turbine engine where the probes are located in between two different sections of the turbine.

IVSI — *Instantaneous vertical speed indicator*: An instrument that eliminates the lag of a conventional VSI through the use of acceleration operated dashpots.

KIAS — *Knots indicated airspeed*: We also find KCAS and KTAS.

LMM — Compass locator transmitter at the middle marker.

LCD — *Liquid crystal display*: A common type of device used in aircraft instruments and radios that have a lighted display.

LED — *Light emitting diode*: A common type of device used in lighted displays on radios and other equipment.

LOM — Compass locator transmitter at the outer marker.

LRU — *Line replaceable unit*: Modern aircraft have most electronic equipment installed in the form of LRUs which are standard size boxes that contain the equipment and which make replacement and maintenance simpler and more efficient.

MLS — *Microwave landing system*: A new type of precision approach aid that may eventually replace ILS. In limited use at this time.

MM — *ILS middle marker*.

MSL — Altitude in terms of mean sea level.

$N_1$ — A tachometer indication of the low pressure compressor speed in a turbine engine.

$N_2$ — A tachometer indication of the high pressure compressor speed in a turbine engine.

$N_g$ — A tachometer indication of the gas producer speed in a turbine engine. Usually turboprop or turboshaft.

$N_p$ — A tachometer indication of the power section speed in a turbine engine. Usually turboprop or turboshaft.

$N_r$ — A tachometer indication of the rotor speed for a helicopter. Usually the main rotor.

NDB — *Non-directional radio beacon*: The ground based radio transmitter that sends the signals which are received by the aircraft ADF radio navigation receiver.

OM — *ILS outer marker*.

POH — *Pilot's operating handbook*: This is an FAA-approved document which gives operating information for that particular aircraft. Used by both pilots and mechanics. Same as AFM.

PPH — *Pounds per hour*: A unit of measurement for aircraft fuel flow and fuel consumption. Most often used with turbine engines.

PSIA — *Pounds per square inch absolute*: A measurement of pressure compared to a perfect vacuum.

PSID — *Pounds per square inch differential*: A measurement of the differential pressure between two pressures measured at different points.

PSIG — *Pounds per square inch gauge*: A measurement of pressure compared to ambient conditions, usually ambient atmospheric pressure.

P-static — *Precipitation static*: The static electricity charge on an aircraft produced by friction with ice, snow, rain, sand, dust etc. It can cause noise in the radios and other problems.

RAM — *Random access memory*: The memory in a computer that can be affected by operator input and is lost when the computer is turned off.

RF — *Radio frequency*: Refers to frequencies above audio frequencies, or those frequencies above 20,000 Hz (20 KHz).

RLG — *Ring laser gyro*: A laser beam device that can be used to replace spinning gyroscopes to operate aircraft instruments and other aircraft systems.

RNAV — *Area navigation*: The use of a computer to process signals from VOR and DME transmitters, permitting random direct routes to be flown using waypoints designated as a VOR radial and distance such as OMN 243/24.

ROC — *Rate of climb*: An aircraft instrument that gives readings in FPM of the aircraft rate of climb or descent.

ROM — *Read only memory*: Sometimes called hard-wired, this is the memory in a computer which cannot be changed by the operator and is not lost when the computer is turned off.

RVR — *Runway visual range*: A measured visibility along a runway, stated in feet. RVR 2400 = 1/2 mile visibility.

SAS — *Stability augmentation system*: This system is often associated with an autopilot and it is designed to provide additional stability to the aircraft for certain flight conditions. On swept wing jets, for example, it helps to reduce Dutch roll.

SELCAL — *Selective calling*: A communications system which allows the person on the ground to dial a code to contact a specific airplane in flight. Used by the airlines to contact their aircraft for operational reasons.

SWR — *Standing wave ratio*: A measure of the efficiency of an antenna, it is based on forward power and reflected power measurements.

TACAN — *Tactical air navigation*: a radio navigation system in the UHF band designed primarily for military aircraft.

TAS — *True Airspeed*.

TCA — *Terminal control area*: An area of airspace around a busy airport where special restrictions are placed on aircraft flight operations.

TCAS — *Traffic alert and collision avoidance system*: This system is installed in some larger aircraft where it gives warnings to the pilots to prevent mid-air collisions. The TCAS uses transponder principles of operation.

TIT — *Turbine inlet temperature*: Refers to the measurement of gas temperature for a turbine engine where the probes are located just downstream of the combustion chambers or just in front of the first turbine stage. Can also refer to a turbosupercharger temperature.

TOT — *Turbine outlet temperature*: Refers to the measurement of gas temperature for a turbine engine where the probes are located downstream of all the turbine sections. Also called EGT.

V-speeds — Designated airspeeds related to a specific aircraft certification requirement or operating airspeed.

V — Velocity.

Va — Design maneuvering speed.

Vd — Design dive speed.

Vfe — Maximum speed with the flaps extended.

Vle — Maximum speed with the landing gear extended.

Vlo — Maximum landing gear operating speed.

Vmc — Minimum control speed: The lowest speed at which directional control of the aircraft can be maintained with the critical engine failed and the remaining engines at maximum continuous power.

Vmo/Mmo — Maximum operating speed: In terms of airspeed and in terms of Mach number.

Vne — Never exceed speed: the maximum permissable speed under any circumstances.

Vno — Maximum structural cruising speed.

$Vs_1$ — The stalling speed or minimum steady flight speed with the landing gear and flaps retracted.

Vso — The stalling speed or minimum steady flight speed with the landing gear and flaps extended.

Vx — The speed for best angle of climb.

Vy — The speed for best rate of climb.

Vyse — The speed for best rate of climb, single engine operations with one engine inoperative.

VFR — *Visual flight rules*: for VFR the pilot must be able to control the aircraft by visual outside references.

VHF — *Very high frequency*.

VOR — *VHF omnidirectional radio range*: a radio navigation system.

VORTAC — A combined VOR and TACAN transmitter site.

VSI — *Vertical speed indicator*: an aircraft instrument that indicates aircraft rate of change of altitude in FPM.

VSWR — *Voltage standing wave ratio*: Same as SWR (see above).

# INDEX